PHYSICS FOR TODAY
AND TOMORROW

By the same author

Exploring Physics, Books 1–5
Practical Modern Physics
Electronics and Nuclear Physics
Advanced Physics: Materials and Mechanics
Advanced Physics: Fields, Waves and Atoms
Adventures with Electronics
Adventures with Microelectronics
Adventures with Physics
Adventures with Digital Electronics
Physics: a Textbook for Advanced Level Students
Success in Electronics
Electronics for Today and Tomorrow

Tom Duncan

PHYSICS FOR TODAY AND TOMORROW

John Murray

To F.D.B.

Acknowledgements

Thanks are due to the following for permission to reproduce copyright photographs:

Figs. 1*a*, 11.6, Hale Observatories; 1*b*, Cenco; 2*a*, Space Frontiers Ltd; 2*b*, I.B.M. United Kingdom Ltd; 2*c*, Sony (UK) Ltd; 2*d*, E.I. Du Pont de Nemours and Company; 1.2, Central Office of Information; 1.3, John Topham Picture Library; 2.5, 49.10, Central Press Photos Ltd; 3.5*b*. Walden Precision Apparatus Ltd; 6.3*b*, Ronan Picture Library; 6.7, Rank Precision Industries; 8.7, by permission of Penguin Books Ltd (from *Revolution in Optics* by S. Tolansky, copyright 1968); 10.2, 10.4, Kodak Ltd; 10.5, Rolex Ltd; 11.2, R. and J. Beck Ltd; 13.6, 13.8*a*, *b*, 13.12*a*, *b*, 13.14*a*, from Llowarch, *Ripple Tank Studies of Wave Motion* (Clarendon Press, Oxford); 13.13, Hydraulics Research Station; 14.1, Addison-Wesley Publishing Company (from *Modern College Physics* by Richards, Sears, Wehr and Zemansky); 14.3, D. G. A. Dyson; 15.4, Barnes Engineering Company; 15.5, 77.2, by courtesy of the Post Office; 15.7, Westinghouse; 16.6, Wormald International Sensory Aids Ltd; 17.1, G.L.C. Architect's Department; 17.8*a*, *b*, Society of Mining Engineers; 19.1*a*, *b*, British Airways; 19.7, E. Leitz (Instruments) Ltd; 20.3, Mrs. Barbara A. Lyle; 21.1, 26.3, 29.4, 55.1, Popperfoto; 22.1, 37.6, (from *PSSC Physics*) reproduced by permission of D. C. Heath and Co., copyright 1965. Educational Development Center; 26.6*a*, National Institute of Agricultural Engineering; 26.6*b*, London Transport; 27.1, British Petroleum; 28.1, Avon Rubber Company Ltd; 30.6, Barnaby's Picture Library; 30.9, Ford Motor Company; 31.8, Camera Press Ltd; 33.5*a*, Wasafoto; 33.5*b*, Sjohistoriska Museum; 33.6, 49.4*a*, H.M.S.O., Crown copyright; 35.1, A. G. Spalding and Bros. Inc. (first appeared in article 'Dynamics of the Golf Swing' by Dr. D. Williams in *Quarterly Journal of Mechanics and Applied Mathematics*, Published by Clarendon Press, Oxford); 37.2, Italian State Tourist Office; 38.1, British Hovercraft Corporation; 38.5, Parachute Regiment, Aldershot; 39.5, United States Information Service; 40.1, 44.3, British Railways Board; 40.5, Lord Blackett's Estate; 41.1, Scottish Tourist Board; 43.1, 65.7, British Steel Corporation; 44.1, British Oxygen Company; 45.4, Rutherford Laboratory; 48.2, Swiss National Tourist Board; 48.4, Prestige Ltd; 49.4*b*, Fibreglass Ltd; 50.4, James R. Sheppard; 51.8, English Electric Company; 51.7, Cunard Shipping; 53.1, Mullard Ltd; 53.5, Hurst Electric Industries Ltd; 56.9*a*, *b*, *c*, Kodansha Ltd; 60.2*a*, *b*, 76.9*a*, *b*, *c*, R. S. Components Ltd; 64.9, Chloride Group Ltd; 66.6, Stanley Power Tools Ltd; 67.4, Weir Electrical Instrument Company Ltd; 67.7, National Physical Laboratory; 69.7, 70.5, Central Electricity Generating Board; 73.8, by courtesy of Tektronix U.K. Ltd; 74.8*a*, C. T. R. Wilson; 74.8*b*, The Royal Society (from *Proceedings*, A. Vol. 104, Plate 16, Fig. 1, 1923); 74.10, United Kingdom Atomic Energy Authority; 76.1*a*, Casio Electronics Ltd; 76.1*b*, The London Hospital; 76.11*a*, 77.11, R. B. Hunt.

© Tom Duncan 1977, 1983

First edition 1977
Reprinted 1978, 1979, 1980, 1981, 1982
Second edition 1983
Reprinted 1984, 1985
John Murray (Publishers) Ltd
50 Albemarle Street, London W1X 4BD

Printed in Great Britain by Butler and Tanner Ltd, Frome and London

British Library Cataloguing in Publication Data
Duncan, Tom
  Physics for today and tomorrow. —2nd ed.
  1. Physics
  I. Title
  530   QC23

ISBN 0 7195 4002 X

Preface to first edition

The reorganization of secondary education has highlighted the need for courses suited to pupils of a wide ability range. This book is an attempt to cater for those taking G.C.E., C.S.E. and similar examinations.

Thanks are due to Dr. M. L. A. Robinson of Worth School for his careful reading of the manuscript and many helpful suggestions and to my wife for producing the typescript. The experiment on $Q = It$ (p. 171) is due to Mr. J. Marshall of Christ College, Brecon, to whom I am very grateful.

Acknowledgement is made to the following G.C.E. boards:

Associated Examining Board (*A.E.B.*)
Cambridge Local Examination Syndicate (*C.*)
Joint Matriculation Board (*J.M.B.*)
University of London (*L.*)
Northern Ireland G.C.E. Examination Board (*N.I.*)
Oxford Local Examinations (*O.*)
Oxford and Cambridge Examination Board (*O. and C.*)
Southern Universities Joint Board (*S.*)
Welsh Joint Education Committee (*W.*)

and to the following C.S.E. boards:

Associated Lancashire Schools Examining Board (*A.L.*)
East Anglian Examinations Board (*E.A.*)
East Midland Regional Examination Board (*E.M.*)
Metropolitan Regional Examination Board (*Met.*)
Middlesex Regional Examining Board (*Mddx.*)
North West Regional Examinations Board (*N.W.*)
Southern Regional Examinations Board (*S.R.*)
South-East Regional Examinations Board (*S.E.*)
West Midlands Examinations Board (*W.M.*)
West Yorkshire and Lindsey Board (*W.Y.*)

Preface to second edition

The contents and pagination are the same as in the first edition but sections have been added on *Crystals*, *Mechanical properties of materials*, *Beams and structures* and on *Bernoulli's principle*. In response to requests from teachers, this edition contains about 100 revision questions all taken from recent G.C.E. 'O' level papers, by kind permission of the various examination bodies. C.S.E. students may also find these useful.

Contents

Physics and technology

Physicists explore the Universe. Their investigations range from stars that are millions and millions of kilometres away to particles that are smaller than atoms, Fig. 1*a*, *b*.

As well as having to find the *facts* by observation and experiment, they also must try to discover the *laws* that summarize (often as mathematical equations) these facts. Sense has then to be made of the laws by thinking up and testing *theories* (thought-models) to explain the laws. The reward, apart from a satisfied curiosity, is a better understanding of the physical world. Engineers and technologists use physics to solve *practical problems* for the benefit of mankind, though in solving them social, environmental and other problems may arise.

In this book we will study the behaviour of *matter* (the stuff things are made of) and the different kinds of *energy* (such as light, sound, heat, electricity). We will also consider the applications of physics in the home, transport, medicine, industry, communications and electronics, Fig. 2*a*, *b*, *c*, *d*.

Mathematics is an essential tool of physics and a 'reference section' of some of the basic mathematics needed is given at the end of the book. It is printed on coloured pages.

Fig. 1*a*. Astronomers have found that the many millions of stars in the Universe, of which the Sun is just one, are in widely separated groups called galaxies. The spiral galaxy M81 near the Plough is shown at the left. The Sun and its planets belong to the galaxy called the Milky Way.

The number of galaxies is huge. Most appear as tiny blurred specks. It is estimated that the farthest are 5000 million light-years from the Sun. One light-year is the distance travelled by light in 1 year—about 10 000 000 000 000 km.

Fig. 1*b*. The photograph below shows the atoms in the tip of a tungsten needle (the metal used for lamp filaments) magnified about 2 million times. It was taken by an instrument called a field ion microscope.

Fig. 2a. The space shuttle, *right*, is the world's first, and as yet only, re-usable 'Space Transport System' (STS). After being launched like a rocket it glides back to earth like an aeroplane to be used again. Satellites and other materials can be carried in its cargo bay to be placed into orbit when the shuttle is in space. The black tiles on the underside of the vehicle protect it against the fierce heat caused by friction as it re-enters the earth's atmosphere.

Fig. 2b. In the picture *left* the results from tests of the man's lung capacities are sent to a computer. The processed results are displayed in a few seconds on the 'TV screen'. Below the screen are keys which the laboratory assistant can use to instruct the computer or to give it certain kinds of information.

Fig. 2c. The pocket-sized battery-operated black and white television receiver, *above*, is smaller than a paperback book. Its compact size is due to a flat screen, the electron beam producing the picture comes in from the side and is deflected by an electrostatic field rather than travelling in a straight line as in traditional sets. A hand-held flat colour TV is now under development.

Fig. 2d. The Gossamer Penguin, *left*, is the first manned aircraft to fly for any length of time powered only by the sun. The solar panels perched above the wings convert the sun's light into electricity which powers a motor connected to a large propeller at the rear. Flying at about 15 mph and at a maximum height of 12 ft in full sun, the 'Penguin' glides gracefully back to earth when shaded by cloud.

1 Light rays

You can see an object only if light from it enters your eyes. Some objects such as the sun, electric lamps and candles make their own light. We call these *luminous* sources.

Most things you see do not make their own light but reflect it from a luminous source. They are *non-luminous* objects. This page, you and the moon are examples. Fig. 1.1 shows some others.

luminous source emitting light
non–luminous objects reflecting light

Fig. 1.1

Luminous sources radiate light when their atoms become 'excited' as a result of receiving energy. In a light bulb, for example, the energy comes from electricity. The 'excited' atoms give off their light haphazardly in most luminous sources.

A light source that works differently is the *laser*, invented in 1960. In it the 'excited' atoms act together and emit a narrow, very bright beam of light which can cut a hole through a key 2 mm thick in a thousandth of a second, Fig. 1.2. Other uses are being found for the laser in industry and medicine.

Fig. 1.2

Rays and beams

Fig. 1.3

Sunbeams streaming through trees, Fig. 1.3, and light from a cinema projector on its way to the screen both suggest that *light travels in straight lines*. The beams are visible because dust particles in the air reflect light into our eyes.

The direction of the path in which light is travelling is called a *ray* and is represented in diagrams by a straight line with an arrow on it. A *beam* is a stream of light and is shown by a number of rays; it may be parallel, diverging (spreading out) or converging (getting narrower), Fig. 1.4.

Fig. 1.4

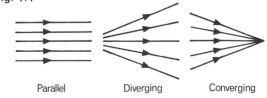

Parallel   Diverging   Converging

Experiment: the pinhole camera

One is shown in Fig. 1.5*a*. Make a small pinhole in the centre of the black paper. Half-darken the room. Hold the box at arm's length so that the pinhole end is nearest to and about 1 metre from a luminous object, e.g. a carbon filament lamp or a candle. Look at the *image* on the screen (an image is a likeness of an object and need not be an exact copy).

Can you see *three* ways in which the image differs

Fig. 1.5

from the object? What is the effect of moving the camera closer to the object?

Make the pinhole larger. What happens to the (*i*) brightness, (*ii*) sharpness, (*iii*) size of the image?

Make several small pinholes round the large hole, Fig. 1.5*b*, and view the image again. What do you see?

The way a pinhole camera forms an image is shown in Fig. 1.6.

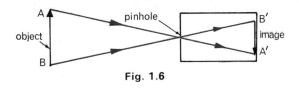

Fig. 1.6

Shadows

Shadows are formed because light travels in straight lines. A very small source of light, called a *point* source, gives a sharp shadow which is equally dark all over. This may be shown as in Fig. 1.7*a* where the small hole in the card acts as a point source.

If the card is removed the lamp acts as a large or *extended* source, Fig. 1.7*b*. The shadow is then larger and has a central dark region, the *umbra*, surrounded by a ring of partial shadow, the *penumbra*. You can see by the rays that some light reaches the penumbra but none reaches the umbra.

Fig. 1.7

Eclipses

There is an eclipse of the sun by the moon when the sun, moon and earth are in a straight line. The sun is an extended source (like the bulb in Fig. 1.7*b*). People in the umbra of the moon's shadow, at B in Fig. 1.8, see a *total* eclipse of the sun (that is, they can't see the sun at all). Those in the penumbra, at A, see a *partial* eclipse (part of the sun is still visible).

Sometimes the moon is farther from the earth (it does not go round the earth in a perfect circle), and then the tip of the umbra does not reach the earth, Fig. 1.9. When this happens people at A still see a partial eclipse, but those at B see an *annular* eclipse (the central region of the sun is hidden but not its outer parts).

A total eclipse seen from one place may last for up to 7 minutes. During this time, although it is day, the sky is dark, stars are visible, the temperature falls and birds stop singing.

Questions

1. How would the size and brightness of the image formed by a pinhole camera change if the camera was made longer?

2. What changes would occur in the image if the single pinhole in a camera was replaced by (*a*) four pinholes close together, (*b*) a hole 1 cm wide?

3. A long narrow bench has two small identical lamps mounted one at each end as in Fig. 1.10. A vertical rod is placed on the

Fig. 1.10

bench. Copy the diagram and draw the shadows formed, showing the correct size and position. State, giving a reason, which shadow is the darker. (*E.A.*)

4. Draw a diagram to show a possible position of the moon for a lunar eclipse to be seen on earth.

Fig. 1.8

Fig. 1.9

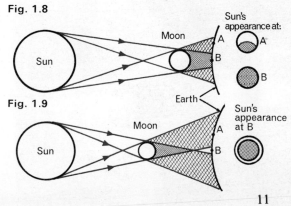

2 Reflection of light

If we know how light behaves when it is reflected we can use a mirror to change the direction in which it is travelling. This happens when a mirror is placed at the entrance of a concealed drive to give warning of approaching traffic.

An ordinary mirror is made by depositing a thin layer of silver on one side of a piece of glass and protecting it with paint. The silver—at the *back* of the glass—acts as the reflecting surface.

Experiment: reflection by a plane mirror

Draw a line AOB on a sheet of paper and using a protractor mark angles on it. Measure them from the perpendicular ON, which is at right angles to AOB. Set up a plane (flat) mirror with its reflecting surface on AOB.

(*a*) *Ray method.* Shine a narrow ray of light along say the 30° line, onto the mirror, Fig. 2.1.

Fig. 2.1

Mark the position of the reflected ray, remove the mirror and measure the angle between the reflected ray and ON. Repeat for rays at other angles. What can you conclude?

(*b*) *Pin method.* Insert two pins P_1 and P_2 on the 30° line, Fig. 2.2, to indicate a 'ray' of light falling at

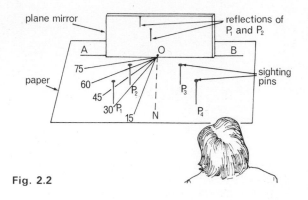

Fig. 2.2

this angle on the mirror. Look into the mirror and insert two sighting pins P_3 and P_4 so that they are in line with the reflections (images) of P_1 and P_2. P_3P_4 gives the path of 'ray' P_1P_2 after it is reflected.

Remove P_3 and P_4 and mark their positions with crosses (lettered P_3 and P_4). Remove the mirror and draw a straight line through P_3 and P_4 to meet the mirror; this should be at O. Measure angle P_4ON. Repeat for other angles. What do you conclude?

Laws of reflection

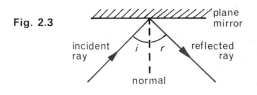

Fig. 2.3

Terms used in connection with reflection are shown in Fig. 2.3. The perpendicular to the mirror at the point where the incident ray strikes it is called the *normal*. Note that the angle of incidence *i* is the angle between the incident ray and the *normal*; similarly for the angle of reflection *r*. There are two laws of reflection.

1. *The angle of incidence equals the angle of reflection.*

2. *The incident ray, the reflected ray and the normal all lie in the same plane.* (This means that they can all be drawn on a flat sheet of paper.)

Periscope

Fig. 2.4

obstacle

Fig. 2.5

A simple periscope consists of a tube containing two plane mirrors, fixed parallel to and facing one another. Each makes an angle of 45° with the line joining them, Fig. 2.4. Light from the object is turned through 90° at each reflection and an observer is able to see over a crowd, for example, Fig. 2.5, or over the top of an obstacle.

In more elaborate periscopes like those used in submarines, prisms replace mirrors (see p. 21).

Regular and diffuse reflection

If a parallel beam of light falls on a plane mirror it is reflected as a parallel beam, Fig. 2.6*a*, and *regular* reflection is said to occur. Most surfaces however reflect light irregularly and the rays in an incident parallel beam are reflected in many directions, Fig. 2.6*b*.

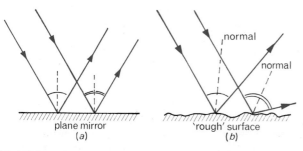

plane mirror
(*a*)

'rough' surface
(*b*)

Fig. 2.6

Irregular or *diffuse* reflection is due to the surface of the object not being perfectly smooth like a mirror. At each point on the surface the laws of reflection are obeyed but the angle of incidence and so the angle of reflection varies from point to point. The reflected rays are scattered haphazardly. Most objects, being rough, are seen by diffuse reflection.

Questions

1. Fig. 2.7 shows a ray of light PQ striking a mirror AB. The mirror AB and the mirror CD are at right angles to each other. QN is a normal to the mirror AB.

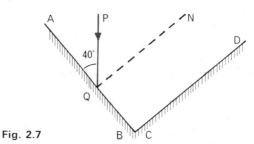

Fig. 2.7

(*a*) What is the value of the angle of incidence of the ray PQ on the mirror AB?

(*b*) Copy the diagram and continue the ray PQ to show the path it takes after reflection at both mirrors.

(*c*) Mark on your diagram the value of the angle of reflection on AB, the angle of incidence on CD and the angle of reflection on CD.

(*d*) What do you notice about the path of the ray PQ and the final reflected ray? (*E.M.*)

2. When a ray of light incident on a plane mirror at an angle of incidence of 70° is reflected from the mirror it subsequently strikes a second plane mirror placed so that the angle between the mirrors is 45°. The angle of reflection at the second mirror, in degrees, is

A 20 **B** 25 **C** 45 **D** 65 **E** 70 (*N.I.*)

3. A person is looking into a tall mirror in front, Fig. 2.8. What part of the mirror is actually needed to see from eye to toes? (*S.R.*)

Fig. 2.8

13

3 Plane mirrors

When you look into a plane mirror on the wall of a room you see an image of the room behind the mirror; it is as if there was another room. Restaurants sometimes have a large mirror on one wall just to make them look larger. You may be able to say how much larger after the next experiment.

The position of the image formed by a mirror depends on the position of the object.

Experiment: position of image

Fig. 3.1

Support a piece of thin glass on the bench, as in Fig. 3.1. It must be *vertical* (at 90° to the bench). Place a small paper arrow O about 10 cm from the glass. The glass acts as a poor mirror and an image of O will be seen in it; the darker the bench top the brighter is the image. How do the sizes of O and its image compare?

Lay another identical arrow I on the bench behind the glass; move it until it coincides with the image of O. Measure the distances of the points of O and I from the glass along the line joining them. How do they compare? Try O at other distances.

Real and virtual images

A *real* image is one which can be produced on a screen and is formed by rays that actually pass through it.

A *virtual* image cannot be formed on a screen and is produced by rays which seem to come from it but do not pass through it. The image in a plane mirror is virtual. Rays from a point on an object are re-flected at the mirror and appear to come from the point behind the mirror where the eye imagines the rays intersect when produced backwards, Fig. 3.2.

Fig. 3.2

Rays IA and IB do not exist; they are virtual and are represented by dotted lines.

Lateral inversion

Fig. 3.3

If you close your left eye your image in a plane mirror seems to close the right eye. In a mirror image, left and right are interchanged and the image is said to be *laterally inverted*. The effect occurs whenever an image is formed by one reflection and is very evident if print is viewed in a mirror, Fig. 3.3. What happens if two reflections occur as in a periscope?

Properties of image

The image in a plane mirror is

(*i*) as far behind the mirror as the object is in front and the line joining the object and image is perpendicular to the mirror

(*ii*) the same size as the object

(*iii*) virtual

(*iv*) laterally inverted.

Uses of plane mirrors

Apart from their everyday use, plane mirrors can improve the accuracy of measurements in science.

(*a*) *Pointer instruments.* A reading made on a meter which has a pointer moving over a scale is correct only if your eye is directly over the pointer. In any other position there is an error, called the 'parallax' error. (There is parallax between two objects—here the pointer and the scale—if they appear to move in opposite directions when you move your head sideways. It arises when objects do not coincide; if they do coincide they move together.)

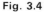

Fig. 3.4

If a plane mirror is fitted in the scale the correct position is found by moving your head until the image of the pointer in the mirror is hidden behind the pointer, Fig. 3.4. (A similar error occurs when reading a ruler, due to its thickness, if you do not look at right angles to it.)

(*b*) *Optical lever.* Meters for measuring small electric currents are called galvanometers and sometimes have a tiny mirror M, Fig. 3.5*a*, attached to the coil of wire which rotates when current flows in it. A beam of light from a lamp falls on M and the reflected beam, which acts as a 'pointer', produces a spot of light L on a scale S. A small rotation of

Fig. 3.5*a*

Fig. 3.5*b*

M causes appreciable movement of L if the 'pointer' is long. A light-beam galvanometer is shown in Fig. 3.5*b*.

Questions

1. Fig. 3.6 shows a plan view of a jar of water and a vertical sheet of glass in a box, the inside of which is painted black.

Fig. 3.6

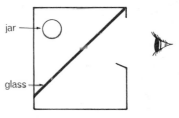

(*a*) Copy the diagram and show where a candle might be placed so that it appears to the viewer to burn in the jar of water.
(*b*) Trace the path of two rays of light from the candle to the eye and show with dotted lines how they appear to come from inside the jar.
(*c*) What does the glass do to the light to get this effect?
(*S.E.*)

2. The image in a plane mirror of a modern clock (with dots instead of numbers) looks as in Fig. 3.7.

Fig. 3.7

The correct time is
   A 2.25   **B** 2.35   **C** 8.35   **D** 9.25   (*W.M.*)

3. If a girl walks away from a plane mirror at a speed of 1 metre per second, in what direction does her image move and with what speed?

4 Curved mirrors

For some purposes curved mirrors are more useful than plane mirrors. You can see the images they give by looking into both sides of a polished spoon.

A *concave* mirror curves inwards like a cave, Fig. 4.1*a*, a *convex* one curves outwards, Fig. 4.1*b*. Many curved mirrors have spherical surfaces and the *principal axis* of such a mirror is the line joining the *pole* P or centre of the mirror to the *centre of curvature* C. C is the centre of the sphere of which the mirror is a part; it is in front of a concave mirror and behind a convex one.

The *radius of curvature r* is the distance CP.

Fig. 4.1

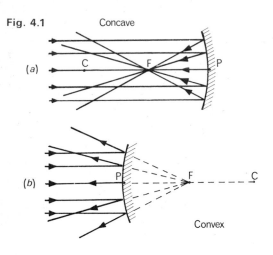

Principal focus

When a beam of light parallel to the principal axis is reflected from a concave mirror, the laws of reflection hold and it converges to a point on the axis called the *principal focus* F. Since light does pass through it, it is a real focus and can be obtained on a screen. A convex mirror has a virtual principal focus behind the mirror, from which the reflected beam appears to diverge.

The *focal length f* is the distance FP and experiment and theory show that $FP = CP/2$ or $f = r/2$, i.e.

focal length = half the radius of curvature

These statements apply only to small mirrors or to large mirrors if the beam is close to its axis. A large mirror does not form a point focus of a wide

Fig. 4.2

parallel beam but causes the reflected rays to form a curve called a *caustic*. One may be seen on the surface of tea in a cup, Fig. 4.2. Why?

Ray diagrams

Facts about the images formed by spherical mirrors can be found by drawing *two* of the following rays.

1. *A ray parallel to the principal axis which is reflected through the principal focus* F.

2. *A ray through the centre of curvature* C *which hits the mirror normally, is reflected back along its own path* (the radius of a sphere is perpendicular to the surface where it meets the surface).

3. *A ray through the principal focus* F *which is reflected parallel to the principal axis.*

In diagrams a curved mirror is represented by a *straight* line. A good-sized object can then be shown and rays from it regarded as forming a point focus, i.e. the mirror behaves as a small one. In numerical questions *horizontal* distances have sometimes to be scaled down (see Qn. 12, p. 33).

Images in a concave mirror

The ray diagrams in Fig. 4.3 show the images for four object positions. In each case two rays are drawn from the top A of an object OA and where they intersect after reflection gives the top B of the image IB. The foot I of each image is on the axis since ray OP hits the mirror normally and is reflected back along the axis. In (*d*) the dotted rays and the image are virtual (not real).

(a) *Object beyond* C

Image is between C and F, real, inverted, smaller

(b) *Object at* C

Image is at C, real, inverted, same size

(c) *Object between* C *and* F

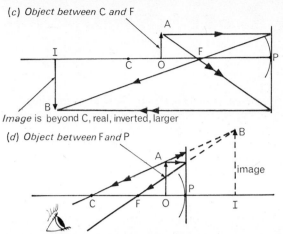

Image is beyond C, real, inverted, larger

(d) *Object between* F *and* P

Image is behind mirror, virtual, erect, larger

Fig. 4.3

Experiment: *f* of a concave mirror

We use the fact that when an object is placed at the centre of curvature C of a concave mirror, a real image is formed also at C, Fig. 4.4a.

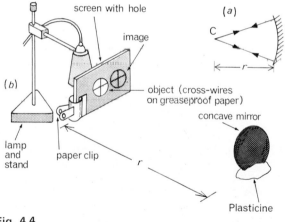

Fig. 4.4

Move the mirror, arranged as in Fig. 4.4b, until a *sharp* image of the cross-wire is obtained on the screen. Measure the distance r from the screen to the mirror, then $f = r/2$.

Uses of curved mirrors

(a) *Shaving mirror*. This is often concave. It forms a magnified, virtual, erect image of an object inside F, Fig. 4.3d, but the view is limited.

(b) *Reflector*. When a point source of light is at the principal focus of a concave mirror, the reflected beam is parallel if the mirror is small. To obtain a

wide parallel beam in, for example, a searchlight, the mirror must be parabolic, Fig. 4.5.

Fig. 4.5

(c) *Driving mirror*. A convex mirror gives a wider field of view than a plane mirror of the same size, Figs. 4.6a, b. For this reason and because it always gives an erect (but smaller) image, it is used as a car driving mirror.

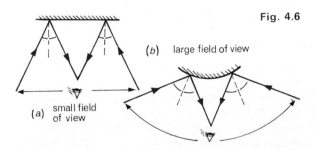

Fig. 4.6

(b) large field of view

(a) small field of view

Questions

1. Draw diagrams to represent (a) a convex mirror and (b) a concave mirror. Mark on each the principal axis, the principal focus F and the centre of curvature C if the focal length of (a) is 3 cm and of (b) 4 cm.

2. A concave mirror has a focal length of 4 cm and a real object 2 cm tall is placed 9 cm away from it. By means of an accurate full size diagram find where the image would be and measure its length. *(A.L.)*

17

5 Refraction of light

If you place a coin in an empty cup and move back until you *just* cannot see it, the result is surprising if someone *gently* pours in water. Try it.

Although light travels in straight lines in one transparent material, e.g. air, if it passes into a different material, e.g. water, it changes direction at the boundary between the two, i.e. it is bent. The *bending of light* when it passes from one material (called a medium) to another is called *refraction*. It causes effects like the coin trick.

Experiment: refraction in glass

Shine a ray of light at an angle on to a glass block (which has its lower face painted white or frosted), Fig. 5.1. Draw the outline ABCD of the block on the sheet of paper under it. Mark the positions of the various rays in air and in glass.

Remove the block and draw the normals on the paper at the points where the ray enters AB (see Fig. 5.1) and where it leaves CD.

What *two* things happen to the light falling on AB? When the ray enters the glass at AB is it bent towards or away from the part of the normal in the block? How is it bent at CD? What can you say about the direction of the ray falling on AB and the direction of the ray leaving CD?

What happens if the ray hits AB at right angles?

Laws of refraction

Terms used in refraction and the two laws are illustrated in Fig. 5.2.

Fig. 5.2

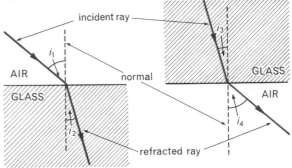

1. *Light is bent towards the normal when it enters a denser medium at an angle and away from the normal when it enters a less dense medium at an angle.*
2. *The incident ray, the refracted ray and the normal all lie in the same plane.*

Real and apparent depth

Rays of light from a point O on the bottom of a pool are refracted away from the normal at the water surface since they are passing into a less dense medium, i.e. air, Fig. 5.3. On entering the eye they appear to come from a point I *above* O; I is the virtual image of O formed by refraction. The apparent depth of the pool is less than its real depth. A straight stick seems bent in water. Why?

Fig. 5.3

Fig. 5.1

Refractive index (*n*)

If i_1 is the angle between the normal and a ray in *air* and i_2 is the angle between the normal and the same ray in a *material*, experiment shows that for all pairs of values of i_1 and i_2

$$\frac{\sin i_1}{\sin i_2} = \text{a constant}$$

This is *Snell's law* of refraction and is true whether the ray travels from air to the material or vice versa. The constant is called the *refractive index* (*n*) of the material. For glass *n* is about 1.5 (3/2) and for water 1.33 (4/3). The larger *n* is for a material the more does it bend light. How will a ray be refracted when it passes from water to glass?

In Fig. 5.2, $n = \sin i_1/\sin i_2 = \sin i_4/\sin i_3$.

Experiment: *n* by real and apparent depth

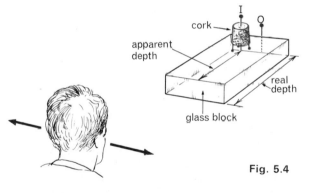

Fig. 5.4

Stick a pin O at the end of a glass block, Fig. 5.4, and mount a second pin I with its point on top of the block. (The mounting can be a cork with three small pins as legs.) View O through the block and at the same time move I nearer or farther from O till I and the image of O remain together in the same straight line when you move your head to the right or left. I then occupies the position of the image of O (and there is no parallax between them).

Measure the real and apparent depths of the block. It can be shown for perpendicular viewing (of O in this case) that

$$\text{refractive index } (n) = \frac{\text{real depth}}{\text{apparent depth}}$$

Refraction by a prism

Fig. 5.5

In a triangular glass prism, Fig. 5.5*a*, the deviation of a ray due to refraction at the first surface is added to the deviation at the second surface, Fig. 5.5*b*. The deviations do not cancel out as in a parallel-sided block where the emergent ray, although displaced, is parallel to the incident ray.

Questions

1. Fig. 5.6 shows a ray of light entering a rectangular block of glass. (*a*) Copy the diagram and draw the normal at the point of entry, (*b*) sketch the approximate path of the ray through the block and out of the other side.

Fig. 5.6

2. Draw two rays from a point on a fish in a stream to show where someone on the bank must aim to spear the fish.

3. If the refractive index of water is 4/3 how deep will a pond really be if it appears to be 6 cm when looking vertically downwards? *(A.L.)*

4. Fig. 5.7 shows a ray of light XY striking a glass prism and then passing through it. Which of the rays A to E is the correct representation of the emerging ray? *(J.M.B./A.L./N.W. 16+)*

Fig. 5.7

6 Total internal reflection

When light passes at small angles of incidence from a denser to a less dense medium, e.g. from glass to air, there is a strong refracted ray and a weak ray reflected back into the denser medium, Fig. 6.1a.

Slowly rotate the paper so that the angle of incidence increases until total internal reflection *just* occurs. Mark the incident ray. Measure the angle of incidence; it equals the critical angle.

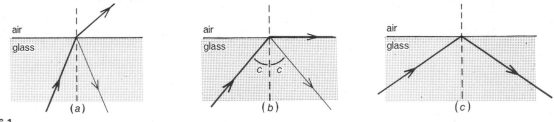

Fig. 6.1

Increasing the angle of incidence increases the angle of refraction.

At a certain angle of incidence, called the *critical angle c*, the angle of refraction is 90°, Fig. 6.1b. For angles of incidence greater than *c*, the refracted ray disappears and *all* the incident light is reflected inside the denser medium, Fig. 6.1c. The light does not cross the boundary and is said to suffer *total internal reflection*.

Experiment: critical angle of glass

Place a semicircular glass block on a sheet of paper, Fig. 6.2, and draw the outline LOMN where O is the centre and ON the normal at O to LOM. Direct a narrow ray (at an angle of about 30°) *along a radius towards O*. The ray is not refracted at the curved surface. Why? Note the refracted ray in the air beyond LOM and also the weak internally reflected ray in the glass.

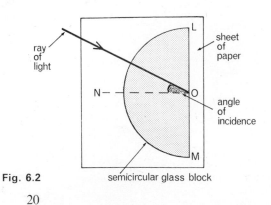

Fig. 6.2

semicircular glass block

Multiple images in a mirror

An ordinary mirror silvered at the back forms several images of one object, due to multiple reflection inside the glass, Fig. 6.3a, b. These blur the main image I (which is formed by one reflection at the silvering), especially if the glass is thick. The trouble is absent in front-silvered mirrors but they are easily damaged.

Fig. 6.3

(b)

Totally reflecting prisms

The defects of mirrors are overcome if 45° right-angled glass prisms are used. The critical angle of ordinary glass is about 42° and a ray falling normally on face PQ of such a prism, Fig. 6.4a, hits face PR at 45°. Total internal reflection occurs and the ray is turned through 90°. Totally reflecting prisms replace mirrors in good periscopes.

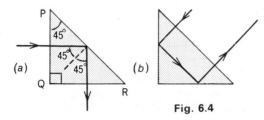

Fig. 6.4

Light can also be reflected through 180° by a prism, Fig. 6.4b; this happens in binoculars.

Mirages

They can often be seen on a hot day as a pool of water on the road some distance ahead. One explanation is that the light from the sky is gradually refracted away from the normal as it passes through layers of warm but less dense air near the hot road. Warm air has a slightly smaller refractive index than cool air and when the light meets a layer at the critical angle, it suffers total internal reflection, Fig. 6.5. To an observer the reflection of the sky appears as a puddle in the road.

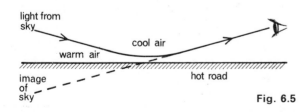

Fig. 6.5

Light pipes

Light can be trapped by total internal reflection inside a bent glass rod and 'piped' along a curved path, Fig. 6.6. A single, very thin glass fibre behaves in the

Fig. 6.6

Fig. 6.7

same way. If several thousand are taped together a flexible light pipe is obtained that can be used (e.g. by doctors and engineers) to light up some awkward spot for inspection. Fig. 6.7 shows a motorway sign lit by light pipes. The latest telephone 'cables' are optical fibres using laser light.

Refractive index and critical angle

From Fig. 6.1b and the definition of refractive index

$$n = \frac{\text{sin of angle between ray in air and normal}}{\text{sin of angle between ray in glass and normal}}$$

$$\therefore \quad n = \frac{\sin 90°}{\sin c} = \frac{1}{\sin c} \quad (\sin 90° = 1)$$

If $n = 3/2$, $\sin c = 2/3$ and $c = 42°$.

Questions

1. Fig. 6.8 shows rays of light in a semicircular glass block.
   (a) Explain why the ray entering the glass at A is not bent.
   (b) Explain why the ray AB is reflected at B and not refracted.
   (c) Ray CB does not stop at B. Copy the diagram and draw its approximate path after it leaves B. (*W.Y.*)

Fig. 6.8

2. Copy Fig. 6.9a and b and complete the paths of the rays.

Fig. 6.9

21

7 Lenses

Lenses are used in many optical instruments (p. 28); they often have spherical surfaces and there are two types. A *convex* lens is thickest in the centre and is also called a *converging* lens because it bends

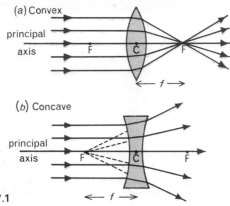

(a) Convex

principal axis

(b) Concave

principal axis

Fig. 7.1

light inwards, Fig. 7.1*a*. You may have used one as a magnifying glass, Fig. 7.2*a*, or as a burning glass. A *concave* or *diverging* lens is thinnest in the centre and spreads light out, Fig. 7.1*b*; it always gives a diminished image, Fig. 7.2*b*.

The centre of a lens is its *optical centre* C; the line through C at right angles to the lens is the *principal axis*.

Principal focus

When a beam of light parallel to the principal axis passes through a convex lens it is refracted so as to converge to a point on the axis called the *principal focus* F. It is a real focus. A concave lens has a virtual principal focus behind the lens, from which the refracted beam seems to diverge.

Since light can fall on both faces of a lens it has two principal foci, one on each side, equidistant from C. The distance CF is the *focal length f* of the lens; it is an important property of a lens.

Fig. 7.2

(a)   (b)

Ray diagrams

Information about the images formed by a lens can be obtained by drawing *two* of the following rays.

1. *A ray parallel to the principal axis which is refracted through the principal focus* F.

2. *A ray through the optical centre* C *which is undeviated.* (The central part of a lens acts as a small parallel-sided block which slightly displaces but does not deviate a ray passing through it; for a thin lens the displacement can be ignored.)

3. *A ray through the principal focus* F *which is refracted parallel to the principal axis.*

In diagrams a thin lens is represented by a *straight* line at which all the refraction is considered to occur.

Images formed by a convex lens

In the formation of images by lenses two important points on the principal axis are F and 2F; 2F is at a distance of twice the focal length from C.

In each ray diagram in Fig. 7.3 two rays are drawn from the top A of an object OA and where they intersect after refraction gives the top B of the image IB. The foot I of each image is on the axis since ray OC passes through the lens undeviated. In (*d*) the dotted rays, and the image, are virtual.

Experiment: *f* of a convex lens

(*a*) *Distant object method.* We use the fact that rays from a *point* on a very distant object, i.e. at infinity, are nearly parallel, Fig. 7.4*a*.

(*a*)
Object beyond 2F

Image is between F and 2F, real, inverted, smaller

(*b*)
Object at 2F

Image is at 2F, real, inverted, same size

Fig. 7.3

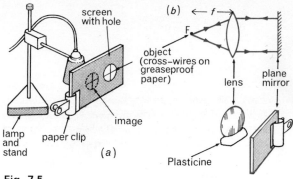

Fig. 7.5

(a) distant point

close point
diverging beam

almost parallel beam

very distant point

parallel beam

(b)

light from window at other side of room

lens   ruler   screen or wall

Fig. 7.4

Move the lens, arranged as in Fig. 7.4*b*, until a *sharp* image of a window at the other side of the room is obtained on the screen. The distance between the lens and the screen is *f* roughly. Why?

(*b*) *Plane mirror method.* Using the apparatus in Fig. 7.5*a* move the lens until a *sharp* image of the object, i.e. the illuminated cross-wire, is formed on the screen beside the object. When this happens, light from the object must travel back along nearly the same path and hit the mirror normally, Fig. 7.5*b*. The object is then at the lens' principal focus F. Why?

Magnification

The linear magnification *m* is given by

$$m = \frac{\text{height of image}}{\text{height of object}}$$

From Fig. 7.3 it can be shown that in all cases triangles OAC and BIC are similar and so

$$m = \frac{\text{IB}}{\text{OA}} = \frac{\text{IC}}{\text{OC}} = \frac{\text{distance of image from lens}}{\text{distance of object from lens}}$$

(*c*)
Object between 2F and F

Image is beyond 2F, real, inverted, larger

(*d*)

Object between F and C

Image is behind object, virtual, erect, larger

Power of a lens

The shorter the focal length of a lens, the more does it converge or diverge light. The *power F* of a lens of *focal length f* is defined by

$$\text{POWER} = \frac{1}{\text{FOCAL LENGTH}} \quad \text{or} \quad F = \frac{1}{f}$$

If *f* is in *metres*, *F* is in *dioptres* (D). If *f* = 1 m, *F* = 1 D; if *f* = 10 cm = 0.10 m, *F* = 1/0.10 = 10 D. The power of a convex lens is taken as positive and of a concave lens as negative. Opticians measure lens 'strengths' in dioptres.

Questions

1. A small electric lamp when placed at the focal point of a converging lens will produce a

    A parallel beam of light   **B** converging beam of light
    C diffuse beam of light   **D** diverging beam of light
                                              (*W.M.*)

2. (*a*) What kind of lens is shown in Fig. 7.6?

focus   focus   principal axis

Fig. 7.6

(*b*) Copy the diagrams and complete them to show the path of the light after passing through the lens.

(*c*) Fig. 7.7 shows an object AB 6 cm high placed 18 cm in front of a lens of focal length 6 cm. Draw the diagram to scale and by tracing the paths of rays from A find the position and size of the image formed.   (*S.E.*)

A
B   focus
     ← 18 cm →   ← 6 cm →

Fig. 7.7

3. An object is placed 4 cm in front of a convex lens. A real image is produced 16 cm from the lens.

(*a*) What is the magnification produced by the lens?

(*b*) By means of a full size diagram determine the focal length of the lens. Mark the principal focus.   (*E.M.*)

4. What is the power of lenses of focal length (*a*) 2 m, (*b*) 0.5 m, (*c*) 25 cm?

23

8 The eye

An image is formed on the *retina* of the eye, Fig. 8.1, by successive refraction at the *cornea*, the *aqueous humour*, the *lens* and the *vitreous humour*. Electrical signals then travel along the *optic nerve* to the brain to be interpreted. In good light, the *yellow spot* (*fovea*) is most sensitive to detail and the image is automatically formed there.

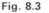

sclerotic (white of eye)
ciliary muscle
choroid (black)
retina
iris (eye colour)
yellow spot (fovea)
pupil
lens
optic nerve
cornea (transparent)
blind spot
aqueous humour (watery liquid)
vitreous humour (jelly)

Fig. 8.1

Objects at different distances are focused by the *ciliary muscles* changing the shape and so the focal length of the lens—a process called *accommodation*. The lens fattens to view near objects. The *iris* has a central hole, the *pupil*, whose size it decreases in bright light and increases in dim light.

Experiment: the eyes

(*a*) *Blind spot*. This is the small area of the retina where the optic nerve leaves the eye. It has no light-sensitive nerve endings and in each eye it is closer to the nose than the yellow spot.

To show its existence, close your left eye and look at the cross in Fig. 8.2. You will also see the black dot. *Slowly* bring the book towards you. At a certain distance the dot disappears; its image has fallen on the blind spot of your right eye.

Fig. 8.2

(*b*) *Binocular vision*. Your eyes see an object from slightly different angles, giving two slightly different images which the brain combines to give a three-dimensional impression. This also helps us to judge distances.

paper tube

Fig. 8.3

Roll a sheet of paper into a tube and hold it to your right eye with your right hand, Fig. 8.3. Close your left eye and place your left hand halfway along the tube. Open your left eye. Is there a 'hole' in your hand to 'see' through? Explain.

(*c*) *Image inverted on retina*, Fig. 8.4*a*. To show this make a pinhole in a piece of paper and hold it about 10 cm away. Close one eye and look at the hole against the sky or something bright. Hold a pin, head up, very close to your eye, Fig. 8.4*b*. Keep looking at the hole and move the pin about slowly until you 'see' it inverted in the hole. Make several pinholes round the first and look again. What do you see?

The pin is too close to the eye for a real image (except a large blur) to be formed on the retina, but a sharp *upright shadow* is produced by light from the pinhole and this falls directly (i.e. *still upright*) on the retina. But as you 'see' it upside-down you

object
eye
inverted image
(*a*)
pinhole
paper
pin
(*b*)

Fig. 8.4

know that the brain must turn it upside-down. If the brain does that with the shadow it will do the same with any image falling on the retina. So, as you normally see an upright object as upright, the image must be upside-down on the retina.

Defects of vision

The average adult eye can focus objects comfortably from about 25 cm (the *near point*) to infinity (the *far point*). Your near point may be less than 25 cm; it gets farther away with age.

(*a*) *Short sight*. A short-sighted person sees near objects clearly but his far point is closer than infinity. The image of a distant object is formed in

Fig. 8.5

SHORT SIGHT   (*b*)

front of the retina because the eyeball is too long, Fig. 8.5*a*. The defect is corrected by a concave spectacle lens which diverges the light before it enters the eye, to give an image on the retina, Fig. 8.5*b*.

(*b*) *Long sight*. A long-sighted person sees distant objects clearly but his near point is beyond 25 cm.

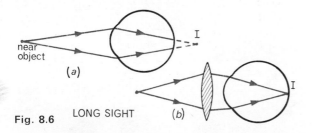

Fig. 8.6   LONG SIGHT   (*b*)

The image of a near object is focused behind the retina because the eyeball is too short, Fig. 8.6*a*. A convex spectacle lens corrects the defect, Fig. 8.6*b*.

Contact lenses

These can be worn instead of spectacles and consist of tiny plastic lenses, Fig. 8.7, held on the cornea by eye fluid.

Fig. 8.7

Persistence of vision

An image lasts on the retina for about one-tenth of a second after the object has disappeared, as can be shown by spinning a card like that in Fig. 8.8.

spin rapidly

front of card

glass tube secured to card

Fig. 8.8   back of card

The effect makes possible the production of motion pictures. Twenty-four separate pictures, each slightly different from the previous one, are projected on to the screen per second and give the impression of continuity. In a TV receiver twenty-five complete pictures are produced every second.

Questions

1. Name the part of the eye (*a*) which controls how much light enters it, (*b*) on which the image is formed, (*c*) which changes the focal length of the lens.

2. Refraction of light in the eye occurs at
   A the lens only   **B** the iris   **C** the cornea only
   D the pupil   **E** both the cornea and the lens   (*W.Y.*)

3. A short-sighted person has a near point of 15 cm and a far point of 40 cm.
   (*a*) Can he see clearly an object at a distance of (*i*) 5 cm, (*ii*) 25 cm, (*iii*) 50 cm?
   (*b*) To see clearly an object at infinity what kind of spectacle lens does he need?

4. The near point of a long-sighted person is 50 cm from the eye.
   (*a*) Can he see clearly an object at (*i*) a distance of 20 cm, (*ii*) infinity?
   (*b*) To read a book held at a distance of 25 cm will he need a convex or a concave spectacle lens?

9 Colour

Colourful clothes, colour TV and the flashing coloured lights in a discotheque all help to make life brighter. It was Newton who, in 1666, set us on the road to understanding how colours may arise. He produced them by allowing sunlight (which is white) to fall on a triangular glass prism, Fig. 9.1.

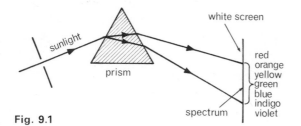

Fig. 9.1

The band of colours he obtained is called a *spectrum*. He concluded that (*i*) white light is a mixture of many colours of light which the prism separates out because (*ii*) the refractive index of glass is different for different colours.

Experiment: a pure spectrum

A pure spectrum is one in which the colours do not overlap, as they do when a prism alone is used. It needs a lens to focus each colour as in Fig. 9.2*a*.

Arrange a lens L, Fig. 9.2*b*, so that it forms an image of the vertical filament of a lamp on a screen at S_1, 1 m away. The filament acts as a narrow source of white light. Insert a 60° prism P and move the screen to S_2, keeping it at the same distance from L, to receive the spectrum; rotate P until the spectrum is pure.

Place different colour filters between P and S_2.

Recombining the spectrum

The colours of the spectrum can be recombined to form white light by

(*a*) arranging a second prism so that the light is deviated in the opposite direction, Fig. 9.3*a*, or

(*b*) using an electric motor to rotate at high speed a disc with the spectral colours painted on its sectors, Fig. 9.3*b*. (The whiteness obtained is slightly grey because paints are not pure colours.)

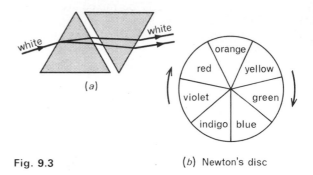

Fig. 9.3 (*b*) Newton's disc

Colour of an object

The colour of an object depends on (*i*) the colour of the light falling on it and (*ii*) the colour(s) it transmits or reflects.

(*a*) *Filters.* A filter lets through light of certain colours only and is made of glass or celluloid. For example, a red filter transmits mostly red light and absorbs other colours; it therefore produces red light when white light shines through it.

(*b*) *Opaque objects.* These do not allow light to pass but are seen by reflected light. A white object

Fig. 9.2

reflects all colours and appears white in white light, red in red light, blue in blue light, etc. A blue object appears blue in white light because the red, orange, yellow, green and violet colours in white light are absorbed and only blue reflected. It also looks blue in blue light but in red light it appears black since no light is reflected and blackness indicates the absence of colour.

Mixing coloured lights

In science red, green and blue are *primary* colours (they are not the artist's primary colours) because none of them can be produced from other colours of light. However, they give other colours when suitably mixed.

The primary colours can be mixed by shining beams of red, green and blue light on to a white screen so that they partially overlap, Fig. 9.4a. The results are summarized in the 'colour triangle' of Fig. 9.4b.

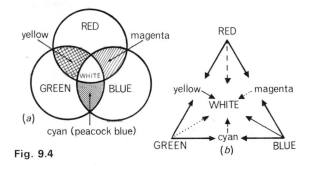

Fig. 9.4

The colours formed by adding two primaries are called *secondary* colours; they are yellow, cyan (turquoise or peacock blue) and magenta. The three primary colours give white light, as do the three secondaries. We would also expect a primary colour and the secondary opposite it in the colour triangle to give white. Why? Any *two* colours producing white light are *complementary* colours, e.g. blue and yellow.

Mixing coloured pigments

Pigments are materials which give colour to paints and dyes by reflecting light of certain colours only and absorbing all other colours. Most pigments are

impure, i.e. they reflect more than one colour. When they are mixed the colour reflected is the one common to all. For example, blue and yellow paints give *green* because blue reflects indigo and green (its neighbours in the spectrum) as well as blue, whilst yellow reflects green, yellow and orange, Fig. 9.5. Only *green* is reflected by both.

Fig. 9.5

Mixing coloured pigments is a process of *subtraction*; coloured lights are mixed by *addition*.

Questions

1. Copy the diagram, Fig. 9.6, mark and label (*a*) the reflected ray of light at the first surface, (*b*) the path followed by the light through and out of the prism, (*c*) what is seen on the screen AB. (*E.M.*)

Fig. 9.6

2. A sheet of white paper is viewed through a piece of blue glass and the paper looks blue. This is because

A the colour of the glass is reflected onto the paper

B blue light is absorbed by the glass

C blue light travels faster than red through glass

D the glass absorbs all colours except blue

E the glass adds blue light to the light coming from the paper. (*O./S.R. 16+*)

3. (*a*) What colour is formed when the following beams of equally bright light are shone onto a white screen and completely overlap: (*i*) yellow and blue, (*ii*) cyan (turquoise) and red?

(*b*) A book which looks red in white light is viewed in magenta light: what colour does it appear?

(*c*) White light is viewed through a piece of yellow filter and a piece of red filter held in contact. What colour light is seen? (*N.W.*)

10 Simple optical instruments

Camera

A camera is a light-tight box in which a convex lens forms a real image on a film, Fig. 10.1. The film contains chemicals that change on exposure to light; it is 'developed' to give a negative. From the negative a photograph is made by 'printing'.

Fig. 10.1

(a) *Focusing.* In simple cameras the lens is fixed and all distant objects, i.e. beyond about 2 metres, are in reasonable focus. Roughly how far from the film will the lens be if its focal length is 5 cm? In other cameras exact focusing of an object at a certain distance is done by altering the lens position. For near objects it is moved away from the film, the correct setting being shown by a scale on the focusing ring.

(b) *Shutter.* When a photograph is taken, the shutter is opened for a certain time and exposes the film to light entering the camera. Sometimes exposure times can be varied and are given in fractions of a second, e.g. 1/1000, 1/60, etc. Fast-moving objects require short exposures.

(c) *Stop.* The brightness of the image on the film depends on the amount of light passing through the lens when the shutter is opened and is controlled by the size of the hole (aperture) in the stop. In some cameras this is fixed but in others, Fig. 10.2, it can be made larger for a dull scene and smaller for a bright one.

The aperture may be marked in *f-numbers.* The diameter of an aperture with f-number 8 is $\frac{1}{8}$ of the focal length of the lens and so the *larger* the f-number the *smaller* the aperture. The numbers are chosen so that on passing from one to the next higher, e.g. from 8 to 11, the area of the aperture is halved.

Fig. 10.2

Projector

A projector forms a real image on a screen of a slide in a slide projector, and a film in a cine-projector. The image is usually so highly magnified that very strong but even illumination of the slide or film is needed if the image is also to be bright. This is

Fig. 10.3

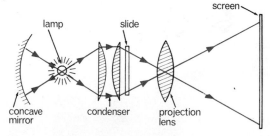

achieved by directing light from a small but powerful lamp on to the 'object' by means of a concave mirror and a condenser lens system arranged as in Fig. 10.3. The image is produced by the projection lens which can be moved in and out of its mounting to focus the picture.

How must the slide be placed in a projector like that in Fig. 10.4 to give an erect image the right way round?

Fig. 10.4

Magnifying glass

A watchmaker's magnifying glass is shown in use in Fig. 10.5.

The sleepers on a railway track are all the same length but those nearby seem longer. This is because they enclose a larger angle at your eye than more distant ones: as a result their image on the retina is larger so making them appear bigger.

Fig. 10.5

A convex lens gives an enlarged, upright virtual image of an object placed inside its principal focus F, Fig. 10.6a. It acts as a magnifying glass since the angle β made at the eye by the image, formed at the near point, is greater than the angle α made by the object when it is viewed directly at the near point without the magnifying glass, Fig. 10.6b.

Fig. 10.6

The fatter (more curved) a convex lens is, the shorter is its focal length and the more does it magnify. Too much curvature however distorts the image.

Questions

1. Fig. 10.7a shows a camera focused on an object in the middle distance. Is the camera shown in Fig. 10.7b focused on a distant or a close object? Give a reason. (*E.A.*)

Fig. 10.7

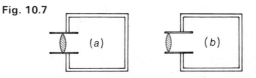

2. (*a*) In the diagram of the projector, Fig. 10.3, if the concave mirror has a focal length of 2 cm, how far must it be from the lamp to reflect the light as shown?

(*b*) If a projector is moved farther away from the screen on which it was giving a sharp image of a slide, state (*i*) *three* changes that occur in the image, (*ii*) how the projection lens must be adjusted to re-focus the image.

3. (*a*) Three converging lenses are available having focal lengths of 4 cm, 40 cm and 4 m respectively. Which one would you choose as a magnifying glass?

(*b*) An object 2 cm high is viewed through a converging lens of focal length 8 cm. The object is 4 cm from the lens. By means of a ray diagram find the position, nature and magnification of the image.

11 Microscopes and telescopes

Compound microscope

A compound microscope gives much greater magnification than a magnifying glass and less distortion. In its simplest form it consists of two *short-focus* convex lenses arranged as in Fig. 11.1.

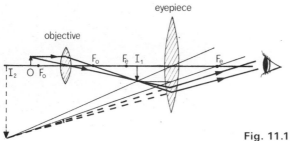

Fig. 11.1

The one nearer the object, called the *objective*, forms a real enlarged, inverted image I_1 of a small object O placed just outside its principal focus F_0. I_1 is just inside the principal focus F_e of the second lens, the *eyepiece*, which treats I_1 as an object and acts as a magnifying glass to give a further enlarged, virtual image I_2.

The thicker arrowed lines are actual rays from O, by which the eye sees the top of I_2. The thin lines without arrows are construction lines drawn to find the position of I_2.

To reduce distortion in a microscope, Fig. 11.2, the objective and eyepiece each consist of several lenses. The object is seen inverted.

Fig. 11.2

Refracting astronomical telescope

A lens astronomical telescope consists of two convex lenses, a *long-focus* objective and a *short-focus* eyepiece. Rays from a *point* on a distant object, e.g. a star, are nearly parallel on reaching the telescope (see p. 23). The objective forms a real, inverted, diminished image I_1 of the object at its principal focus F_o, Fig. 11.3. The eyepiece acts as a magnifying glass treating I_1 as an object and forming a magnified, virtual image. Normally the eyepiece is adjusted to give this final image at infinity, i.e. a long way off, and so I_1 will be at the principal focus F_e of the eyepiece. That is, F_o and F_e coincide. The object is seen inverted.

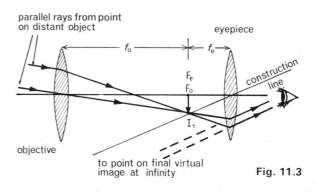

Fig. 11.3

A telescope magnifies because the final image it forms, subtends a much greater angle at the eye than does the distant object viewed without the telescope. Fig. 11.3 shows that the longer the focal length of the objective, the larger is I_1, and so for greatest magnification the objective should have a long focal length and the eyepiece a short one (like any magnifying glass).

Experiment: simple lens telescope

Arrange a carbon filament lamp at the far end of the room. Mount a long-focus convex lens (e.g. 50 cm) at eye-level, Fig. 11.4a. Point it at the lamp and find its image on a piece of greaseproof paper.

Insert a short-focus convex lens (e.g. 5 cm) as the eyepiece and adjust it so that you can see the image on the greaseproof paper clearly, Fig. 11.4b. Remove the paper and view the image of the lamp. Look at a book beside the lamp and outside objects.

Fig. 11.4

Fig. 11.6

Reflecting astronomical telescope

The objective of a telescope must have a large diameter as well as a large focal length. This (*i*) gives it good light-gathering power so that faint objects can be seen and (*ii*) enables it to reveal detail.

The largest *lens* telescope has an objective of diameter 1 metre; anything more would sag under its own weight. The biggest astronomical telescopes use long-focus *concave mirrors* as objectives; they can be supported at the back. Fig. 11.5 shows how parallel rays from a distant point object are reflected at the objective and then intercepted by a small plane mirror before they form a real image I_1. This image is magnified by the eyepiece.

The Mount Palomar telescope in California, Fig. 11.6, has a mirror of diameter 5 metres.

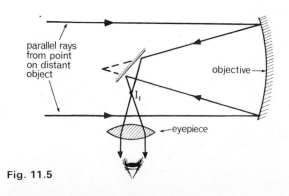

Fig. 11.5

Questions

1. Select from the list **A** to **E** the pairs of lenses most suitable for (*a*) a compound microscope, (*b*) an astronomical telescope.

A Two concave lenses of focal lengths 100 cm and 5 cm.
B Two convex lenses of focal lengths 100 cm and 5 cm.
C Two concave lenses of focal lengths 5 cm and 3 cm.
D Two convex lenses of focal lengths 5 cm and 3 cm.
E A convex lens of focal length 5 cm and a concave lens of focal length 3 cm. (*J.M.B.*)

Fig. 11.7

2. A and B are two convex lenses correctly set up as a telescope to view a distant object, Fig. 11.7. One has focal length 5 cm and the other 100 cm.

(*a*) What is A called and what is its focal length?
(*b*) How far from A is the first image of the distant object?
(*c*) What is B called?
(*d*) What acts as the 'object' for B and how far must B be from it if someone looking through the telescope is to see the final image at the same distance as the distant object?
(*e*) What is the distance between A and B with the telescope set up as in (*d*)?

3. (*a*) What is used as the objective in (*i*) an optical refracting telescope, (*ii*) an optical reflecting telescope?

(*b*) Give *two* reasons for an optical telescope having an objective of large diameter. (*J.M.B./A.L./N.W.16+*)

31

12 Further questions

Light rays

1. Which one of the following statements about the image produced in a pinhole camera is correct?

  A The image is bigger if the object is further away.

  B The image is smaller if the screen is nearer the pinhole.

  C The image is brighter if the object is further away.

  D The image is sharper if the pinhole is made bigger.

  E The image is bigger if the object is brighter.
                           (*O./S.R.16+*)

2. The diagram (Fig. 12.1) shows an illuminated arrow of length 6 cm placed 40 cm in front of a pinhole camera 16 cm in length having two small holes, H_1 and H_2, 4 cm apart.

Fig. 12.1

  (*a*) Make a scale diagram and draw suitable rays from the luminous arrow to show how two images are formed on the back of the box.

  (*b*) Show why one large blurred image is obtained if the cardboard between the small holes is cut away to form one large circular hole of diameter 4 cm.   (*L.*)

3. A boy finds that by holding an opaque circular disc, 8.0 mm in diameter, at a distance of 90 cm from his eye he can just cover the full moon. Calculate the diameter of the moon if it is at a distance of 380 000 km. Upon what property of light does this test depend?   (*S.*)

4. Eclipses of the sun can be described as total, partial or annular. Explain with the aid of diagrams, how the three types of eclipse are formed.

  Show clearly where observers must be to see each of these eclipses.   (*J.M.B.*)

Reflection of light: plane mirrors

5. The image in a plane mirror is

  A upright, real with a magnification of 2

  B upright, virtual with a magnification of 1

  C inverted, real with a magnification of $\frac{1}{2}$

  D inverted, virtual with a magnification of 1

  E inverted, real with a magnification of 2

6. Describe an experiment to determine the position of the image formed by a plane mirror. State the expected result of such an experiment.

  Explain the meaning of the term 'parallax errors' as applied to the reading of a pointer on a scale and describe how this error may be reduced by using a plane mirror.

Fig. 12.2

  Three plane mirrors are arranged along three sides of a square as shown in Fig. 12.2 and a ray of light is incident on the mirror AB at its mid-point with an angle of incidence of 40° so that the ray is afterwards reflected by BC and CD. Copy the diagram, sketch the approximate path of the ray and calculate the angle through which the ray is turned at each of the three reflections.   (*J.M.B.*)

7. Show by a ray diagram how a suitably placed eye sees an image of a point object which is placed 10 cm in front of a plane mirror. Show clearly the position of the image and give two reasons why it is described as virtual.   (*L.*)

Curved mirrors

8. An object stands at the centre of curvature of a concave mirror. What sort of image appears?

  A Virtual and upright

  B Upright and magnified

  C Magnified and real

  D Real and inverted

  E Inverted and virtual.   (*S.R.*)

9. State the *laws of reflection of light.* Copy Fig. 12.3 and indicate clearly the paths of the *incident* rays before reflection at (*a*) the plane mirror, (*b*) the convex mirror having its centre of curvature at C.

Fig. 12.3

What advantage does this indicate that a convex mirror may have over a plane mirror? (*L.*)

10. A parallel beam of light is produced by reflection from a concave mirror when the point source of light is

A at the principal focus of the mirror F
B at the centre of curvature C
C between C and F
D between the mirror and F
E further from the mirror than C. (*J.M.B.*)

11. An object is placed 20 cm in front of (*a*) a plane mirror, (*b*) a concave mirror of focal length 10 cm. State the similarities and differences between the images in each case. (Diagrams are not essential.) (*S.*)

12. Find by means of ray diagrams drawn to suitable scales, the size, nature and position of the image of a small object 2.0 cm high which is placed (*a*) 50 cm, (*b*) 10 cm in front of a concave mirror of focal length 15 cm. The object is perpendicular to, and has one end on, the axis of the mirror.

Refraction: total internal reflection

13. Fig. 12.4 shows the end view of a glass prism whose angles are 30°, 60° and 90°. Light passes into the prism in the direction AB and some of it after reflection in the face XY emerges in the direction BA. What is the angle of refraction of the ray AB at B? If the refractive index of the glass is 1.5, what is the angle of incidence *i*? (*O. and C.*)

Fig. 12.4

14. An observer whose eye is at E, 3.0 metres above the surface of the water, stands upright on the edge of a tank which has a horizontal bottom and is 10 metres wide. He looks straight across to the opposite side and notices that a small block of wood floating on the surface of the water obscures the deepest point X, on the opposite side when the block is 6.0 metres away from the nearer side of the tank, as shown in Fig. 12.5.

Fig. 12.5

Note: diagram not to scale

Assuming the refractive index of water relative to air is 4/3 determine, by scale drawing or otherwise,

(*i*) the apparent depth of the point X to the observer, and

(*ii*) the actual depth of water in the tank. (*L.*)

15. Light travels up through a pond of water of refractive index 4/3. What happens at the surface if the angle of incidence is (*a*) 30°, (*b*) 60°?

Lenses

16. An illuminated object is placed at a distance of 15 cm from a convex lens of focal length 10 cm. The image obtained on a screen is

A upright and magnified
B upright and the same size
C inverted and magnified
D inverted and the same size
E inverted and diminished (*N.I.*)

17. An object is set up 0.20 m (20 cm) in front of lens *A* and the details of the image are noted and are shown below. The process is repeated for a different lens *B*.

Lens A. Real, inverted, magnified and at a great distance.

Lens B. Real, inverted and same size as the object.

State the type of each lens and give as definite a value as possible for each focal length, explaining how you arrive at the values given. (*J.M.B.*)

18. (a) What is meant by the focal length of a converging (convex) lens?

(b) Define magnification.

(c) How would you determine by an experiment the focal length of a converging lens, first approximately and then more accurately?

(d) An object 1.5 cm high stands upright on the axis of a converging lens of focal length 4.0 cm. The object is placed in turn at distances 8.0 cm, 7.0 cm and 2.0 cm from the lens. For each of these positions determine the position, nature and size of the image.
(*J.M.B./A.L./N.W.16+*)

19. Fig. 12.6 shows a pin AB, a converging lens L and a plane mirror M. The pin and the mirror are held perpendicular to the principal axis of the lens, and the point A, of the pin, is at the principal focus of the lens.

Fig. 12.6

Make two copies of this arrangement. On one copy, trace the paths of *two* rays of light from the point A of the pin, passing through the lens and reflected by the mirror through the lens again. On the second copy, trace the paths of *two* rays from the head B of the pin, passing through the lens and reflected by the mirror through the lens again.
(*C.*)

20. Three lenses L_1, L_2 and L_3 have powers of +5, +2.5 and −20 D respectively.

(a) Which is/are convex and which concave?

(b) Which would be the 'strongest' magnifying glass?

(c) What is the focal length of each one?

The eye

21. Fig. 12.7 shows a simplified section of a human eye.

Fig. 12.7

(a) Name the parts labelled A, B and C and explain what happens there.

(b) What is the effect if light goes through the lens on to the nerve ending D?

(c) Why does the eye automatically turn to look straight at an object if possible? (*S.R.*)

22. What changes occur in the normal eye when, after looking at a dimly lit distant object, one reads a brightly lit book? (*O. and C.*)

23. A man is obliged to hold a newspaper at arm's length in order to read it.

(a) State a defect of vision which would cause this.

(b) What type of spectacle lenses would he require to correct this defect?

Colour

24. Draw a diagram showing an arrangement of apparatus to project a pure spectrum from white light onto a screen and indicate the paths of rays that produce the blue and red parts of the spectrum.

Account for the separation of the colours. (*L.*)

25. Three lamphouses A, B and C, each with a filter of one of the primary colours as shown in Fig. 12.8, are set up equal distances apart on a line parallel to a white screen so as to direct beams of equal intensity onto the centre of the screen. An opaque

Fig. 12.8

rectangular object painted white is placed halfway between the line of the lamps and the screen as shown. If the width of this object is slightly less than the distance between adjacent lamps, describe and explain the appearance of the object and the screen, using a diagram to indicate the parts of the screen referred to in your description. (*J.M.B.*)

26. Why is the result of mixing blue and yellow paints very different from that of mixing blue and yellow lights?

Optical instruments

27. (a) Draw a ray diagram to show the action of the converging (convex) lens in a variable focus camera when it is being used to photograph a very close object. Mark the position of the principal focus of the lens and label it F.

(b) If we now wish to take a photograph of a more distant object we must adjust the focusing. How will this adjustment affect the distance between the lens and the film in the camera?

(*J.M.B./A.L./N.W.16+*)

28. Compare the optical system of the eye with that of a camera. Discuss in particular the focusing of objects at different distances, the regulation of the amount of light entering the system and the nature of the images formed. (*N.I.*)

29. Draw a diagram of a slide projector and use it to explain the function of the condenser lens and the concave mirror placed behind the light source.

What advantage has a matt white surface for the screen over a glossy surface?

A slide projector using a slide $5\,\text{cm} \times 5\,\text{cm}$ produces a picture $3\,\text{m} \times 3\,\text{m}$ on a screen placed at a distance of $24\,\text{m}$ from the projection lens. How far from the lens must the slide be? Make an approximate estimate of the focal length of the projection lens. If this lens gets broken and the only substitute available is one of about half its focal length, what would you do to arrange that the picture is still the same size? (*O. and C.*)

30. Draw a ray diagram to show the action of a magnifying glass. Is the image real or virtual? Explain your answer.

31. Draw a ray diagram to show how two lenses may be used to construct a compound microscope. State the type of each lens and its approximate focal length. Show on the diagram the positions of the principal foci of the lenses in relation to the object and image positions. (*J.M.B.*)

32. (a) Draw a simple ray diagram of a reflecting telescope.

(b) What advantages has this type of telescope over a refractor?

(c) Why should the objective of the telescope be as large as possible?

(d) What factors determine the magnification obtained?

(e) What observational advantage is gained by putting an optical telescope in orbit in a satellite? (*A.L.*)

13 Water waves

Many kinds of wave occur in physics. A wave can be produced simply by fixing one end of a rope (or spring) and jerking the other end, Fig. 13.1. The humps and hollows forming the wave, travel along

Fig. 13.1

the rope but each part of the rope moves to and fro *at right angles* to the direction of the wave. Such a wave is called a *transverse* wave.

Waves carry energy from one place to another.

Describing waves

Fig. 13.2 helps to explain the terms used.

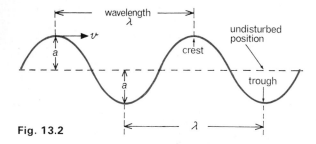

Fig. 13.2

(*a*) *Wavelength*, represented by the Greek letter λ (lambda), is the distance between successive crests.

(*b*) *Frequency f* is the number of complete waves generated per second. If the end of a rope is jerked up and down twice in a second, two waves are produced in this time. The frequency of the wave is 2 vibrations per second or 2 *hertz* (2 Hz; the hertz being the unit of frequency) as is the frequency of jerking of the end of the rope. That is, the frequencies of the wave and its source are equal.

The frequency of a wave is also the number of crests passing a chosen point per second.

(*c*) *Speed v* of the wave is the distance moved by a crest or any point on the wave in 1 second.

(*d*) *Amplitude a* is the height of a crest or the depth of a trough measured from the undisturbed position of what is carrying the wave, e.g. a rope.

The wave equation

The faster the end of a rope is waggled the shorter is the wavelength of the wave produced. That is, the higher the frequency of a wave the smaller its wavelength. There is a useful connection between f, λ and v which is true for all types of wave.

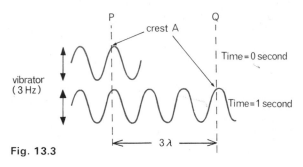

Fig. 13.3

Suppose waves of wavelength $\lambda = 20$ cm travel on a long rope and three crests pass a certain point every second. The frequency $f = 3$ Hz. If Fig. 13.3 represents this wave motion then if crest A is at P at a particular time, 1 second later it will be at Q, a distance from P of three wavelengths, i.e. $3 \times 20 = 60$ cm. The speed of the wave $v = 60$ cm per second (60 cm/s). Therefore

$$\text{speed of wave} = \text{frequency} \times \text{wavelength}$$

or,

$$v = f\lambda$$

Experiments: the ripple tank

The behaviour of water waves can be studied in a ripple tank. This consists of a transparent tray containing water, having a lamp above and a white screen below, Fig. 13.4.

Pulses (i.e. short bursts) of ripples are obtained by dipping a finger in the water for circular ones and a ruler for straight ones. *Continuous* ripples are

Fig. 13.4

Fig. 13.6

generated by an electric motor on a bar which gives straight ripples if it just touches the water and circular ripples if the bar is raised and a small ball fitted to it so as to be in the water.

Continuous ripples are studied more easily if they are *apparently* stopped ('frozen') by viewing the screen through a disc, with equally spaced slits, that can be spun by hand, i.e. a stroboscope.

In the effects that follow it is best to look at pulses first and continuous ripples afterwards.

Reflection

Fig. 13.5

In Fig. 13.5 *straight* water waves are represented falling on a metal strip placed in a ripple tank at an angle of 60°, i.e. the angle i between the direction of travel of the waves and the normal to the strip is 60°, as is the angle between the wavefront and the strip. The angle of reflection r is 60°. Incidence at other angles shows that the angles of reflection and incidence are always equal.

The pattern given by a *circular* pulse starting at A and falling on a straight strip is shown in Fig.

13.6. The reflected pulse seems to come from B which is as far behind the strip as A is in front.

Reflection at spherical surfaces is shown in Fig. 13.7. In (a) the incident straight wave, which is another way of representing a parallel beam, is converged after reflection to the principal focus F as a circular wave. In (b) the incident circular wave from F is reflected as a straight wave. In (c) the incident straight wave produces a reflected circular wave which appears to come from a virtual principal focus F behind the reflector.

Water waves evidently behave in the same way as light when reflected.

Fig. 13.7

Refraction

Fig. 13.8

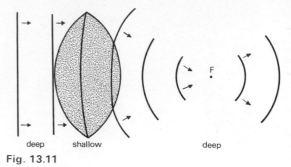

Fig. 13.11

Refraction of a straight wave at a curved surface can be shown by the focusing action of a lens-shaped area of shallow water formed by having a convex piece of perspex in the tank, Fig. 13.11.

If a glass plate is placed in a ripple tank so that the water is about 1 mm deep over it but 5 mm elsewhere, continuous straight waves in the shallow region are found to have a shorter wavelength than those in the deeper parts, Fig. 13.8a. Both sets of waves have the frequency of the vibrating bar and since $v = f\lambda$, then if λ has decreased so has v, since f is fixed. Hence *waves travel more slowly in shallow water.*

When the plate is at an angle to the waves, Fig. 13.8b, their direction of travel in the shallow region is bent towards the normal, Fig. 13.9, i.e. refraction

Diffraction

In Figs. 13.12a, b, straight water waves in a ripple tank are falling on gaps formed by obstacles. In (a) the gap width is about the same as the wavelength of the waves (1 cm); those passing through are circular and spread out in all directions. In (b) the gap is wide (10 cm) compared with the wavelength and the waves continue straight on; some spreading occurs but it is less obvious.

The spreading of waves at the edges of obstacles is called *diffraction*; when designing harbours, engineers use models like that in Fig. 13.13 to study it.

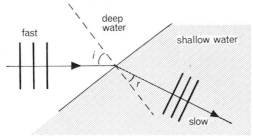

Fig. 13.9

Fig. 13.12

occurs. To see that this is due to the change of speed, consider three people A, B, C marching in line and in step, on a road. On approaching a marsh obliquely, Fig. 13.10, A is slowed first and takes shorter paces to keep in step with the others. The line therefore wheels round.

Fig. 13.10

(a)

(b)

38

Fig. 13.13

Interference

When two sets of continuous circular waves cross in a ripple tank, a pattern like that in Fig. 13.14a is obtained.

Fig. 13.14

(a)

(b)

crest
crest
+
=
crest

crest
+
=
water at rest
trough

At points where a crest from S_1 arrives at the same time as a crest from S_2, a bigger crest is formed and the waves are said to be *in phase*. At points where a crest and a trough arrive together, they cancel out (if their amplitudes are equal); the waves are exactly *out of phase* (due to travelling different distances from S_1 and S_2) and the water is undisturbed, Fig. 13.14b. The dark 'spokes' radiating from S_1 and S_2 join such points.

Interference is the combination of waves to give a larger or a smaller wave.

Study the effect with two ball 'dippers' about 3 cm apart on the bar. Also observe the result of changing (*i*) the frequency, (*ii*) the separation of the 'dippers': use a stroboscope when necessary.

Similar patterns are obtained if straight waves fall on two small gaps: interference occurs between the emerging (circular), diffracted waves.

Questions

1. The lines in Fig. 13.15 are crests of straight ripples.
   (*a*) What is the wavelength of the ripples?
   (*b*) If ripple A occupied 5 seconds ago the position now occupied by ripple F, what is the frequency of the ripples?
   (*c*) What is the speed of the ripples?

Fig. 13.15

2. A straight ripple ABC is shown in Fig. 13.16 moving towards a wall XY. Draw one diagram to show the position of the ripple when B reaches the wall and another when C reaches it. On each diagram mark the angles which are 30°.

Fig. 13.16   Fig. 13.17

3. One side of a ripple tank ABCD is raised slightly, Fig. 13.17, and a ripple started at P by a finger. After a second the shape of the ripple is as shown.
   (*a*) Why is it not circular?
   (*b*) Which side of the tank has been raised?

4. Fig. 13.18 gives a full-scale representation of the water in a ripple tank 1 second after the vibrator was started. The dark lines represent crests.

Fig. 13.18

(*a*) What is represented at A at this instant?
(*b*) Estimate (*i*) the wavelength, (*ii*) the speed of the waves, and (*iii*) the frequency of the vibrator.
(*c*) Sketch a suitable attachment which could have been vibrated up and down to produce this wave pattern.
(*d*) Explain how the waves combine (*i*) at B and (*ii*) at C.

39

14 Light waves

Although we cannot see how light travels it displays the properties of waves.

Diffraction

Fig. 14.1

Diffraction occurs when light passes the edge of an object but it is not easy to detect. This suggests that it has a very small wavelength since we saw that diffraction of water waves is most obvious at a gap when its width is comparable with the wavelength of the waves. Fig. 14.1 is the diffraction pattern of a very narrow vertical slit and shows how light has spread into regions that would be in shadow if it went exactly in straight lines.

Interference

When light falls on two narrow slits very close together, Fig. 14.2, a pattern of equally spaced bright and dark bands (called *fringes*) is obtained on a screen, Fig. 14.3. It can be explained by assuming that diffraction occurs at each slit and in the

Fig. 14.3

region where the two diffracted beams cross, interference occurs, Fig. 14.4a.

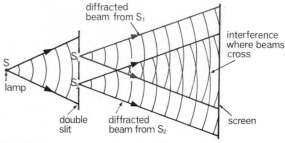

Fig. 14.4a

At points on the screen where a 'crest' from one slit arrives at the same time as a 'crest' from the other, the waves are in phase and there are bright bands. Dark bands occur where 'crests' and 'troughs' arrive simultaneously and the waves cancel. We then have: light + light = darkness. This makes sense only if we regard light as having a wave

Fig. 14.2

nature. A similar experiment was performed by Young in 1801.

With white light all the bright bands except the centre one are coloured. With red light the bright bands are red and they are farther apart than the blue bands obtained with blue light. We will show below that the wavelength λ of the light used is given by

$$\lambda = \frac{\text{slit separation} \times \text{bright band separation}}{\text{distance of slits from screen}}$$

This shows that red light has a longer wavelength than blue light.

Fig. 14.4*b*

In Fig. 14.4*b*, S_1 and S_2 are the two slits, O is the position of the *central* bright band, A is the position of the *first* bright band and C is the mid-point of S_1S_2. S_2A must be one wavelength (λ) longer than S_1A. If S_1P is drawn perpendicular to CA then S_2P will be approximately equal to λ. The shaded triangles S_1S_2P and CAO will be similar for all practical purposes. Therefore

$$\frac{S_2P}{OA} = \frac{S_1S_2}{CA}$$

$$\therefore \quad S_2P = \frac{S_1S_2 \times OA}{CA}$$

In symbols,
$$\lambda = \frac{a \times y}{D}$$

Experiment: wavelength of light by double slit

Arrange the apparatus as in Fig. 14.2 ensuring that the filament of the lamp is *vertical*, is parallel to the double slit and at the same height. Darken the room and shield the screen from stray light. View the fringes from behind the screen.

Three measurements must be made.

(i) *Bright band separation* (*y*). The distance from the centre of one bright band to the centre of the next has to be found. This is done by measuring across as many bands as can be seen (they are equally spaced). To do this make two marks at appropriate

places on the screen whilst looking at the bands. Measure the distance afterwards in daylight with a mm scale. In the case shown in Fig. 14.2 the distance measured is 4*y*.

(ii) *Distance of slits from screen* (*D*). Measure this with a metre rule (about 2 m).

(iii) *Slit separation* (*a*). Do this in daylight by one of the following methods. Lay the double slit and a $\frac{1}{2}$ mm transparent scale on white paper and compare them with a lens. A second, better method is to examine them together under a microscope. A third alternative is to hold both double slit and scale in a slide projector and view their images on a distant wall.

Substitute your measurements in $\lambda = ay/D$ and obtain an estimate for the average wavelength of white light in m.

Diffraction grating

A diffraction grating consists of a piece of glass or plastic with a large number of parallel lines marked on it. The lines scatter light and in effect are opaque. The thin clear strips between the lines transmit light and act as slits.

When white light from a straight filament lamp is viewed through a grating a number of spectra (plural of spectrum) are seen, each like that given by a prism. The spectra are said to be of various 'orders'. A 'fine' grating with say 300 lines per mm gives the zero, first and second orders, Fig. 14.5. A 'coarse' grating, e.g. 100 lines per mm, gives more

Fig. 14.5

orders closer together and the 'coarser' the grating the more does the pattern resemble the two-slits one.

The slits are only a few wavelengths wide and when light falls on them, diffraction occurs causing cylindrical waves to spread out from each one. In certain *directions* the diffracted waves are in phase and if brought to a focus by a lens or the eye, they reinforce. In other directions they more or less cancel.

In Fig. 14.6a suppose a first order spectrum is formed in a direction making an angle θ with the incident light of wavelength λ. The diffracted waves from each slit must travel a distance λ more (or less) than those from the next slit, i.e. the path difference between the waves is one wavelength. What will it be for (i) the zero order spectrum, (ii) a second order spectrum?

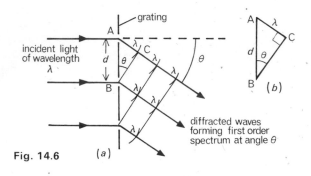

Fig. 14.6   (a)

In triangle ABC, Fig. 14.6b, if d is the separation of adjacent slit centres (the *grating spacing*), then

$$\sin \theta = \lambda/d \quad \text{or} \quad \lambda = d \sin \theta$$

If we know d and measure θ, λ can be calculated. In general if n is the order of the spectrum

$$n\lambda = d \sin \theta$$

Experiment: wavelength of light by grating

Arrange the apparatus as in Fig. 14.7. Get someone to move a pencil along the metre rule until you see it in the centre of the first order spectrum. Measure x and l, then $\sin \theta = x/l$.

If the grating has 300 slits per mm, the slit separa-

Fig. 14.7

tion d is 1/300 mm or 1/300 000 m. Estimate the average wavelength of light using $\lambda = d \sin \theta$.

Refraction

Just as the refraction of water waves is considered to be due to a change of speed so the refraction of light waves is attributed to the fact that light travels more slowly in a denser medium. It can be shown that

$$\text{refractive index} = \frac{\text{speed of light in air}}{\text{speed of light in medium}}$$

Red sunset: blue sky

The wavelength of red light is about twice that of blue light. The longer the wavelength the more penetrating is the light, while the shorter the wavelength the more easily is it scattered.

When the sun is setting the light from it has to travel through a greater thickness of the earth's atmosphere and only the longer wavelength red light is able to get through. Sunsets are therefore red.

The shorter wavelengths, like blue, are scattered in all directions by the atmosphere, which is why the sky looks blue.

Questions

1. In Fig. 14.8, L is a source of light, wavelength λ, $S_1 S_2$ a double slit and O, O_1 and O_2 are points on a screen.

Fig. 14.8

(a) If the central bright band is formed at O, how do the distances $S_1 O$ and $S_2 O$ compare?

(b) If the first dark band next to the central bright band is formed at O_1, how do $S_1 O_1$ and $S_2 O_1$ compare?

(c) If the first bright band occurs at O_2 next to the first dark band, how do $S_1 O_2$ and $S_2 O_2$ compare?

2. In a double slit experiment with white light the slit separation is 0.25 mm, the fringe width is 4 mm and the distance from the slits to the screen is 2 m. Find the average wavelength of white light in micrometres (μm). ($1 \, \mu$m $= 10^{-6}$ m.)

3. Light of wavelength 6.0×10^{-7} m is incident normally on a diffraction grating which has 6000 rulings per cm.

(a) What is the grating spacing, in metres?

(b) At what angle to the straight-through direction does the first diffracted beam emerge?   (*O./S.R.16+*)

4. Calculate the speed of light in glass of refractive index 1.5 if its speed in air is 3.0×10^8 m/s.

15 Electromagnetic spectrum

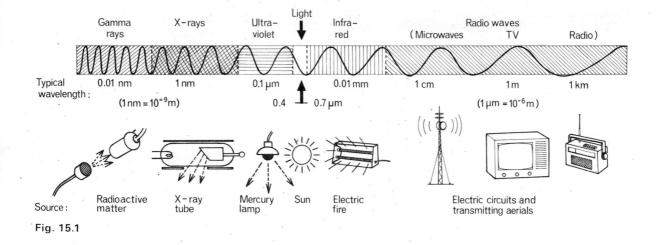

Fig. 15.1

The members of the electromagnetic spectrum, Fig. 15.1, are wave-like radiations which carry energy and exhibit interference and diffraction. They all travel at 300 million metres per second (3×10^8 m/s) in air. This is the speed of light. Their different wavelengths λ and frequencies f are related to their speed v by $v = f\lambda$.

Whilst each is produced differently, most result from electrons suffering some kind of energy change. For example, radio waves are emitted when electrons are accelerated in an aerial. Because of their electrical origin and ability to travel in a vacuum (e.g. from the sun to the earth), they are regarded as a combination of travelling electric and magnetic forces which vary in value and are directed at right angles to each other and to the direction of travel, i.e. they are transverse-type 'waves', Fig. 15.2.

Infrared radiation

The presence of infrared (i.r.) in the radiation from the sun or from the filament of an electric lamp can be detected by placing a phototransistor just beyond the red end of the spectrum formed (as explained on p. 26) by a prism, Fig. 15.3. Our bodies detect i.r. (also called 'radiant heat' or 'heat radiation') by its heating effect.

Anything which is hot but not glowing, i.e. below 500 °C, emits i.r. alone. At about 500 °C a body becomes red-hot and emits red light as well as i.r.; the heating element of an electric fire is an example. At about 1000 °C things such as lamp filaments are white-hot and radiate i.r. and white light, i.e. all the colours of the spectrum.

Infrared is also detected by special photographic films and pictures can be taken in the dark like that

Fig. 15.2

Fig. 15.3

Fig. 15.4

in Fig. 15.4 of a car; the white parts are hottest. Infrared lamps are used to dry the paint on cars during manufacture and in the treatment of muscular complaints. Infrared control units are used to operate TV sets remotely.

Ultraviolet radiation

Ultraviolet (u.v.) rays have shorter wavelengths than light and can be detected just beyond the violet end of the spectrum (due to the sun or a filament lamp) by fluorescent paper. They cause sun-tan and produce vitamins in the skin but an overdose can be harmful, especially to the eyes.

Ultraviolet causes teeth, finger nails, fluorescent paints and clothes washed in detergents to fluoresce, i.e. they glow by reradiating as light the energy they absorb as u.v. The shells of fresh eggs fluoresce with a reddish colour, those of 'bad' eggs appear violet.

A u.v. lamp used for scientific or medical purposes contains mercury vapour and this emits u.v. when an electric current passes through it. Fluorescent tubes also contain mercury vapour and their inner surfaces are coated with powders which radiate light when struck by u.v.

Radio waves

Radio waves vary in wavelength from a few mm to several km. The shortest are called microwaves and are radiated by 'saucer-shaped' aerials like those in Fig. 15.5. They are used in radar and in a new method of cooking which cooks food right through quickly. VHF and TV signals have wavelengths of a few metres and travel in straight lines from sender to receiver. Long distance radio waves rely on 're-flection' from the *ionosphere*; this consists of layers of electrically charged gases between 80 and 400 km

Fig. 15.5

above the earth. For satellite communication, signals with wavelengths less than 10 m or so must be used since only they can penetrate the ionosphere.

Fig. 15.6

The wave nature of microwaves can be shown using the two-slits apparatus of Fig. 15.6 to demonstrate interference: the meter reading rises and falls on the receiver as it is moved across behind the metal plates.

X-rays

X-rays have smaller wavelengths than u.v. Their production is considered later (p. 221).

X-rays can penetrate solid objects and affect a film; Fig. 15.7 is an X-ray photograph of someone shaving. Very penetrating X-rays are used in hospitals to kill cancer cells. They also damage healthy cells so careful shielding of the X-ray tube with lead is needed. Less penetrating X-rays have longer wavelengths and penetrate flesh but not bone: they are used in dental X-ray photography.

In industry they are used to inspect welded joints and castings for faults.

Gamma rays are more penetrating and dangerous than X-rays and will be studied on pp. 222–3.

Fig. 15.7

Questions

1. Name *four* properties common to all electromagnetic waves.
2. Which of the following types of radiation has the largest frequency?

   A u.v.   B radio waves   C light   D X-rays   E i.r.

3. Name one type of electromagnetic radiation which (*a*) causes sun-tan, (*b*) bounces off the earth's upper atmosphere, (*c*) passes through a thin sheet of lead, (*d*) is used to take photographs in haze.

16 Sound waves

Sources of sound such as a drum, a guitar and the human voice have some part which *vibrates*. The sound travels through the air to our ears and we hear it. That the air is necessary may be shown by pumping out a glass jar containing a ringing electric bell, Fig. 16.1; the sound disappears though the striker can still be seen hitting the gong. Evidently sound cannot travel in a vacuum like light.

Fig. 16.1

glass jar

ringing electric bell

sponge pad

to battery

to vacuum pump

Other materials, including solids and liquids, transmit sound. 'Cathedral chimes' may be heard if you jingle together some spoons tied to a piece of string with its ends in your ears, Fig. 16.2. Not only does string (a solid) transmit sound but it does so better than air.

string

table spoons

Fig. 16.2

Sound also gives interference and diffraction effects, as we will see. Because of this and its other properties, we believe it is a form of energy (as the damage from supersonic booms shows) which travels as a wave, but of a type called *longitudinal*.

Longitudinal waves

In a longitudinal wave the particles of the transmitting medium vibrate in the *same direction* as that in which the wave is travelling and not at right angles to it as in a transverse wave. A longitudinal wave can be sent along a spring, stretched out on the bench and fixed at one end if the free end is repeatedly pushed and pulled sharply. Compressions C (where the coils are closer together) and rarefactions R (where the coils are farther apart), Fig. 16.3, travel along the spring.

Fig. 16.3

wave

C R C R C

fixed end

long spring

A sound wave produced for example by a loudspeaker consists of a train of compressions and rarefactions in the air, Fig. 16.4. The speaker has

Fig. 16.4

C R C R C

loudspeaker cone

λ λ

wave

a cone which is made to vibrate in and out by an electric current. When the cone moves out the air in front is compressed; when it moves in the air is rarefied (goes 'thinner'). The wave progresses through the air but the air as a whole does not move. The air particles vibrate backwards and forwards a little as the wave passes, and this causes the sound you hear when the wave reaches your ears.

The number of compressions produced per second is the frequency f of the sound wave (and equals the frequency of the vibrating cone); the distance between successive compressions is the wavelength λ. As for transverse waves the speed $v = f\lambda$.

Human beings hear only sounds with frequencies from about 20 Hz to 20 000 Hz (20 kHz). These are the *limits of audibility*; they decrease with age.

Reflection and echoes

Sound waves are reflected well from hard, flat surfaces such as walls or cliffs and obey the same laws of reflection as light. The reflected sound forms an *echo*.

If the reflecting surface is nearer than 15 m, the echo joins up with the original sound which then seems to be prolonged. This is called *reverberation*. Some is desirable in a concert hall to stop it sounding 'dead', but too much causes 'confusion'. In the Royal Festival Hall, London (p. 48), walls and seats are covered with sound-absorbing material.

Speed of sound

If you stand about 100 m from a high wall and clap your hands, echoes are obtained. When the clapping rate is such that each clap coincides with the echo of the previous one, the sound has travelled to the wall and back in the time between two claps, i.e. an interval. By timing 30 intervals with a stopwatch and knowing the distance to the wall, the speed of sound can be found roughly.

It is about 330 m/s in air at 0°C and increases at higher temperatures. In steel it is 6000 m/s.

Diffraction and interference

(*a*) *Diffraction*. A doorway has a width of 1 m which is comparable with the wavelength of much speech and music. It is therefore not surprising that sound is diffracted at such openings and we hear it round corners.

signal generator (2 kHz)

½ m

loudspeakers

Fig. 16.5

(*b*) *Interference*. In Fig. 16.5 the notes from two loudspeakers interfere to cause variations in the loudness of the sound heard when you pass them.

Ultrasonics

Sound waves with frequencies above 20 kHz are called *ultrasonic* waves. They are emitted by bats and enable them to judge the distance of an object from the time taken by the reflected wave to return. The same idea is used in spectacles for the blind; these contain an ultrasonic sender and receiver, Fig. 16.6.

Fig. 16.6

In the echo-sounding system called *sonar*, ships use ultrasonic waves to measure the depth of the sea and to detect shoals of fish. In industry they are used to reveal flaws in welded joints; also holes of any shape or size are cut in glass and steel by ultrasonic drills.

Questions

1. A coastguard sees a distress rocket burst in the sky and 5 seconds later he hears the bang. If the speed of sound is 330 m/s, how far is the exploding rocket from the coastguard?

    A 66 m   **B** 335 m   **C** 1100 m   **D** 1650 m
    E 3300 m.   (*S.E.*)

2. The time-keeper of a 110 m race stands near the finishing tape and starts his stop-watch on hearing the bang from the starting pistol.

    (*a*) When should he have started his stop-watch?
    (*b*) Give a reason for your answer to (*a*).
    (*c*) Calculate the error in his timing assuming he makes no further errors. (Speed of sound = 330 m/s.)   (*E.M.*)

3. (*a*) What is the relationship connecting the frequency of a sound source with its wavelength and the speed of sound in air?

    (*b*) An echo sounder in a ship produces a sound pulse and an echo is received from the sea bed after 0.4 s. Assuming the speed of sound in sea water to be 1500 m/s calculate the depth of the sea bed.

    (*c*) If the echo sounder had produced continuous waves of frequency 6000 Hz (6 kHz), what would have been their wavelength in the sea water? Give your value in cm.   (*N.W.*)

4. If 5 s elapse between a lightning flash and the clap of thunder how far away is the storm? Speed of sound = 330 m/s.

17 Musical notes

Fig. 17.1

Irregular vibrations cause *noise*, regular vibrations such as occur in the instruments of an orchestra, Fig. 17.1, produce *musical notes* which have three properties—pitch, loudness and quality.

Pitch

The pitch of a note depends on the frequency of the sound wave reaching the ear, i.e. on the frequency of the source of sound. A high-pitched note has a high frequency and a short wavelength. The frequency of middle C is 256 vibrations per second or 256 Hz and that of upper C is 512 Hz. Notes are an *octave* apart if the frequency of one is twice that of the other. Pitch is like colour in light; both depend on the frequency.

Notes of known frequency can be produced in the laboratory by a signal generator supplying alternating electric current (a.c.) to a loudspeaker. The cone of the speaker vibrates at the frequency of the a.c. which can be varied and read off a scale on the generator. A set of tuning forks with frequencies marked on them can also be used. A tuning fork, Fig. 17.2, has two steel prongs which vibrate when struck; the prongs move in and out *together*, generating compressions and rarefactions.

Loudness

A note is louder when more sound energy enters our ears per second than before and is caused by the source vibrating with a larger amplitude. If a violin string is bowed more strongly, its amplitude of vibration increases as does that of the resulting sound wave and the note heard is louder because more energy has been used to produce it.

Quality

The same note on different instruments sounds different; we say the notes differ in *quality* or *timbre*. The difference arises because no instruments

Fig. 17.2

prong

stem

(except a tuning fork and a signal generator) emit a 'pure' note, i.e. of one frequency. Notes consist of a main or *fundamental* frequency mixed with others, called *overtones*, which are usually weaker and have frequencies that are exact multiples of the fundamental. The number and strength of the overtones decides the quality of a note. A violin has more and stronger higher overtones than a piano. Overtones of 256 Hz (middle C) are 512 Hz, 768 Hz and so on.

The *waveform* of a note played near a microphone connected to a c.r.o. (p. 219) can be displayed on the c.r.o. screen. Those for the *same* note on three instruments are given in Fig. 17.3. Their different

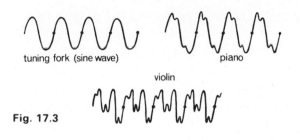

tuning fork (sine wave) piano

violin

Fig. 17.3

shapes show that while they have the same fundamental frequency, their quality differs. The 'pure' note of a tuning fork has a *sine* waveform and is the simplest kind of sound wave. *N.B.* Although the waveform on the c.r.o. screen is transverse it represents a longitudinal sound wave.

Vibrating strings

In a string instrument such as a guitar the 'string' is a tightly-stretched wire or length of gut. When it is plucked transverse waves travel to both ends, which are fixed, and are reflected. Interference occurs between the incident and reflected waves and a *stationary* or *standing* wave pattern is formed. In this, certain points on the string, called *nodes*, are at rest whilst points mid-way between each pair of nodes are in continuous vibration with maximum amplitude; they are called *antinodes*.

A string can vibrate in various ways. If the standing wave has one loop. Fig. 17.4*a*, the fundamental note is emitted. If there is more than one loop, Figs. 17.4*b*, *c*, overtones are produced, but in all cases the *separation of the nodes N and the antinodes A is one-quarter of the wavelength* of the wave on the string causing the note. In an instrument, a string vibrates in several ways at the same time depending on where it is plucked, this decides the quality of the note.

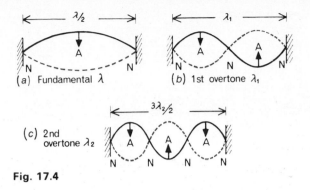

(a) Fundamental λ (b) 1st overtone λ_1

(c) 2nd overtone λ_2

Fig. 17.4

The standing wave patterns of a vibrating string (or rubber cord) may be viewed as in Fig. 17.5.

Fig. 17.5

Frequency of a vibrating string

The frequency *f* of the *fundamental* note emitted by a vibrating string of length *l*, mass per unit length *m* and under tension *T* is given by

$$f = \frac{1}{2l}\sqrt{\frac{T}{m}}$$

Hence *f* increases if *l* is reduced or *T* increased or *m* reduced; short, thin, tightly stretched wires therefore emit high notes.

These relationships can be verified experimentally using a *sonometer*, Fig. 17.6. For example, to see how *l* affects *f*, a tuning fork say of frequency 256 Hz is struck and, keeping A fixed, B is moved until the note given by plucking the centre of the

Fig. 17.6

wire is the same as that of the fork. Non-musicians can do this by a resonance method (see later) in which a small V-shaped strip of paper (a 'rider') is placed inverted at the centre of the wire and the length adjusted while the stem of the vibrating fork is held on one of the bridges. When the wire is tuned to the fork the rider jumps off. With the same wire under the same tension the lengths for other forks are found and if $f \propto 1/l$ then $f \times l$ should be constant.

Resonance

All objects have a natural frequency of vibration. The vibration can be started and increased by another object vibrating at the same frequency. The effect is called *resonance*. For example, when the heavy pendulum X in Fig. 17.7 is set swinging, it forces all the light ones to swing at the same frequency, but D, which has the same length as X, does so with a much larger amplitude, i.e. D resonates with X.

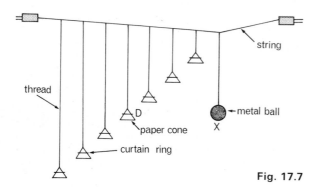

Fig. 17.7

If a large structure such as a suspension bridge starts vibrating at its natural frequency the result can be disastrous. The collapse of the Tacoma Narrows Bridge, USA, in 1940 was due to a cross-wind of just the 'right' speed to cause resonant vibrations, Fig. 17.8a, b. Models of new bridges are now tested

Fig. 17.8   (a)   (b)

in wind tunnels to check that their natural frequencies are not dangerous.

Resonance also occurs in sound. We have seen how it is used to tune a sonometer wire to a fork; other examples follow.

Vibrating air columns

In wind instruments musical notes are produced by *standing longitudinal* waves in a column of air in a tube open at one or both ends. A disturbance at one end of the tube causes sound waves to travel to the other end where they are reflected. Interference occurs between the incident and reflected waves and a standing wave is formed. In an organ pipe the disturbance is created by a jet of air hitting a sharp edge.

An air column, like a stretched string, can vibrate in various ways. The closed end of a tube must always be a node N since the air there cannot vibrate longitudinally. At an open end the air can vibrate freely and this is always an antinode A. The fundamental frequency is emitted when the standing wave is the simplest possible, i.e. Fig. 17.9a for a closed tube and Fig. 17.10a for an open tube.

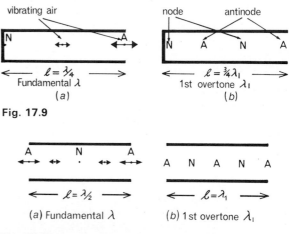

Fig. 17.9

Fig. 17.10

Overtones occur with more nodes and antinodes in the column, Figs. 17.9b and 17.10b. As with strings, *nodes and antinodes are one-quarter of a wavelength apart.*

The different vibrations of an air column may be shown as in Fig. 17.11. At certain frequencies (about 250, 500, 750 etc. Hz for a 65 cm long *open* tube), which can be read off from the signal generator, the air in the tube resonates with the note from the loudspeaker.

glass tube open both ends / small speaker / to signal generator

Fig. 17.11

The pipes of the Festival Hall organ can be seen in Fig. 17.1; the longest emit the lowest notes.

Experiment: speed of sound in air by resonance tube

If we know the frequency f of a tuning fork and measure the wavelength λ of the note it emits, the speed of sound v can be found from $v = f\lambda$.

Strike a tuning fork (e.g. 512 Hz) and hold it at the top of a very short air column in a tube with its lower end in water, Fig. 17.12. Slowly raise the

Fig. 17.12

tuning fork
glass tube
water
large glass jar

tube until the sound becomes a maximum. The air column is then resonating with the fork and is vibrating at its fundamental frequency, i.e. f; this is called the *first position of resonance*. Measure l_1, then

$$l_1 + c = \lambda/4 \quad \text{(Fig. 17.9a)} \quad (1)$$

where c is the *end correction*, i.e. the unknown distance which has to be added to l_1 because the antinode is not exactly at the top of the tube but is above it.

Raise the tube still further until a *second position of resonance* is found with the same fork. Measure l_2, the length of the longer air column which is producing its first overtone of frequency f. We can say

$$l_2 + c = 3\lambda/4 \quad \text{(Fig. 17.9b)} \quad (2)$$

Subtracting (1) from (2) eliminates c and gives

$$\lambda/2 = l_2 - l_1 \quad \text{or} \quad \lambda = 2(l_2 - l_1)$$

Then v is calculated from

$$v = f\lambda = 2f(l_2 - l_1)$$

Beats

When two notes of almost equal pitch are sounded together, the loudness rises and falls regularly and *beats* are said to be heard. The effect may be demonstrated with two signal generators each connected to a loudspeaker. Alternatively, two tuning forks of the same frequency can be used, one with a little Plasticine on one prong to lower its frequency slightly. They are struck at the same time and the stems pressed on the bench.

It can be proved that if f_1 and f_2 are the frequencies of the two notes, the number of beats per second, i.e. the beat frequency f, is $f_1 - f_2$. f decreases as f_1 and f_2 get closer.

Beats are due to interference and offer more evidence for the wave nature of sound.

Questions

1. (*a*) Draw the waveform of (*i*) a loud, low-pitched note and (*ii*) a soft, high-pitched note.

(*b*) If the speed of sound is 340 m/s what is the wavelength of a note of frequency (*i*) 340 Hz, (*ii*) 170 Hz?

2. (*a*) What change does your ear detect when you are listening to a sound if (*i*) the *amplitude* is raised, (*ii*) the *frequency* is raised?

(*b*) A certain length of guitar string gives the note middle C. (*i*) What note do you get with half the length? (*ii*) How could you raise the pitch of the note without changing the length?

(*c*) A trombone has a section which can move out to increase the tube length. What happens to the pitch of the note when the tube length is increased?

(*d*) When two tuning forks of almost the same frequency are sounded together, beats are heard. (*i*) What is meant by 'beats'? (*ii*) What is one wave doing to the other to cause the effect? (*iii*) A piano tuner listens to the beats between his tuning fork and the note on the piano. How can he tell that the note is improving? (*S.R.*)

3. A wire is stretched over bridges A, B and C as shown in Fig. 17.13. The bridges rest on a hollow box (a sonometer). X, Y and Z are light paper riders resting on the wire.

A   B   X   Y   Z   C

AB = BY = YC
BX = XY = YZ = ZC

Fig. 17.13

weights

When the wire is plucked gently midway between A and B, X and Z fall off but Y stays on the wire. Explain this, stating the names given to the points on the wire at X, Y and Z.

The same effect may be produced if the stem of a vibrating tuning fork is placed on the sonometer box. Why is this? (*L.*)

18 Further questions

Water waves

1. A straight vibrator causes water ripples to travel across the surface of a shallow tank. The waves travel a distance of 33 cm in 1.5 s and the distance between successive wave crests is 4.0 cm. Calculate the frequency of the vibrator.   (*W.*)

2. Fig. 18.1 shows a series of waves as might be produced in a laboratory experiment with a ripple tank. The waves are travelling from region A to region B.

Fig. 18.1

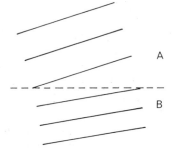

(*a*) Describe how these waves are produced.
(*b*) What is happening along the dotted line?
(*c*) By measurement, determine the wavelength of the waves in the region A and the region B.
(*d*) What can you say about the frequency of the waves in region A and region B?
(*e*) What can you say about the speed of waves in region A and region B?
(*f*) Where is the water deepest—at A or B?
    (*E.M.*)

3. Figs. 18.2*a* and *b* show ripples approaching metal plates with gaps in them. Gap (*a*) is narrow compared with the wavelength and gap (*b*) is wide compared with the wavelength.

Fig. 18.2

Copy the diagrams and draw the shapes of the ripples after passing through the gaps.   (*W.Y.*)

Light waves

4. Fig. 18.3 represents a wavefront PQ passing from air to another medium and producing a new wavefront RS after refraction. What is the refractive index of the medium?

Fig. 18.3

A sin 60/sin 70   **B** sin 20/sin 30
C sin 30/sin 20   **D** sin 70/sin 60
E sin 60/sin 20   (*J.M.B.*)

5. Fig. 18.4 represents wavefronts of light spreading from a point source O towards a converging lens.

Fig. 18.4

Draw diagrams of the wavefronts travelling from the lens when O is at (*i*) the principal focus and (*ii*) twice the distance of the principal focus from the lens.   (*A.E.B.*)

6. In a double slits experiment with light of wavelength 6×10^{-7} m the slits are 0.6 mm apart and the screen is 2 m away from the slits.

(*a*) Calculate the separation of successive bright bands.
(*b*) What would you see on the screen if one of the slits were covered up?

7. If you held a diffraction grating with its lines vertical close to the eye in a darkened room and looked through the grating at a small, bright source of white light some distance away, describe and explain what you might expect to see.

What is meant by the *order of a spectrum*?

If the second order spectrum of light of wavelength 6450×10^{-10} m coincides with the third order spectrum of some other wavelength, what is this wavelength? *(O. and C.)*

Electromagnetic spectrum

8. The strip in Fig. 18.5 represents part of the electromagnetic spectrum extending on both sides of the region of visible light C. If A is the region of shortest wavelengths and F the region of longest wavelengths, name which section will represent the *(a)* u.v. region, *(b)* X-rays, *(c)* i.r. region.

Fig. 18.5

State one difference between the behaviour of ultraviolet and X-rays. *(L.)*

9. Light travels at 3×10^8 m/s in air (300 000 000 m/s).
(a) How fast do radio waves travel in air?
(b) What is the wavelength of the 80 MHz waves used for broadcasting on VHF? (1 MHz = 1 000 000 Hz.)
(c) What is the frequency of the 1500 m radio waves used on the Long Wave Band? *(S.R.)*

Sound waves

10. The property which distinguishes longitudinal waves from transverse waves is the
A wavelength
B velocity
C ability to be refracted
D need for a material medium
E relative directions of oscillation and propagation *(J.M.B.)*

11. *(a)* Explain *(i)* how sound is transmitted through air and *(ii)* why several echoes may be heard when a sharp sound is made in a large hall.
(b) Describe an experiment which shows that sound waves require a material medium for their transmission.
(c) A boy claps his hands once every second and hears the echo from a tall building. When he is 85 m away from the building, he hears the echo of each clap mid-way between it and the next clap. Calculate the speed of sound. *(A.E.B.)*

12. Two loudspeakers play the same note from a signal generator. A person moving across the line between them, Fig. 18.6, finds the note is loud in some places and soft in others.

Fig. 18.6

(a) Why is the note loud in some positions and soft in others?
(b) What difference would it make to use a higher frequency note? Why? *(O./S.R.16+)*

Musical notes

13. A vibrating wire of length L under tension T emits a note of fundamental frequency f. If a similar wire will emit a note of fundamental frequency $2f$ its length and tension could be
A $2L, T/2$ B $2L, T$ C $2L, 2T$
D $L/2, T/2$ E $L/2, T$ *(J.M.B.)*

14. What is meant by *resonance*? Describe how to determine the frequency of a tuning fork using a vibrating column of air, assuming the speed of sound in air to be known.
A sonometer wire was tuned to a fundamental frequency of 250 Hz. The vibrating wire was then under a tension of 10 N and was 87 cm long. Calculate how to tune the wire to a fundamental frequency of 375 Hz by adjusting its *(a)* length only, *(b)* tension only. *(A.E.B.)*

15. Describe a simple experiment to show that sound is not transmitted through a vacuum.
A tuning fork of frequency 320 Hz is set in vibration at the open end of a long narrow tube. The effective length of the tube may be varied and it is closed at the other end. Calculate the two shortest lengths of the tube for which the fork and the air column are in resonance. (Speed of sound in air = 336 m/s.) Describe briefly the motion of the air particles in the tube for the shortest resonant length. *(S.)*

16. A resonance tube open at both ends is 10 m long. If the speed of sound is 340 m/s the frequency in Hz of the second harmonic (the first overtone) is
A 8.5 B 17.0 C 34.0 D 68.0 E 340.0 *(N.I.)*

19 Measurements

Fig. 19.1*a*

Before a measurement can be made, a standard or *unit* must be chosen. The size of the quantity to be measured is then found with an instrument having a scale marked in the unit.

Many types of measuring instruments have been designed. Those on the flight deck of Concorde, Fig. 19.1*a, b*, provide the pilot with information about the performance of the aircraft.

Three basic quantities we have to measure in physics are *length*, *mass* and *time*. Units for other quantities are based on them. The SI (Système International d'Unités) system is a set of metric units now used in many countries. It is a decimal system in which units are divided or multiplied by 10 to give smaller or larger units.

Powers of ten shorthand

This is a neat way of writing numbers especially if they are large or small. It works like this.

$$4000 = 4 \times 10 \times 10 \times 10 = 4 \times 10^3$$
$$400 = 4 \times 10 \times 10 = 4 \times 10^2$$
$$40 = 4 \times 10 = 4 \times 10^1$$
$$4 = 4 \times 1 = 4 \times 10^0$$
$$0.4 = 4/10 = 4/10^1 = 4 \times 10^{-1}$$
$$0.04 = 4/100 = 4/10^2 = 4 \times 10^{-2}$$
$$0.004 = 4/1000 = 4/10^3 = 4 \times 10^{-3}$$

Fig. 19.1*b*

The small figures 1, 2, 3 etc., are called *powers of ten* and give the number of times the number has to be multiplied by 10 if it is greater than 1 and divided by 10 if it is less than 1. Note that 1 is also written as 10^0 and for numbers less than 1 the power has a negative sign.

Length

The unit of length is the *metre* (m) and is the distance, believed never to alter, occupied by a certain number of wavelengths of a particular colour of light. Previously it was the distance between two marks on a metal bar. Submultiples are:

$$1 \text{ centimetre (cm)} = 10^{-2} \text{ m}$$
$$1 \text{ millimetre (mm)} = 10^{-3} \text{ m}$$
$$1 \text{ micrometre} (\mu\text{m}) = 10^{-6} \text{ m}$$
$$1 \text{ nanometre (nm)} = 10^{-9} \text{ m}$$

A multiple for large distances is

$$1 \text{ kilometre (km)} = 10^3 \text{ m} \ (\tfrac{5}{8} \text{ mile approx.})$$

Many length measurements are made with rulers; the correct way to read one is shown in Fig. 19.2. The reading is 76 mm or 7.6 cm. Your eye must be

Fig. 19.2

right over the mark on the scale or the thickness of the ruler causes errors due to 'parallax' (p. 15).

Accuracy

Scientific results are written as a power of the number multiplied by another number which has just one figure before the decimal point. For example, the distance of the moon from the earth is 3.84403×10^5 km and indicates that we believe the measurement is reliable to the fifth figure after the decimal point. Using a ruler marked in mm we might state that a length is 8.3 cm. An answer of say 8.34 cm could be given but the last figure would be a guess. If a measurement of 0.035 cm is written 3.5×10^{-2} cm it shows it is thought to be accurate to the first decimal place.

Vernier scales

When a reading is between two marks on a scale it can be given more accurately if the instrument has a *vernier* scale. Such scales are used on calipers (for finding the outside or inside diameter of a tube), on microscopes and on barometers.

A vernier scale for use with a millimetre scale is 9 mm long and has ten equal divisions, Fig. 19.3a.

$$1 \text{ vernier division} = 9/10 \text{ mm} = 0.9 \text{ mm}$$

Fig. 19.3

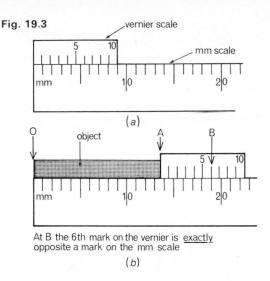

(a)

At B the 6th mark on the vernier is <u>exactly</u> opposite a mark on the mm scale

(b)

The object in Fig. 19.3b is between 13 mm and 14 mm long. The next figure is obtained by finding the mark on the vernier scale which is exactly opposite (or nearest to) a mark on the mm scale. Here it is the 6th mark and the reading is 13.6 mm since

$$OA = OB - AB = 19.0 - 6 \times 0.9$$
$$= 19.0 - 5.4 = 13.6 \text{ mm}$$

Micrometer screw gauge

This measures very small lengths such as the diameter of a wire, Fig. 19.4.

$$t = 2.83 \text{ mm}$$

Fig. 19.4

One complete turn of the drum, which is joined to the screw, opens the jaws by one division on the scale on the shaft; this is usually 0.5 mm. (The *pitch* of the screw is said to be 0.5 mm.) If the drum has a scale of 50 divisions round it, turning it by one division opens the jaws by 0.5/50 = 0.01 mm. The thickness t of the object shown

$$= 2.5 \text{ mm on shaft scale} + 33 \text{ divs on drum scale}$$
$$= 2.5 + 33 \times 0.01 = 2.83 \text{ mm}$$

Volume

Volume is the amount of space occupied. The unit of volume is the *cubic metre* (m^3) but as this is rather large, for most purposes the *cubic centimetre* (cm^3) is used. The volume of a cube with 1 cm edges is $1\,cm^3$.

For a regularly-shaped object

VOLUME = LENGTH × BREADTH × HEIGHT

The volume of a sphere of radius r is $\frac{4}{3}\pi r^3$ and of a cylinder of radius r and height h is $\pi r^2 h$.

Fig. 19.5   Fig. 19.6

The volume of a liquid may be obtained by pouring it into a measuring cylinder, Fig. 19.5, or a known volume can be run off more accurately from a burette, Fig. 19.6. When making a reading both vessels must be upright and the eye level with the bottom of the curved liquid surface, i.e. the meniscus. The meniscus formed by mercury is curved oppositely to that of other liquids and the top is read.

Liquid volumes are also expressed in litres (l); 1 litre = $1000\,cm^3$. One millilitre (1 ml) = $1\,cm^3$.

Mass

The mass of an object is a measure of the amount of matter in it. The unit of mass is the *kilogram* (kg) and is the mass of a piece of platinum alloy at the Office of Weights and Measures in Paris. The gram (g) is one-thousandth of a kilogram.

$$1\,g = 1/1000\,kg = 10^{-3}\,kg = 0.001\,kg$$

The term *weight* is often used when mass is really meant. In science the two ideas are distinct and have different units as we shall see later. The confusion is not helped by the fact that mass is found on a

Fig. 19.7

balance by a process we unfortunately call 'weighing'!

There are several kinds of balance. In the *beam balance* the unknown mass in one pan is balanced against known masses in the other pan. In the *lever balance* a system of levers acts against the mass when it is placed in the pan. A direct reading is obtained from the position on a scale of a pointer joined to the lever system. A modern *top pan balance* is shown in Fig. 19.7.

Time

The unit of time is the *second* which until 1968 was based on the length of a day, this being the time for the earth to revolve once on its axis. However, days are not all of exactly the same duration and the second is now defined as the time interval for a certain number of energy changes to occur in the caesium atom.

Time-measuring devices rely on some kind of constantly repeating oscillations. In many clocks and watches a small wheel (the balance wheel) oscillates to and fro; in modern clocks and watches the oscillations are produced by a tiny quartz crystal. A swinging pendulum controls a pendulum clock.

Experiment: simple pendulum

A simple pendulum consists of a piece of thread which is fixed at one end and has a small metal ball, called the bob, on the other end.

The *periodic time T* of the pendulum is the time for a complete swing or oscillation. The *length l* of the pendulum is the distance from the point of sup-

56

port to the centre of gravity (p. 71) of the bob. The *amplitude* (angular) of a swing is the angle between the extreme and rest positions of the thread.

Experiments show that if the amplitude does not exceed 10° or so, T depends only on l and is unaffected by the mass of the bob and the amplitude. The connection between T and l can be found in this experiment.

Fig. 19.8

Set up a pendulum as in Fig. 19.8. Find the time for 50 oscillations of *small amplitude* for different lengths (e.g. 25, 36, 49, 64, 81, 100 cm). Count 3, 2, 1, 0, 1, 2, ... 50 as the thread passes its rest position in the *same direction*. Start the clock on 0 and stop it on 50. Check each timing.

l(cm)	$50T$	T(s)	$\sqrt{l}$	$T/\sqrt{l}$
.				

Enter the results in a table as shown. Work out T (time for 1 swing) and $\sqrt{l}$. If $T/\sqrt{l}$ has a constant value, then $T \propto \sqrt{l}$, i.e. if l is quadrupled, T doubles. Check this for 100 cm and 25 cm.

If a graph of T against $\sqrt{l}$ is plotted and is a straight line through the origin, this shows that the *periodic time is proportional to the square root of the length of the pendulum*, i.e. there is a one-to-one correspondence between T and $\sqrt{l}$.

Questions

1. How many millimetres are there in (a) 1 cm, (b) 4 cm, (c) 0.5 cm, (d) 6.7 cm, (e) 1 m?

2. What are these lengths in metres: (a) 300 cm, (b) 550 cm, (c) 870 cm, (d) 43 cm, (e) 100 mm?

3. (a) Write the following in powers of ten form with one figure before the decimal point:

100 000; 3500; 428 000 000; 504; 27 056

(b) Write out the following in full:

10^3; 2×10^6; 6.9×10^4; 1.34×10^2; 10^9

4. (a) Write these fractions in powers of ten form:

$1/1000$; $7/100\,000$; $1/10\,000\,000$; $3/60\,000$

(b) Express the following decimals in powers of ten form with one figure before the decimal point;

0.5; 0.084; 0.000 36; 0.001 04

5. The pages of a book are numbered 1 to 200 and each leaf is 0.10 mm thick. If each cover is 0.20 mm thick, what is the thickness of the book?

6. What are the lengths of the objects in Figs. 19.9a, b?

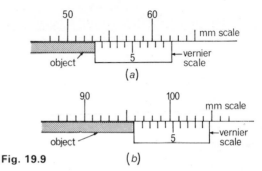

Fig. 19.9 *(b)*

7. What are the screw gauge readings in Figs. 19.10a, b?

Fig. 19.10

8. A metal block measures 10 cm × 2 cm × 2 cm. What is its volume? How many blocks each 2 cm × 2 cm × 2 cm are there in it?

9. How many blocks of ice cream each 10 cm × 10 cm × 4 cm can be stored in the compartment of a deep freeze measuring 40 cm × 40 cm × 20 cm?

10. A Perspex box has a 6 cm square base and contains water to a height of 7 cm, Fig. 19.11.

Fig. 19.11

(a) What is the volume of the water?

(b) A stone is lowered into the water so as to be completely covered and the water rises to a height of 9 cm. What is the volume of the stone?

20 Density

In everyday language lead is said to be 'heavier' than wood. By this is meant that a certain volume of lead is heavier than the same volume of wood. In science such comparisons are made by using the term *density*. This is the *mass per unit volume* of a substance and is calculated from

$$\text{DENSITY} = \frac{\text{MASS}}{\text{VOLUME}}$$

The density of lead is 11 grams per cubic centimetre (11 g/cm³) and means that a piece of lead of volume 1 cm³ has mass 11 g. A volume of 5 cm³ of lead would have mass 55 g. Knowing the density of a substance the mass of *any* volume can be calculated. This enables engineers to work out the weight of a structure if they know from the plans the volumes of the materials to be used and their densities. Strong enough foundations can then be made.

The SI unit of density is the *kilogram per cubic metre*. To convert a density from g/cm³, normally the most suitable unit for the size of sample we use, to kg/m³, we multiply by 10^3. For example the density of water is 1.0 g/cm³ or 1.0×10^3 kg/m³.

Simple density measurements

If the mass m and volume V of a substance are known its density d can be found from $d = m/V$.

(a) *Regularly-shaped solid*. The mass is found on a balance and the volume by measuring the length, breadth and height with a ruler, vernier calipers or a micrometer screw gauge depending on the size.

(b) *Irregularly-shaped solid*, e.g. a pebble or a glass stopper. The solid is weighed and its volume measured by one of the methods shown in Fig. 20.1a, b. In (a) the volume is the difference between the first and second readings. In (b) it is the volume of water collected in the measuring cylinder.

(c) *Liquid*. A known volume is transferred from a burette or a measuring cylinder into a weighed beaker which is reweighed to give the mass of liquid.

(d) *Air*. A 500 cm³ round-bottomed flask is weighed full of air and then after removing the air with a vacuum pump; the difference gives the mass of air in the flask. The volume of air is found by filling the flask with water and pouring it into a measuring cylinder.

Relative density

In the simple methods just outlined for finding density, the volume measurement is usually less accurate than the mass one. Using the idea of relative density, density can be found more reliably by methods requiring only weighings.

The relative density of a substance is defined by

$$\text{RELATIVE DENSITY} = \frac{\text{DENSITY OF SUBSTANCE}}{\text{DENSITY OF WATER}} \quad (1)$$

The density of aluminium is 2.7 g/cm³ and taking the density of water as 1.0 g/cm³, the relative density of aluminium = 2.7. Relative density has no units and equals numerically the density of the substance in g/cm³. A relative density measurement is in effect a density measurement.

An equation can be obtained from (1) which is useful for relative density experiments. We have

$$\text{relative density} = \frac{\text{density of substance}}{\text{density of water}}$$

$$= \frac{\text{mass of substance}}{\text{volume of substance}} \div \frac{\text{mass of water}}{\text{volume of water}}$$

$$= \frac{\text{mass of substance}}{\text{volume of substance}} \times \frac{\text{volume of water}}{\text{mass of water}}$$

If the substance and water have equal volumes, then

$$\text{RELATIVE DENSITY} = \frac{\text{MASS OF SUBSTANCE}}{\text{MASS OF SAME VOLUME OF WATER}} \quad (2)$$

Fig. 20.1

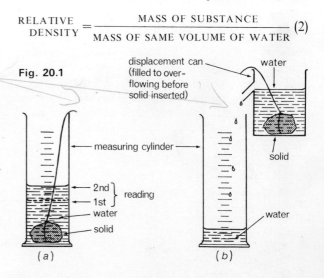

Experiment: relative density of a liquid by density bottle

A density bottle has a ground glass stopper with a narrow hole through it, Fig. 20.2. When the bottle

stopper

density bottle

Fig. 20.2

is full and the stopper inserted, the excess liquid rises up the hole and spills over. The bottle always contains exactly the same volume when the liquid level is at the top of the hole.

Weigh a dry density bottle with stopper when empty and then when full of liquid, e.g. methylated spirit. Return the liquid to its stock bottle, rinse out the density bottle with water, fill it with water and weigh again. Always ensure that the outside of the bottle is dry before weighing.

The measurements may be set out as shown and the result worked out using equation (2).

Mass of empty bottle	= g
Mass of bottle full of liquid	= g
∴ Mass of liquid	= g
Mass of bottle full of water	= g
∴ Mass of same volume of water	= g

Note. Another method for finding the relative density (and so the density) of solids and liquids using Archimedes' principle is described on p. 90.

Floating and sinking

An object sinks in a liquid of smaller density than its own; otherwise it floats, partly or wholly submerged. For example, a piece of glass of density $2.5 \, g/cm^3$ sinks in water (density $1.0 \, g/cm^3$) but floats in mercury (density $13.6 \, g/cm^3$). An iron nail sinks in water but an iron ship floats because its average density is less than that of water. Why is it easy to float in the Dead Sea, Fig. 20.3?

More will be said about this topic later (p. 90).

Questions

The formula $d = m/V$ is useful in calculations; it can also be written: $m = V \times d$ and $V = m/d$.

1. (*a*) If the density of wood is $0.5 \, g/cm^3$ what is the mass of (*i*) $1 \, cm^3$, (*ii*) $2 \, cm^3$, (*iii*) $10 \, cm^3$?

(*b*) What is the density of a substance of (*i*) mass 100 g and volume $10 \, cm^3$, (*ii*) volume $3 \, m^3$ and mass 9 kg?

(*c*) The density of gold is $19 \, g/cm^3$. Find the volume of (*i*) 38 g, (*ii*) 95 g of gold.

2. A piece of steel has a volume of $12 \, cm^3$ and a mass of 96 g. What is its density in (*a*) g/cm^3, (*b*) kg/m^3?

3. What is the mass of $5 \, m^3$ of cement of density $3000 \, kg/m^3$?

4. What is the mass of air in a room measuring $10 \, m \times 5.0 \, m \times 2.0 \, m$ if the density of air is $1.3 \, kg/m^3$?

5. A perspex box has a 10 cm square base and contains water to a height of 10 cm. A piece of rock of mass 600 g is lowered into the water and the level rises to 12 cm.

(*a*) What is the volume of water displaced by the rock?

(*b*) What is the volume of the rock?

(*c*) Calculate the density of the rock. (*E.M.*)

6. A density bottle has mass 70 g when empty, 90 g when full of water and 94 g when full of a liquid. What is the relative density of the liquid?

Fig. 20.3

21 Weight and springs

A *force* is a push or a pull. It can cause a body at rest to move or if the body is already moving it can change its speed or direction of motion. A weight-lifter in action exerts both a pull and a push, Fig. 21.1.

Weight

We all constantly experience the force of gravity, i.e. the pull of the earth. It causes an unsupported body to fall from rest to the ground.

The weight of a body is the force of gravity on it.

The nearer a body is to the centre of the earth the more does the earth attract it. Since the earth is not a perfect sphere the weight of a body varies over the earth's surface. It is greater at the poles than at the equator.

The newton

The SI unit of force is the *newton* (N). It will be defined later (p. 109) but the definition is based on the change of speed a force can produce on a body. Weight is a force and therefore should be measured in newtons. The weight of an average-sized apple is about 1 newton.

The weight of a body can be measured by hanging it on a *spring balance* marked in newtons, Fig.

Fig. 21.1

Fig. 21.2

21.2, and letting the pull of gravity stretch the spring in the balance. The greater the pull the more does the spring stretch. On most of the earth's surface

the weight of a body of mass 1 kg is 9.8 N.

Often this is taken as 10 N. A mass of 2 kg has a weight of 20 N and so on. The mass of a body is the same wherever it is and does not depend on the presence of the earth as does weight.

Mass is measured by a lever, beam or top-pan balance; weight is measured by a spring balance. However, many spring balances are marked in kg or g; a reading of 1 kg would correspond to 10 N and 100 g to 1 N (on the earth).

Experiment: stretching a spring

Fig. 21.3

Arrange a steel spring as in Fig. 21.3. Read the scale opposite the bottom of the hanger. Add 100 g loads one at a time and take the reading after each one. Enter the readings in a table.

Load g	Scale reading mm	Total extension mm

Do the results suggest any rule about how the spring behaves when it is stretched?

Sometimes it is easier to discover laws by displaying the results on a graph. Do this on graph paper by plotting *load* readings along the *y*-axis and *total extension* readings along the *x*-axis. Every pair of readings will give a point; mark them by small crosses and draw a smooth line through them. What is its shape?

Hooke's law

Springs were investigated by Hooke about 300 years ago. He found that the extension was proportional to the stretching force so long as the spring was not permanently stretched. This means that doubling the force doubles the extension, trebling the force trebles the extension and so on. Using the sign for proportionality we can write *Hooke's law*

extension ∝ *stretching force*

It is true only if the *elastic limit* of the spring is not exceeded, i.e. if the spring returns to its original length when the force is removed.

Fig. 21.4

The graph of Fig. 21.4 is for a spring stretched beyond its elastic limit E. OE is a straight line passing through the origin O and is graphical proof that Hooke's law holds over this range. If the force for point A on the graph is applied to the spring, the elastic limit is passed, and on removing the force, some of the extension (OS) remains. Over which part of Fig. 21.4 does a spring balance work?

Questions

1. If a body of mass 1 kg has weight 10 N at a certain place what will be the weight of (*a*) 100 g, (*b*) 5 kg, (*c*) 50 g?

2. The force of gravity on the moon is said to be one-sixth of that on the earth. What would a mass of 12 kg weigh (*a*) on the earth and (*b*) on the moon?

3. A spring is fitted with a scale pan as shown in Fig. 21.5 and the pointer points to the 30 cm mark on the scale. When some sand is placed in the pan the pointer points to the 15 cm mark. When a 20 g mass is placed on top of the sand the pointer points to the 5.0 cm mark.

(*a*) What extension is produced by the sand?

(*b*) What extension is produced by the 20 g mass?

(*c*) What is the mass of the sand? (*A.L.*)

Fig. 21.5

4. Fig. 21.6 shows four diagrams, not to scale, of the same spring which obeys Hooke's law. (*a*) What is the length *x*? (*b*) What is the mass *M*? (*E.A.*)

Fig. 21.6

22 Molecules

Fig. 22.1

Matter is made up of tiny particles or *molecules* which are too small for us to see directly. But they can be 'seen' by scientific 'eyes'. One of these is the electron microscope: Fig. 22.1 is a photograph taken with such an instrument showing molecules of a protein. Molecules consist of even smaller particles called *atoms* and are in continuous motion.

Experiment: Brownian motion

The apparatus is shown in Fig. 22.2*a*. First fill the glass cell with smoke using a burning drinking straw (made of paper), Fig. 22.2*b*. Replace the lid on the apparatus and set it on the microscope platform. Connect the lamp to a 12 V supply; the glass rod acts as a lens and focuses light on the smoke.

Fig. 22.2

Carefully adjust the microscope until you see bright specks dancing around haphazardly, Fig. 22.2*c*. The specks are smoke particles seen by reflected light; their random motion is due to collisions with fast-moving air molecules in the cell. The effect is called *Brownian motion*.

Kinetic theory of matter

As well as being in continuous motion, molecules also exert strong electrical forces on one another when they are close together. The forces are both attractive and repulsive. (The former hold molecules together and the latter cause matter to resist compression.) The *kinetic theory* can explain the existence of the solid, liquid and gaseous states.

(*a*) *In solids* the molecules are close together and the attractive and repulsive forces between neighbouring molecules balance. Each molecule vibrates to and fro about one position. Solids therefore have a regular, repeating molecular pattern, i.e. are crystalline, and their shape is definite.

(*b*) *In liquids* the molecules are usually slightly farther apart than in solids and, as well as vibrating, they can at the same time move rapidly over short distances. However they are never near another molecule long enough to get trapped in a regular pattern and a liquid can flow.

(*c*) *In gases* the molecules are much farther apart than in solids or liquids (about ten times). They dash around at very high speed (500 m/s for air molecules) in all the space available. It is only during the brief spells when they collide with other molecules or with the walls of the container that the molecular forces act.

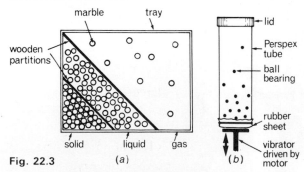

Fig. 22.3

A model illustrating the states of matter is shown in Fig. 22.3*a*. The tray is rotated to and fro on the bench and the motion of the marbles (molecules) observed. Fig. 22.3*b*, is a model of a gas; if a polystyrene ball (1 cm diameter) is dropped into the tube its irregular motion demonstrates Brownian motion on a large scale.

Experiment: size of a molecule

(a) *Method.* Pour water into a waxed tray till it is overbrimming. Lightly dust the surface with lycopodium.

Obtain a drop of olive oil on a V-shaped loop of thin wire by dipping the end into the oil and *quickly* removing it. Fix the loop in a holder with a $\frac{1}{2}$ mm scale, Fig. 22.4a, and view the drop and the scale through a hand lens. If the diameter of the drop is not about $\frac{1}{2}$ mm, discard it and take up another one.

Fig. 22.4

card
loop of wire
hand lens
½ mm scale
oil drop
holder
(a)
lycopodium powder
oil drop
waxed boom
waxed tray overbrimming with water
rubber wedge for levelling
(b)

Remove the loop from the holder and dip the end into the centre of the water, Fig. 22.4b. The oil spreads, pushing the powder before it and leaving a clear circular film. Measure its diameter.

Clean the water surface by drawing two waxed booms across it from the middle of the tray. Repeat the experiment with other $\frac{1}{2}$ mm diameter drops.

(b) *Calculation.* If d is the diameter of the drop then, assuming it is a sphere

$$\text{volume of drop} = \tfrac{4}{3}\pi(d/2)^3 = \pi d^3/6$$

If D is the diameter of the film, assumed to be a flat cylinder of height h, then

$$\text{volume of film} = \pi(D/2)^2 h = \pi D^2 h/4 \qquad \text{(p. 56)}$$

Also, volume of film = volume of drop

$$\therefore \ \pi D^2 h/4 = \pi d^3/6$$

$$\therefore \ h = \frac{2d^3}{3D^2}$$

But $\quad d = 0.5\,\text{mm} = 0.5 \times 10^{-3}\,\text{m} = 5 \times 10^{-4}\,\text{m}$

$$\therefore \ h = 2(5 \times 10^{-4})^3/(3D^2)\,\text{m}$$

$$= 250 \times 10^{-12}/(3D^2)\,\text{m}$$

Substitute the average value of D and so find h.

Chemical studies show that olive oil molecules are long and narrow with one end which is attracted strongly to water. In the film the molecules stand upright and, assuming that the film is one molecule

thick when the spreading stops, the thickness h of the film equals the *length* of one molecule.

This experiment only gives a rough result but other methods give values in the region of $2.0 \times 10^{-9}\,\text{m} = 2\,\text{nm}$. This means 500 million olive oil molecules could lie lengthways along a metre rule.

Crystals

Crystals have hard, flat sides and straight edges. Whatever their size, crystals of the same substance have the same shape. This can be seen by observing through a microscope, very small cubic salt crystals growing as water evaporates from salt solution on a glass slide, Fig. 22.5.

trimming knife
calcite crystal

Fig. 22.5   Fig. 22.6

A calcite crystal will split cleanly if a trimming knife, held exactly parallel to one side of the crystal, is struck by a hammer, Fig. 22.6.

These facts suggest crystals are made of small particles (e.g. atoms) arranged in an orderly way in planes. Metals consist of tiny crystals.

Questions

1. When viewing Brownian motion in a smoke cell the observer sees moving specks of light which are

   A molecules moving in random motion
   B molecules vibrating regularly
   C molecules colliding with each other
   D smoke particles vibrating regularly
   E smoke particles in random motion   (*J.M.B.*)

2. Why are gases more easily squeezed than liquids or solids?

3. (a) A tray is 50 cm long and 40 cm wide and has $2.0 \times 10^3\,\text{cm}^3$ of water poured into it. What is the depth of water?

   (b) A drop of oil of volume $1.0 \times 10^{-3}\,\text{cm}^3$ spreads out on a clean water surface to a film of area $1.0\,\text{m}^2$ ($1.0 \times 10^4\,\text{cm}^2$). Calculate the thickness of the film.

4. 100 identical drops of oil, of density $800\,\text{kg/m}^3$, are found to have a total mass of $2 \times 10^{-4}\,\text{kg}$. One of these drops is placed on a large clean water surface and it spreads to form a uniform film of area $0.2\,\text{m}^2$.

   (a) What is the mass of one drop?
   (b) What is the volume of one drop?
   (c) What is the thickness of the film?
   (d) If a second oil drop of the same mass were placed on the film, what would you expect the new area of the film to be? Explain.   (*O.*)

23 Properties of matter

Diffusion

Smells, pleasant or otherwise, travel quickly and are caused by rapidly moving molecules. The spreading of a substance of its own accord is called *diffusion* and is due to molecular motion.

Diffusion of gases can be shown if some brown nitrogen dioxide gas is made by pouring a mixture of equal volumes of concentrated nitric acid and water on copper turnings in a gas jar. When the action has stopped, a gas jar of air is inverted over the bottom jar, Fig. 23.1. The brown colour spreads into the upper jar showing that nitrogen dioxide molecules diffuse upwards against gravity. Air molecules also diffuse into the lower jar.

The speed of diffusion of a gas depends on the speed of its molecules and is greater for light molecules. The apparatus of Fig. 23.2 shows this. When hydrogen surrounds the porous pot, the liquid in the U-tube moves in the direction of the arrows. This is due to the lighter, faster molecules of hydrogen diffusing into the pot faster than the heavier, slower molecules of air diffuse out. The opposite happens when carbon dioxide surrounds the pot. Why?

Diffusion in liquids can be seen as in Fig. 23.3. After 24 hours the blue copper sulphate solution has diffused upwards into the water.

Surface tension

A needle, though made of steel which is denser than water, will float on a *clean* water surface. A film formed by dipping an inverted funnel in a detergent solution, rises *up* the funnel, Fig. 23.4a. When the film inside the cotton loop in Fig. 23.4b, is broken, the loop forms a *circle*, Fig. 23.4c.

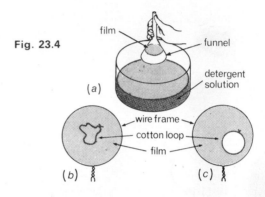

Fig. 23.4

These facts suggest that the surface of a liquid (in a vessel or on a film) behaves as if covered with an elastic skin that is trying to shrink. The effect is called *surface tension*. It can be reduced if the liquid is 'contaminated' by adding, for example, detergent: a needle floating in water then sinks.

Surface tension is due to the molecules in a liquid surface being slightly farther apart than normal, like those in a stretched wire.

Adhesion and cohesion

The force of attraction (p. 62) between molecules of the same substance is known as *cohesion*, that between molecules of different substances is *adhesion*. The adhesion of water to glass is greater than the cohesion of water and water spilt on clean glass wets it by spreading to a thin film. By contrast, mercury on glass forms small spherical drops or large flattened ones because cohesion of mercury is stronger than its adhesion to glass.

The cleaning action of detergents depends on their ability to weaken the cohesion of water. Instead of forming drops on greasy clothes, the water penetrates the fabric and releases dirt.

Fig. 23.1   Fig. 23.2

Fig. 23.3

Capillarity

If a glass tube of narrow bore (a capillary tube) is dipped into water, the water rises up in the tube to a height of a few centimetres, Fig. 23.5a. The narrower the tube the greater the rise. Adhesion between water and glass exceeds cohesion between water molecules, the meniscus curves up and the water rises.

Fig. 23.5

The action of blotting paper is due to capillary rise in the narrow spaces between the fibres it contains. The rise of oil up a lamp wick occurs in the same way. The damp-course in a house, i.e. the layer of non-porous material in the walls just above ground level but below the floor, prevents water rising up the pores in the bricks by capillary action from the ground and causing dampness. Mercury is depressed in a capillary tube, Fig. 23.5b.

Mechanical properties of materials

When selecting a material for a particular job we need to know how it behaves when forces act on it, i.e. what its mechanical properties are.

(a) *Strength*. A strong material requires a large force to break it. The strength of some materials depends on how the force is applied. For example, concrete is strong when compressed but weak when stretched, i.e. in tension.

(b) *Stiffness*. A stiff material resists forces which try to change its shape or size or both. It is not flexible. All materials 'give' to some extent although the change may be very small. Steel is strong and stiff, putty is neither. Rope is not stiff but can be strong in tension.

(c) *Elasticity*. An elastic material such as rubber recovers its original shape and size after the force deforming it has been removed. A material which does not recover but is deformed permanently, like Plasticine, is plastic. (Note that man-made plastics are not always 'plastic'; they are so-called because during manufacture they behave in that way.)

(d) *Ductility*. Materials which can be rolled into sheets, drawn into wires or worked into other useful shapes without breaking, are ductile. Metals owe much of their usefulness to this property.

(e) *Brittleness*. A brittle material is fragile and breaks suddenly. Bricks, cast iron and glass (if dropped) are brittle.

Stretching a wire

Useful information about mechanical properties is obtained from stretching a long wire of material by gradually loading it as in Fig. 23.6.

Fig. 23.6

The graph obtained by plotting load against extension is similar to that for stretching a spring (Fig. 21.4, p. 61). Between O and the *elastic limit* E, it is a straight line showing that *extension ∝ stretching force*, i.e. Hooke's law holds. At A, the *yield point*, the wire 'runs' and greater extensions than before are produced by a given increase of load but larger loads can be supported.

Up to E the molecules are pulled slightly farther apart; the deformation is elastic and the wire recovers its original length when the load is removed. Beyond A, layers of atoms slip over each other; the deformation is plastic and if unloaded the wire does not return to its previous length.

Metals used in engineering structures should carry loads which only deform them elastically.

Questions

1. Explain why (a) diffusion occurs more quickly in a gas than in a liquid, (b) diffusion is still quite slow even in a gas, (c) an inflated balloon gradually goes down even when tied.

2. Explain the following observations as fully as you can.

(a) A small needle may be floated on the surface of water, but if a drop of detergent is added to the water the needle sinks.

(b) Damp-courses are used in modern houses.

(c) Gases can be easily compressed but liquids cannot.

(*E.A.*)

24 Further questions

Measurements

1. Explain the use of the vernier.

Fig. 24.1

Fig. 24.1 shows a portion of the scale fitted to a mercury barometer. The vernier part has its zero mark level with the top of the meniscus. What is the barometric height? (*O. and C.*)

2. The diameter of a uniform wire is measured using a micrometer screw gauge. The five readings obtained are: 1.20 mm, 1.19 mm, 1.70 mm, 1.18 mm, 1.20 mm. On the basis of these observations, what value would you take for the radius of the wire? (*N.I.*)

Density

3. Two solid cubes weigh the same, but their surface areas are in the ratio 4:1. What is the ratio of their densities? Choose from

A 1:2 **B** 1:4 **C** 1:8 **D** 1:16
E 1:24 (*S.R.*)

4. Fig. 24.2 shows a measuring cylinder containing some sugar (mass 32.0 g) in paraffin oil (mass 56.4 g, density 0.80 g/cm³) which does not dissolve the sugar. The total volume of the substances in the cylinder is 90.5 cm³. Calculate (*a*) the volume of the paraffin oil, (*b*) the volume of the sugar, (*c*) the density of the sugar. (*C.*)

5. (*a*) Why does a piece of wood float and a piece of lead sink in water?

(*b*) A wooden block, whose volume is 16 cm³, has a hole with a volume of 1.0 cm³ drilled in it. The hole is filled with lead. Will the block sink or float in water? (Give reasons for your answer and show any calculations you make.) Density of lead = 11 g/cm³: density of wood = 0.50 g/cm³: density of water = 1.0 g/cm³.

(*c*) Which is denser, milk or cream? (*S.E.*)

Weight and springs

6. A vertical spring of unstretched length 30 cm is rigidly clamped at its upper end. When an object of mass 100 g is placed in a pan attached to the lower end of the spring, its length becomes 36 cm. For an object of mass 200 g in the pan the length becomes 40 cm. Calculate the mass of the pan. Name and state clearly the law you have assumed. (*S.*)

7. A light helical spring hangs vertically with its upper end fixed. A light pointer, attached to its lower end, can be used to take readings on a vertical scale when masses of various sizes are attached to the lower end of the spring. The following table gives the scale readings of the pointer for different attached masses.

Mass attached in kg	0	0.2	0.4	0.6	0.8
Scale reading in mm	120	126	132	138	144

(*a*) Make a table showing corresponding values of the force on the spring in newtons and its resulting extension in metres.

(*b*) Plot a graph of force (*y*-axis) against extension (*x*-axis).

(*c*) State Hooke's law. Are the readings for this spring consistent with it? Explain.

(*d*) Use your graph to find the force that produces an extension of 15 mm.

(Weight of 1 kg is 10 N.) (*O.*)

Fig. 24.2

volume 90.5 cm³

paraffin oil 56.4 g (density 0.80 g/cm³)

sugar 32.0 g

Molecules

8. Describe the differences between solids, liquids and gases in terms of (*a*) the arrangement of the molecules throughout the bulk of the material, (*b*) the separation of the molecules, and (*c*) the motion of the molecules. (*J.M.B.*)

9. Smoke particles in an air cell viewed under a microscope exhibit Brownian motion.

Fig. 24.3

(*a*) Copy Fig. 24.3 and draw a suitable arrangement to show how the particles in the air cell can be illuminated.

(*b*) How is the motion of the smoke particles best described?

(*c*) What accounts for the motion of the smoke particles?

(*d*) The motion is viewed using bigger smoke particles. What difference in the motion would this lead to? Give the reason for the difference. (*O./S.R.16+*)

10. A drop of oil of volume 0.010 cm³ is allowed to fall on some clean water in a dish and it spreads to form a circle of radius 14 cm. Estimate the upper limit of the diameter of an oil molecule.

In such an experiment describe (*a*) what is done in order that the circle may be clearly visible, (*b*) what apparatus is used and any precautions that are taken. (*L.*)

Properties of matter

11. Describe experiments, one in each case, to show (*a*) diffusion in liquids, (*b*) diffusion in gases.

Use the kinetic theory to explain the result of your experiment demonstrating the diffusion of gases. (*J.M.B.*)

12. A porous pot holding air is fitted with a tube dipping into water, Fig. 24.4.

(*a*) When the pot is surrounded by hydrogen, air bubbles rapidly out of the water, but after a short time the bubbles slow down and stop. Explain these stages.

(*b*) If now the jar of hydrogen is removed, water rises rapidly up the tube, slows down and stops, and very slowly returns. Explain these stages.

(*c*) What difference does it make when the experi-

Fig. 24.4

ment is repeated using carbon dioxide instead of hydrogen. Why? (*S.R.*)

Fig. 24.5

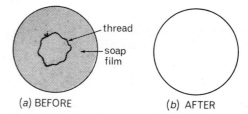

(*a*) BEFORE   (*b*) AFTER

13. (*a*) A piece of thread is carefully placed in a soap film which has been formed on a metal ring, Fig. 24.5*a*. Copy Fig. 24.5*b* and show clearly what happens if the soap film inside the thread is pierced by a needle.

(*b*) What name is given to the force acting on the thread? (*E.M.*)

Fig. 24.6

14. (*a*) Name the effect shown in tube A of Fig. 24.6.

(*b*) Copy the diagram and mark the water levels in B and C and the mercury levels in D and E.

15. The graph shown in Fig. 24.7 represents the behaviour of a wire in an experiment to investigate Hooke's law. Copy the graph. Label each axis and add appropriate labels to the guide lines. (*E.A.*)

Fig. 24.7

25 Moments and levers

The handle on a door is at the outside edge so that it opens and closes easily. A much larger force would be needed if the handle were near the hinge. Similarly it is easier to loosen a nut with a long spanner than with a short one.

The *turning effect* or *moment of a force* depends on both the size of the force and how far it is applied from the pivot or *fulcrum*. It is measured by multiplying the force by the *perpendicular* distance of the line of action of the force from the fulcrum. The unit is the *newton metre* (N m).

MOMENT OF A FORCE = FORCE × PERPENDICULAR DISTANCE FROM FULCRUM

Fig. 25.1

In Fig. 25.1 a force F acts on a gate, in (a) at right angles, in (b) obliquely. In (a), moment of F about $O = 5\ N \times 3\ m = 15\ N\,m$. In (b), moment of F about $O = 5\ N \times 2\ m = 10\ N\,m$. The turning effect of F is greater in (a); this agrees with the fact that a gate opens most easily when it is pulled at right angles.

Experiment: law of moments

Balance a half-metre rule at its centre, adding Plasticine to one side or the other until it is horizontal.

Hang unequal loads m_1 and m_2 from either side of the ruler and alter their distance d_1 and d_2 from the centre until the ruler is again balanced, Fig. 25.2. Forces F_1 and F_2 are exerted by gravity on m_1

Fig. 25.2

and m_2 and so on the ruler; on 100 g the force is 1 N. Record the results in a table and repeat for other loads and distances.

m_1 (g)	F_1 (N)	d_1 (cm)	$F_1 \times d_1$ (N cm)	m_2 (g)	F_2 (N)	d_2 (cm)	$F_2 \times d_2$ (N cm)

F_1 is trying to turn the ruler anticlockwise and $F_1 \times d_1$ is its moment. F_2 is trying to cause clockwise turning and its moment is $F_2 \times d_2$. When the ruler is balanced or as we say in *equilibrium*, the results should show that the anticlockwise moment $F_1 \times d_1$ equals the clockwise moment $F_2 \times d_2$.

The *law of moments* (also called the *law of the lever*) is stated as follows.

When a body is in equilibrium the sum of the clockwise moments about any point equals the sum of the anticlockwise moments.

Worked example

The see-saw in Fig. 25.3 balances when Sue of weight 320 N is at A, Tom of weight 540 N is at B and Harry of weight W is at C. Find W.

Fig. 25.3

Taking moments about the fulcrum O:
anticlockwise moment
$$= 320 \times 3 + 540 \times 1 = 1500 \text{ N m}$$
clockwise moment $= (W \times 3) \text{ N m}$
By the law of moments,
clockwise moments = anticlockwise moments
$$\therefore 3\,W = 1500$$
$$\therefore \quad W = 500 \text{ N}$$

Levers

A lever is any device which can turn about a pivot. In a lever a force called the *effort* is used to overcome a resisting force called the *load*.

When we use a crowbar to move a heavy boulder, Fig. 25.4a, our hands apply the effort at one end of the bar and the load is the force exerted by the boulder on the other end. If distances from the fulcrum O are as shown and the load is 1000 N, the effort can be calculated from the law of moments. As the boulder *just begins* to move we can say, taking moments about O, that

clockwise moment = anticlockwise moment
$$\text{effort} \times 200 = 1000 \times 10$$
$$\text{effort} = 50 \text{ N}$$

The crowbar in effect magnifies the effort 20 times but the effort must move farther than the load.

Other examples of levers are shown in Fig. 25.4b, c. In (b) the load is between the effort and the fulcrum; in this case as in (a) the effort is less than the load. In (c) the effort (applied by the biceps muscle) is between the load and the fulcrum and is greater than the load, which moves farther than the effort.

Parallel forces

Sometimes a number of parallel forces act on a body so that it is in equilibrium. We can then say:

(*i*) *the sum of the forces in one direction equals the sum of the forces in the opposite direction*
(*ii*) *the law of moments must apply.*

Fig. 25.4

Fig. 25.5

As an example consider two decorators of weights 500 N and 700 N standing at A and B on a plank resting on two trestles, Fig. 25.5. In the next topic we will see (p. 71) that the whole weight of the plank (400 N) may be taken to act vertically downwards at its centre, O. If P and Q are the upwards forces exerted by the trestles on the plank (called *reactions*) then we have from (*i*),

$$P + Q = 500 + 400 + 700 = 1600 \text{ N} \qquad (1)$$

Moments can be taken about any point but taking them about C eliminates the moment due to Q.

Clockwise moment $= P \times 4 \text{ N m}$
Anticlockwise moments
$$= (700 \times 1 + 400 \times 2 + 500 \times 5) \text{ N m}$$
$$= 700 + 800 + 2500 = 4000 \text{ N m}$$

Since the plank is in equilibrium we have from (*ii*),
$$4\,P = 4000 \qquad\qquad \therefore P = 1000 \text{ N}$$
From (1), $\qquad\qquad\qquad\qquad Q = 600 \text{ N}.$

Couples

When you steer a bicycle round a bend with both hands on the handle-bars, two equal and opposite forces are applied, Fig. 25.6. The forces form a *couple* and cause rotation.

Fig. 25.6

(a) Crowbar   (b) Wheelbarrow   (c) Forearm

OA = 10 cm
OB = 200 cm

Beams and structures

(*a*) *Beams*. When a beam bends, one side is compressed, the other is stretched and the centre is unstressed (a neutral plane), Fig. 25.7*a*. I-shaped steel girders, Fig. 25.7*b*, are used in large structures. They are, in effect, beams that have had material removed from the neutral plane and so weigh less. The top and bottom flanges withstand the compression and tension forces due to loading. In a hollow tube the removal of unstressed material gives similar advantages.

Fig. 25.7

(*b*) *Bridges*. In an arched stone bridge, the stone is in compression, since it is weak in tension, Fig. 25.8*a*. A girder bridge has no material in the neutral plane, Fig. 25.8*b*; it is strengthened by diagonal bars.

Fig. 25.8

(*c*) *Cracks and fracture*. A notch, scratch or crack on the surface of a brittle material like concrete and glass, spreads more readily under tension than under compression, Fig. 25.9. Hence pre-stressed concrete contains steel rods that are in tension because they were stretched while the concrete was poured on them and set. As well as resisting tension forces they keep the concrete in compression even

Fig. 25.9

if the whole structure is not. The same principle applies in the use of fibres of glass and carbon to reinforce plastics or of asbestos in concrete for roofing material.

Questions

1. Fig. 25.10 shows half-metre rules which are marked off at intervals of 5 cm. Identical metal discs are placed on the rules as shown. In each case state whether the rules will turn clockwise, anticlockwise or remain in the horizontal position. Show your working. (*E.A.*)

Fig. 25.10

2. The metre rule in Fig. 25.11 is supported at its centre. If the rule is balanced, the values of *x* and *y* respectively are
   A 3 cm (*x*) and 5 cm (*y*)   **B** 5 cm (*x*) and 3 cm (*y*)
   C 6 cm (*x*) and 10 cm (*y*)   **D** 12 cm (*x*) and 20 cm (*y*)
   (*W.M*)

Diagram NOT to scale

Fig. 25.11

3. In Fig. 25.12, the distance AC = CB. Calculate in each case the force X which will keep the system stationary. (*E.M.*)

Fig. 25.12

4. Fig. 25.13 shows three positions of the pedal on a bicycle which has a crank 0.20 m long. If the cyclist exerts the same vertically downwards push of 25 N with his foot, in which case is the turning effect (*i*) 25 × 0.2 = 5 N m. (*ii*) 0, (*iii*) between 0 and 5 N m? Explain your answers.

Fig. 25.13

5. A spade, a bottle opener and a fishing rod are levers. Show by diagrams the positions of the effort, load and fulcrum in each. In which is the effort greater than the load?

26 Centres of gravity

A body behaves as if its whole weight were concentrated at one point, called its *centre of gravity* (c.g.), even though the earth attracts every part of it. The c.g. of a ruler is at its centre and when supported there it balances, Fig. 26.1a. If it is supported at any other point it topples because the moment of its weight W about the point of support is not zero, Fig. 26.1b.

Fig. 26.1

Your c.g. is near the centre of your body and the vertical line from it to the floor must be within the area enclosed by your feet or you will fall over. You can test this by standing with one arm and the side of one foot pressed against a wall, Fig. 26.2. Now try to raise the other leg sideways. Can you do it without falling over?

A tight-rope walker has to keep his c.g. exactly above the rope. Some carry a long pole to help them to balance, Fig. 26.3. The combined weight of the walker and pole is then spread out more and if the walker begins to topple to one side he moves the pole to the other side.

The c.g. of a regularly shaped body of the same density all over is at its centre. In other cases it can be found by experiment.

Fig. 26.2

Fig. 26.3

Experiment: c.g. using a plumb line

Suppose we have to find the c.g. of an irregularly shaped lamina (a thin sheet) of cardboard.

Make a hole A in the lamina and hang it so that it can *swing freely* on a nail clamped in a stand. It will come to rest with its c.g. vertically below A. To locate the vertical line through A tie a plumb line (a thread and a weight) to the nail, Fig. 26.4, and mark its position AB on the lamina. The c.g. lies on AB.

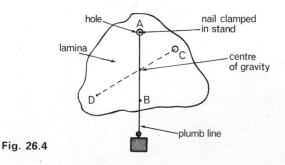

Fig. 26.4

Hang the lamina from another position C and mark the plumb line position CD. The c.g. lies on CD and must be at the point of intersection of AB and CD. Check this by hanging the lamina from a third hole. Also try balancing it at its c.g. on the tip of your forefinger.

Devise a method using a plumb line of finding the c.g. of a tripod.

Toppling

The position of the c.g. of a body affects whether or not it topples over easily. This is important in the design of such things as tall vehicles (which tend to overturn when rounding a corner), racing cars, reading lamps and even tea-cups.

A body topples when the vertical line through its c.g. falls outside its base, Fig. 26.5a. Otherwise it remains stable, Fig. 26.5b.

Fig. 26.5

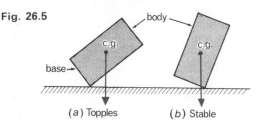

(a) Topples   (b) Stable

Toppling can be investigated by placing an empty can on a plank (with a rough surface to prevent slipping) which is slowly tilted. The angle of tilt is noted when the can falls over. This is repeated with 1 kg in the can. How does this affect the position of the c.g? The same procedure is followed with a second can of the same height as the first but of greater width. It will be found that the second can with the weight in it can be tilted through the greater angle.

The stability of a body is therefore increased by
  (i) lowering its c.g.
  (ii) increasing the area of its base.

In Fig. 26.6a the c.g. of a tractor is being found. It is necessary to do this when testing a new design since tractors are often driven over sloping surfaces and any tendency to overturn must be discovered.

The stability of double-decker buses is being tested in Fig. 26.6b. When the top deck only is fully laden with passengers (represented by sand bags in the test), it must not topple if tilted through an angle of 28°. Racing cars have a low c.g. and a wide wheel base.

Stability

Three terms are used in connection with stability.

(a) A body is in *stable equilibrium* if when slightly displaced and then released it returns to its previous position. The ball at the bottom of the dish in Fig. 26.7a is an example. Its c.g. rises when it is displaced. It rolls back because its weight has a moment about the point of contact.

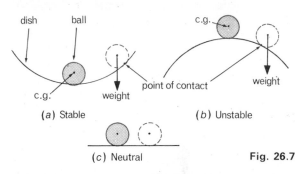

(a) Stable   (b) Unstable

(c) Neutral   **Fig. 26.7**

(b) A body is in *unstable equilibrium* if it moves farther away from its previous position when slightly displaced. The ball in Fig. 26.7b behaves in this way. Its c.g. falls when it is displaced slightly.

(c) A body is in *neutral equilibrium* if it stays in its new position when displaced, Fig. 26.7c. Its c.g. does not rise or fall.

Fig. 26.6   (a)

(b)

Fig. 26.8

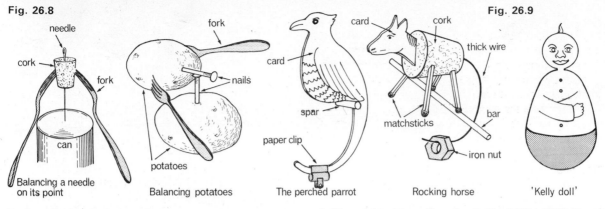

Balancing a needle on its point

Balancing potatoes

The perched parrot

Rocking horse

'Kelly doll'

Fig. 26.9

Balancing tricks and toys

Some tricks that you can try or toys to make are shown in Fig. 26.8. In each case the c.g. is vertically below the point of support and equilibrium is stable.

A self-righting toy (a 'Kelly doll') has a heavy base, Fig. 26.9, and when tilted, the weight acting through the c.g. has a moment about the point of contact. This restores it to the upright position.

Questions

1. Fig. 26.10 shows an irregular shape of plywood suspended by a thin thread at two different points, A and B. Copy diagram (*b*). Mark and label the centre of mass of the plywood. Draw

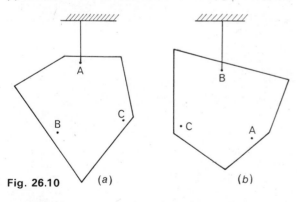

Fig. 26.10   (*a*)   (*b*)

and label across diagram (*b*) a line which would be vertical if the plywood were suspended at point C.   (*E.A.*)

2. Fig. 26.11 shows a Bunsen burner in three different positions. State in which position it is in (*a*) stable equilibrium, (*b*) unstable equilibrium, (*c*) neutral equilibrium.

Fig. 26.11

3. The weight of the uniform bar in Fig. 26.12 is 10 N. Does it balance, tip to the right or tip to the left?

Fig. 26.12

4. (*a*) A uniform metre rule is balanced at the 30 cm mark when a load of 0.80 N is hung at the zero mark, Fig. 26.13*a*.

   (*i*) At what point on the rule is the centre of gravity of the rule?

   (*ii*) Show with an arrow drawn on a copy of the diagram the weight of the rule acting through the centre of gravity.

   (*iii*) Calculate the weight of the rule.

   (*b*) Fig. 26.13*b* shows the jib of a building site crane. What is the purpose of the concrete block at one end of the jib? (*Met.*)

Fig. 26.13

27 Adding forces

In structures like a giant oil platform, Fig. 27.1, two or more forces may act at the same point. It is then often useful for the design engineer to know the value of the single force, i.e. the *resultant*, which has exactly the same effect as these forces. If the forces act in the same straight line the resultant is found by simple addition or subtraction, but if they do not they are added by the parallelogram law.

Experiment: parallelogram law

Arrange the apparatus as in Fig. 27.2a with a sheet of paper behind it on a vertical board. We have to find the resultant of forces P and Q.

Read the values of P and Q from the spring balances. Mark on the paper the directions of P, Q and W as shown by the strings. Remove the paper and using a scale of 1 cm to represent 1 N, draw OA, OB and OD to represent the three forces P, Q and W which act at O, Fig. 27.2b. (W=weight of the 1 kg mass=9.8 N, therefore OD=9.8 cm.)

P and Q together are balanced by W and so their resultant must be a force equal and opposite to W.

Complete the parallelogram OACB. Measure the diagonal OC; if it is equal in size (i.e. 9.8 cm) and

Fig. 27.1

(a)

Fig. 27.2

Scale:
1 cm=1 N

(b)

opposite in direction to W then it represents the resultant of P and Q.

The parallelogram law for adding two forces is:

If two forces acting at a point are represented in size and direction by the sides of a parallelogram drawn from the point, their resultant is represented in size and direction by the diagonal of the parallelogram drawn from the point.

Examples

1. *Two people carrying a heavy bucket.* The weight of the bucket is balanced by the resultant F of F_1 and F_2, Fig. 27.3a.
2. *Two tugs pulling a liner.* The resultant of T_1 and T_2 is forwards, Fig. 27.3b, and so the liner moves forwards.

74

(a)   (b)   **Fig. 27.3**

drawn, its sides OA and OB represent the required components F_1 and F_2 on the same scale as OC represents F. For example if $F = 200$ N and $\angle COB = 30°$ then $F_1 = 100$ N and $F_2 = 173$ N.

If you have done trigonometry you can show that $F_2 = F \cos \theta$ and $F_1 = F \sin \theta$.

Vectors and scalars

A *vector* quantity is one such as force which is described completely only if both its size (magnitude) and direction are stated. It is not enough to say, for example, a force of 10 N, but rather a force of 10 N acting vertically downwards.

A vector can be represented by a straight line whose length represents the magnitude of the quantity and whose direction gives its line of action. An arrow on the line shows which way along the line it acts.

A *scalar* quantity has magnitude only. Mass is a scalar and is completely described when its value is known. Scalars are added by ordinary arithmetic; vectors are added geometrically by the parallelogram law which ensures that their directions as well as their magnitudes are considered.

Resolving a force

The parallelogram law enables us to replace two forces by one. Sometimes we have to do the reverse and split or *resolve* one force into two forces called its *components* which together have the same effect as the single force. Usually it is most useful to take the components at right angles to each other.

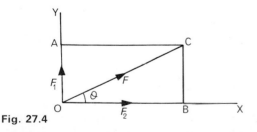

Fig. 27.4

Suppose a force F is represented by OC in Fig. 27.4 and that we wish to find its components along OX and OY ($\angle XOY = 90°$). If rectangle OACB is

Fig. 27.5

Resolving a force helps to explain why a yacht can sail into the wind. It can be shown that the wind causes a force F at right angles to the sail as it blows over it. This force can be resolved into two components F_1 and F_2, Fig. 27.5. F_1 drives the yacht forwards, F_2 would cause it to drift sideways if it did not have a heavy keel. In a wind from the north the yacht could sail alternately NW and NE, i.e. 'tack', and so progress northwards.

Questions

1. Using a scale of 1 cm to represent 10 N find the size and direction of the resultant of forces of 30 N and 40 N acting at (a) right angles to each other, (b) 60° to each other.

2. In Fig. 27.6 the lines represent two forces acting at a point O. Which of the single forces could be the resultant of the two? (*E.A.*)

Fig. 27.6

3. Tom, Dick and Harry are pulling a metal ring. Tom pulls with a force of 100 N and Dick with a force of 140 N at an angle of 70° to Tom. If the ring does not move what force is Harry exerting?

4. Explain why a slack clothes line is less likely to break than a taut one.

28 Work, energy, power

Fig. 28.1

In science the word *work* has a different meaning from its everyday one. Work is done when a force moves. A boat pulling a water skier does work, Fig. 28.1, as does a crane when it lifts a load. However, no work is done in the scientific sense by someone holding a heavy pile of books, an upwards force is exerted but no motion results.

Measuring work

If a building worker carries ten bricks up to the first floor of a building he does more work than if he carries only one brick because he has to exert a larger force. Even more work is required if he carries the ten bricks to the second floor. The amount of work done depends on the *size* of the force applied and the *distance* it moves. We therefore measure work by

> WORK = FORCE × DISTANCE MOVED IN
> DIRECTION OF FORCE   (1)

The unit of work is the *joule* (J) and is the *work done when a force of 1 newton* (N) *moves through 1 metre* (m). For example, if you have to pull with a force of 50 N to move a box steadily 3 m in the direction of the force, Fig. 28.2a, the work done is 50 N × 3 m = 150 N m = 150 J. That is,

JOULES = NEWTONS × METRES

If you lift a mass of 3 kg vertically through 2 m, Fig. 28.2b, you have to exert a vertically upwards force equal to the weight of the body, i.e. 30 N (approximately) and the work done is 30 N × 2 m = 60 N m = 60 J.

Note that we must always take the distance in the direction in which the force acts.

Forms of energy

Energy enables work to be done and people and machines need a supply of it. Experience shows that it exists in many different forms.

(*a*) *Chemical energy.* Food and fuels like coal, oil and gas are stores of chemical energy. The energy of food is released by chemical reactions in our bodies. Fuels release their energy when they are burnt (a chemical reaction) in an engine or other device. A car engine uses chemical energy.

(*b*) *Potential energy* (p.e.). This is energy which a body has because of its position or condition. A body above the earth's surface has p.e. and can do work. The weight in a wound-up grandfather clock or at the top of a pile driver has p.e. which it loses as it falls. The water in a mountain reservoir is another example of something with p.e.

Wound-up watch springs and stretched elastic bands have p.e. because of their 'strained' condition.

(*c*) *Kinetic energy* (k.e.) Any moving body has k.e. and the faster it moves the more k.e. it has. For example as a hammer strikes a nail or an earth-

50 N

3 m

3 kg

2 m

Fig. 28.2 (*a*) (*b*)

moving machine levels the ground it exerts a force and does work because of the k.e. it possesses as a result of its motion.

Kinetic and potential energy are types of mechanical energy.

(*d*) *Other forms.* These include: electrical energy, heat energy, sound energy, light energy, magnetic energy and nuclear energy.

Energy changes

One of the useful things about energy is that it can be changed from one form to another by suitable devices.

The apparatus in Fig. 28.3 may be used to show a battery changing chemical energy to electrical energy which in the electric motor becomes k.e. The motor raises a weight giving it p.e. If the change-over switch is joined to the lamp and the weight is allowed to fall, what energy changes occur?

Some other examples of energy changes are shown in Fig. 28.4. In all cases it is found that *energy cannot be destroyed, it only changes into a different form.* This is known as the *principle of conservation of energy.* If it seems in a change that some energy has disappeared, the 'lost' energy is often converted into heat. For example, when a brick falls its p.e. becomes k.e. As it hits the ground, its temperature and that of the ground rises and heat is produced (and a little sound energy).

Fig. 28.3

In an energy change work is done. We take the *work done as a measure of the amount of energy changed.* For example, if you have to exert an upwards force of 10 N to raise a stone steadily through a vertical distance of 1.5 m, the work done is 15 J. This is also the amount of chemical energy transferred *from* your muscles *to* p.e. of the stone. All forms of energy, as well as work, are measured in joules.

Fig. 28.4

Power

The more powerful a car is the faster it can climb a hill, i.e. the faster it does work. The *power* of a device is the work it does per second, i.e. the *rate at which it does work*. This is the same as the rate at which it changes energy from one form to another.

$$\text{POWER} = \frac{\text{WORK DONE}}{\text{TIME TAKEN}} = \frac{\text{ENERGY CHANGE}}{\text{TIME TAKEN}} \qquad (2)$$

The unit of power is the *watt* (W) and is *a rate of working of 1 joule per second*, i.e. $1 \text{ W} = 1 \text{ J/s}$. Larger units are the kilowatt (kW) and the megawatt (MW).

$$1 \text{ kW} = 1000 \text{ W} = 10^3 \text{ W};$$
$$1 \text{ MW} = 1\,000\,000 \text{ W} = 10^6 \text{ W}$$

If a machine does 500 J of work in 10 s its power is $500 \text{ J}/10 \text{ s} = 50 \text{ J/s} = 50 \text{ W}$. A Mini develops a maximum power of about 25 kW.

Experiment: your own power

Get someone with a stop watch to time you running up a flight of stairs, the longer the better. Find your weight (in newtons). Calculate the total *vertical* height (in metres) you have climbed by measuring the height of one stair and counting the number of stairs.

The work you do (in joules) in lifting your weight to the top of the stairs is (your weight) × (vertical height of stairs). Calculate your power (in watts) from equation (2). About 0.5 kW is good. (1 horse power = 0.75 kW.)

Friction

Friction is the force that opposes one surface moving, or trying to move, over another. It can be a help or a hindrance. We could not walk if it did not exist between the soles of our shoes and the ground. Our feet would slip backwards, as they tend to if we walk on ice. On the other hand engineers try to reduce friction to a minimum in the moving parts of machinery by using lubricating oils and ball bearings.

When a gradually increasing force P is applied through a spring balance to a block on a table, Fig. 28.5, it does not move at first. This is because an equally increasing but opposing frictional force F

Fig. 28.5

acts where the block and table touch. At any instant P and F are equal and opposite.

If P is increased further the block eventually moves; as it does so F has its maximum value, called *starting* or *static* friction. When it is moving at a steady speed the balance reading is slightly less than that for starting friction. *Sliding* or *dynamic* friction is therefore less than static friction.

A weight on the block increases the force pressing the surfaces together and increases friction.

When work is done against friction, the temperatures of the bodies in contact rise (as you can test by rubbing your hands together) and some other form of energy is usually changed into heat energy.

Questions

1. How much work is done when a mass of 3 kg (weighing 30 N) is lifted vertically through 6 m?

2. A hiker climbs a hill 300 m high. If he weighs 50 kg calculate the work he does in lifting his body to the top of the hill. (*W.Y.*)

3. Name one device which changes
   (*a*) electrical energy to light,
   (*b*) sound to electrical energy,
   (*c*) chemical energy to electrical energy,
   (*d*) p.e. to k.e.,
   (*e*) electrical energy to k.e.

4. A cyclist free-wheels from the top of a hill, gathers speed going down the hill, applies his brakes and eventually comes to rest at the bottom of the hill. Which one of the following energy changes takes place?

   A Potential to kinetic to heat energy.
   B Kinetic to potential to heat energy.
   C Chemical to heat to potential energy.
   D Kinetic to heat to chemical energy. (*W.M.*)

5. In loading a lorry a man lifts boxes each of weight 100 N through a height of 1.5 m.
   (*a*) How much work does he do in lifting one box?
   (*b*) If he lifts 4 boxes per minute at what power is he working? (*A.L.*)

6. A boy whose weight is 600 N runs up a flight of stairs 10 m high in a time of 12 s. The average power he develops, in W, is

   A 72   **B** 500   **C** 720   **D** 5000   **E** 7200   (*Met.*)

29 Machines

A machine is any device which enables a force (the *effort*) acting at one point to overcome another force (the *load*) acting at some other point. A lever (p. 69) is a simple machine as are pulleys, gears, screws, etc. They are used to build more complicated machines like the crane in Fig. 29.4.

Definitions

If a load of 50 N is moved by applying an effort of 10 N to a machine, the *mechanical advantage* of the machine is $50/10 = 5$.

$$\text{MECHANICAL ADVANTAGE (M.A.)} = \frac{\text{LOAD}}{\text{EFFORT}}$$

Machines with M.A. greater than 1 allow heavy loads to be moved by smaller efforts. But the effort has to move farther than the load. We define

$$\frac{\text{VELOCITY}}{\text{RATIO (V.R.)}} = \frac{\text{DISTANCE MOVED BY EFFORT}}{\text{DISTANCE MOVED BY LOAD}}$$

V.R. is fixed by the design of the machine. M.A. has to be found experimentally. The V.R. of the lever

load
100 N

Fig. 29.1

in Fig. 29.1 is 10. The effort needed to raise the load is found by taking moments about the fulcrum O. Do this (ignore the weight of the lever). What is the M.A?

Efficiency of a machine

Machines make work easier. No machine is perfect and in practice more work is done by the effort on a machine than by the machine on the load. Work measures energy transfer (or change) and so we can also say that the energy input to a machine is greater than its energy output. Some energy is always wasted to overcome friction and move parts

of the machine itself. In Fig. 29.1 there is friction at the fulcrum and the lever has weight; the effort will therefore be more than 10 N. We define

$$\text{EFFICIENCY} = \frac{\text{ENERGY OUTPUT}}{\text{ENERGY INPUT}}$$

$$= \frac{\text{WORK DONE ON LOAD}}{\text{WORK DONE BY EFFORT}}$$

This is expressed as a percentage and is always less than 100%.

There is a useful relation between M.A., V.R. and efficiency. From the above equation we can say, remembering that work = force × distance,

$$\text{efficiency} = \frac{\text{load} \times \text{distance load moves}}{\text{effort} \times \text{distance effort moves}}$$

$$= \text{M.A.} \times \frac{1}{\text{V.R.}}$$

$$\therefore \quad \text{PERCENTAGE EFFICIENCY} = \frac{\text{M.A.}}{\text{V.R.}} \times 100\%$$

Pulleys

(*a*) *Single fixed pulley*, Fig. 29.2. This enables us to lift a load L more conveniently by applying a *downwards* effort E. E need be only slightly greater than L and if friction in the pulley bearings is negligible then $E = L$ and M.A. = 1. What is the V.R.?

(*b*) *Single moving pulley*, Fig. 29.3. If the effort applied to the free end of the rope is E the total upward force on the pulley is 2E since two parts of the rope support it. A load $L = 2E$ can therefore be raised if the pulley and rope are frictionless and weightless. That is, M.A. = 2 (but less in practice).

To raise the load by 1 m requires each side of the rope to shorten by 1 m. The free end has therefore to take up 2 m of slack and so V.R. = 2.

Fig. 29.2   L   **Fig. 29.3**   L

Fig. 29.4

Load N	Effort N	M.A.	$Efficiency = \dfrac{M.A.}{V.R.} \times 100\%$

(*c*) *Block and tackle.* This type of pulley system is used in cranes (Fig. 29.4) and lifts. It consists of two blocks each with one or more pulleys. In the arrangement of Fig. 29.5*a* the pulleys in the blocks are shown one above the other for clarity; in practice they are side by side on the same axle, Fig. 29.5*b*. The rope passes round each pulley in turn.

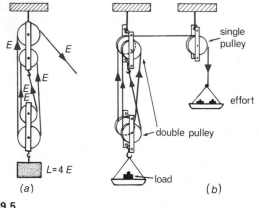

(*a*)

Fig. 29.5

The total upward force on the lower block is 4*E* since it is supported by four parts of the rope and a load *L* = 4*E* can be raised. Hence M.A. = 4 if the pulleys are frictionless and weightless. Using the same reasoning as in (*b*) we see that V.R. = 4, i.e. the number of times the rope passes from one block to the other.

Experiment: efficiency of a pulley system

Set up the system of Fig. 29.5*b* or a similar one. Starting with 50 g in the load pan, add weights to the effort pan until the load just rises steadily. Record the load and effort in a table (100 g has a weight of 1 N) and repeat for greater loads.

The V.R. can be obtained as explained before. Work out the M.A. and the efficiency for each pair of readings of load and effort.

Notes: 1. The lower pulley block and the load pan are also raised by the effort but are not included as part of the load. They become less important as the load increases and the M.A. and the efficiency both increase for this reason. The V.R. is constant for a particular system.

2. The efficiency is less than 100% because the system is not frictionless and the moving parts not weightless.

Other simple machines

Fig. 29.6

(*a*) *Wheel and axle.* A screwdriver and the steering wheel of a car, Fig. 29.6, use the wheel and axle principle. This is shown in Fig. 29.7*a*; the effort is applied to a rope wound round the wheel and the load is raised by another rope wound oppositely on the axle. For one complete turn of the wheel the effort moves a distance $2\pi R$, i.e. the circumference of the wheel, and the load a distance $2\pi r$. Hence

$$V.R. = \frac{2\pi R}{2\pi r} = \frac{R}{r}$$

The M.A. of a frictionless wheel and axle is also R/r as you can prove from Fig. 29.7*b* by taking moments about O.

Fig. 29.7

(*a*)   (*b*)

(b) *Inclined plane.* It is easier to push a barrel up a plank on to a lorry than to lift it vertically. In Fig. 29.8, to raise the load L through a *vertical* height

Fig. 29.8

load L

h, the smaller effort E moves a greater distance d equal to the length of the incline.

$$\text{V.R.} = \frac{\text{length of incline}}{\text{height of incline}} = \frac{d}{h}$$

The M.A. of a *perfect* incline may be calculated from the principle of conservation of energy by assuming

work done on load = work done by effort

i.e. $L \times h = E \times d$

$$\therefore \ \text{M.A.} = \frac{L}{E} = \frac{d}{h}$$

In fact, because of friction, it will be less.

(c) *Screw jack.* In a car jack a screw passes through a nut carrying an arm that fits into the car chassis, Fig. 29.9a. When the effort applied to the lever at

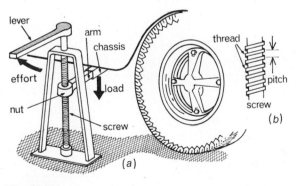

Fig. 29.9

the top of the screw makes one complete turn, the screw (and the load) rises a distance equal to its pitch, i.e. the distance between successive threads, Fig. 29.9b.

$$\text{V.R.} = \frac{\text{circumference of circle made by effort}}{\text{pitch of screw}}$$

The M.A. of a perfect jack can also be calculated assuming conservation of energy.

(d) *Gears.* The V.R. and M.A. of a machine can be changed by gears. In Fig. 29.10 the gear with 10 teeth makes two revolutions for each complete

Fig. 29.10

revolution of the one with 20 teeth. The V.R. is therefore 2 if the effort is applied to the small gear which drives the large gear. Hence

$$\text{V.R.} = \frac{\text{no. of teeth on driven gear}}{\text{no. of teeth on driving gear}}$$

Questions

1. A machine of V.R. 5 is used to raise a load whose weight is 200 N. The effort required is 50 N.
 (a) What is the M.A. of the machine?
  A $\frac{1}{4}$ B 4   C 5   D 10   E 20
 (b) What is the efficiency of the machine?
  A 50%   B 60%   C 75%   D 80%   E 125% (*E.A.*)

2. An effort of 250 N raises a load of 1000 N through 5 m in a pulley system. If the effort moves 30 m, what is (a) the work done in raising the load, (b) the work done by the effort, (c) the efficiency?

3. For each pulley system shown in Fig. 29.11a, b, c, what is (i) the M.A., (ii) the V.R. and (iii) the efficiency?

Fig. 29.11

4. A machine consisting of a wheel of radius 50 cm and an axle of radius 10 cm is used to lift a load of 400 N with an effort of 100 N. For this system calculate: (a) the M.A., (b) the V.R. and (c) the efficiency.

5. A trolley of weight 10 N is pulled from the bottom to the top of the inclined plane in Fig. 29.8 at a steady speed by a force of 2 N. If $h = 2$ m and $d = 20$ m what is (a) the M.A., (b) the V.R. and (c) the efficiency?

6. If gear A has 30 teeth and drives gear B with 75 teeth, how many times does A rotate for each rotation of B?

81

30 Pressure in liquids

To make sense of some effects in which a force acts on a body we have to consider not only the force but also the area on which it acts. For example, wearing skis prevents you sinking into soft snow because your weight is spread over a greater area. We say the *pressure* is less.

Pressure is the force (or thrust) *acting on unit area* (e.g. 1 m²) and is calculated from

$$PRESSURE = \frac{FORCE}{AREA}$$

The pressure exerted on the floor by the same box (*a*) standing on end, (*b*) lying flat, is shown in Fig. 30.1. The unit of pressure is the *pascal* (Pa); it equals 1 newton per square metre (N/m²) and is quite a small pressure. An apple in your hand exerts about 1000 Pa.

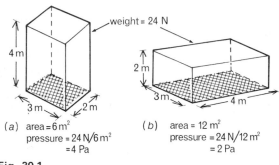

weight = 24 N

(*a*) area = 6 m²
pressure = 24 N/6 m²
= 4 Pa

(*b*) area = 12 m²
pressure = 24 N/12 m²
= 2 Pa

Fig. 30.1

The greater the area over which a force acts the less is the pressure. This is why a tractor with wide wheels can move over soft ground. The pressure is large when the area is small and accounts for a nail having a sharp point. Walnuts can be broken in the hand by squeezing two but not one. Why?

Liquid pressure

1. *Pressure in a liquid increases with depth* because the farther down you go the greater the weight of liquid above. In Fig. 30.2 water spurts out fastest and furthest from the lowest hole.

2. *Pressure at one depth acts equally in all directions.* The can of water in Fig. 30.3 has similar holes all

Fig. 30.2

Fig. 30.3

round it at the same level. Water comes out as fast and as far from each hole. Hence the pressure exerted by the water at this depth is the same in all directions.

3. *A liquid finds its own level.* In the U-tube of Fig. 30.4*a* the liquid pressure at the foot of P is greater than at the foot of Q because the left-hand column

Fig. 30.4

(*a*)   (*b*)

is higher than the right-hand one. When the clip is opened the liquid flows from P to Q until the pressure and the levels are the same, i.e. the liquid finds its own level. Although the weight of liquid in Q is now greater than in P, it acts over a greater area since tube Q is wider.

In Fig. 30.4*b* the liquid is at the same level in each tube and confirms that the pressure at the foot of a liquid column depends only on the *vertical* depth of the liquid and not on the width or shape of the tube.

Water supply system

A town's water supply often comes from a reservoir on high ground. Water flows from it through pipes to any tap or storage tank that is below the level of water in the reservoir, Fig. 30.5. The lower the place supplied the greater is the water pressure at it. In very tall buildings it may be necessary first to pump the water to a large tank in the roof. Why?

Fig. 30.6

reservoir

pump

Fig. 30.5

force
I N

load

piston A
($\frac{1}{100}$ m²)

piston B
($\frac{1}{2}$ m²)

liquid

Fig. 30.7

Reservoirs for water supply or for hydroelectric power stations (p. 208) are often made in mountainous regions by building a dam at one end of a valley. The dam must be thicker at the bottom than at the top due to the large water pressure at the bottom, Fig. 30.6.

Hydraulic machines

Liquids are almost incompressible (i.e. their volume cannot be reduced by squeezing) and they pass on any pressure applied to them. Use is made of these facts in hydraulic machines. Fig. 30.7 shows the principle on which they work. Suppose a downwards force of 1 N acts on a piston A of area $1/100$ m². The pressure transmitted through the liquid is

$$\text{pressure} = \frac{\text{force}}{\text{area}} = \frac{1}{1/100} = 100 \text{ Pa}$$

This pressure acts on piston B of area $\frac{1}{2}$ m². The total upwards force or thrust on B is given by

$$\text{force} = \text{pressure} \times \text{area} = 100 \times \tfrac{1}{2} = 50 \text{ N}$$

A force of 1 N thus produces a force of 50 N.

A *hydraulic jack*, Fig. 30.8, has a platform on top of piston B and is used in garages to lift cars. Both valves open only to the right and they allow B to be raised a long way when A moves up and down repeatedly. A *hydraulic fork lift truck* works similarly. In a *hydraulic press* there is a fixed plate above

reservoir   piston
A

B

valve   valve

Fig. 30.8

83

Fig. 30.9

Fig. 30.11

B, and one like that in Fig. 30.9 shapes car bodies from sheets of steel placed between B and the plate. *Hydraulic car brakes* are shown in Fig. 30.10. When the brake pedal is pushed the piston in the master cylinder exerts a force on the brake fluid and the resulting pressure is transmitted equally to eight other pistons (four are shown). These force the brake shoes or pads against the wheels and stop the car.

Fig. 30.10

Expression for liquid pressure

In designing a dam an engineer has to calculate the pressure at various depths below the water surface.

An expression for the pressure at a depth h in a liquid of density d can be found by considering a horizontal area A, Fig. 30.11. The force acting vertically downwards on A equals the weight of the liquid column of height h and cross-sectional area A above it. Then

$$\text{volume of liquid column} = hA$$

Since mass = volume × density we can say

$$\text{mass of liquid column} = hAd$$

Taking a mass of 1 kg to have weight 10 N,

$$\text{weight of liquid column} = 10\,hAd$$
$$\therefore \text{force on area } A = 10\,hAd$$
$$\therefore \text{pressure} = \text{force/area} = 10\,hAd/A$$
$$= 10\,hd$$

This pressure acts equally in all directions at depth h and depends only on h and d. Its value will be in Pa if h is in m and d in kg/m^3.

Questions

1. A girl in stiletto heels is more likely to damage a wooden floor than an elephant is. Why?

2. (a) What is the pressure on a surface when a force of 50 N acts on an area of (i) 2 m^2 (ii) 100 m^2 (iii) 0.5 m^2?

(b) A pressure of 10 Pa acts on an area of 3 m^2. What is the force acting on the area?

3. A block of concrete weighs 900 N and its base is a square of side 2 m. What pressure does the block exert on the ground? (E.A.)

Fig. 30.12

4. (a) What is the volume of the block in Fig. 30.12?

(b) What is the mass of the block if its density is 2000 kg/m^3?

(c) What is the weight of the block? (Assume a mass of 1 kg has weight 10 N.)

(d) What pressure is exerted on the ground by the block?

(e) If the shaded side of the block is on the ground, what effect, if any, will this have on (i) the force exerted by the block on the ground, (ii) the pressure exerted by the block on the ground?

5. In a hydraulic press a force of 20 N is applied to a piston of area 0.2 m^2. The area of the other piston is 2 m^2. What is (a) the pressure transmitted through the liquid, (b) the force on the other piston?

6. (a) Why must a liquid and not a gas be used as the 'fluid' in a hydraulic machine?

(b) On what other important property of a liquid do hydraulic machines depend?

7. What is the pressure 100 m below the surface of sea water of density 1150 kg/m^3?

8. The pressure in a water pipe in the ground floor of a building is 4×10^5 Pa but three floors up it is only 2×10^5 Pa. What is the height between the ground floor and the third floor? (The water in the pipe may be assumed to be stationary; density of water $= 1 \times 10^3$ kg/m^3.) (N.I.)

31 Atmospheric pressure

The air forming the earth's atmosphere stretches upwards a long way. Air has weight and in a normal room weighs about the same as you do, e.g. 500 N. Owing to its weight the atmosphere exerts a large pressure at sea level, about $100\,000\,\text{N/m}^2 = 10^5\,\text{Pa} = 100\,\text{kPa}$. This pressure acts equally in all directions.

We do not normally feel atmospheric pressure because the pressure inside our bodies is almost the same as that outside. A similar balance exists with external objects, unless air is removed from one place. The effect of atmospheric pressure is then noticeable. A space from which all the air has been withdrawn is a *vacuum*.

Air pressure demonstrations

(*a*) *Collapsing can.* If air is removed from a can, Fig. 31.1*a*, by a vacuum pump, the can collapses because the air pressure inside becomes less than that outside, Fig. 31.1*b*.

(*a*)   (*b*)

Fig. 31.1

(*b*) *Magdeburg hemispheres.* The vacuum pump was invented by von Guericke, the Mayor of Magdeburg. About 1650 he used it to remove the air from two large hollow metal hemispheres, fitted together to give an airtight sphere. So good was his pump

Fig. 31.2

that it took two teams, each of eight horses, to separate the hemispheres. A similar experiment can be done by two people with small brass hemispheres, Fig. 31.2.

Using air pressure

(*a*) *Drinking straw*, Fig. 31.3*a*. When you suck, your lungs expand and air passes into them from the straw. Atmospheric pressure pushing down on the surface of the liquid in the bottle is now greater than the pressure of the air in the straw and so forces the liquid up to your mouth.

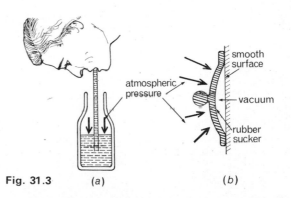

Fig. 31.3   (*a*)   (*b*)

(*b*) *Rubber sucker*, Fig. 31.3*b*. When the sucker is moistened and pressed on a smooth flat surface, the air inside is pushed out. Atmospheric pressure then holds it firmly against the surface. Suckers are used as holders for towels in the home, for attaching car licences to windscreens and in industry for lifting metal sheets.

Pressure gauges

These measure the pressure exerted by a fluid, i.e. by a liquid or a gas.

(*a*) *Bourdon gauge.* It works like the toy in Fig. 31.4*a*. The harder you blow into the paper tube, the more does it uncurl. In a Bourdon gauge, Fig. 31.4*b*, when a fluid pressure is applied, the curved metal tube tries to straighten out and rotates a pointer over a scale. Car oil pressure gauges and the gauges on gas cylinders are of this type.

paper tube

curved metal tube

(a)

Fig. 31.4

(b)

fluid pressure

(b) *U-tube manometer.* In Fig. 31.5a each surface of the liquid is acted on equally by atmospheric pressure and the levels are the same. If one side is connected to, for example, the gas supply, Fig. 31.5b, the gas exerts a pressure on surface A and level B rises until

pressure of gas = atmospheric pressure +
pressure due to liquid
column BC

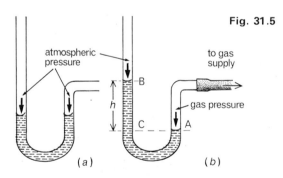

Fig. 31.5

atmospheric pressure

to gas supply

B

h

C

A

gas pressure

(a)

(b)

The pressure of the liquid column BC therefore equals the amount by which the gas pressure *exceeds* atmospheric pressure. It equals $10\,hd$ (in Pa) where h is the vertical height of BC (in m) and d is the density of the liquid (in kg/m^3). The height h is called the *head of liquid* and sometimes, instead of stating a pressure in Pa, we say that it is so many cm of water (or mercury for higher pressures).

Mercury barometer

A barometer is a manometer which measures atmospheric pressure. A simple barometer can be made

by using a small funnel to nearly fill with mercury a thick-walled glass tube about 1 m long. If the tube is slowly inverted several times, with a finger over the open end, the large air bubble runs up and down collecting any small air bubbles trapped in the mercury.

The tube is then filled with mercury, closed with the finger and inverted into a bowl of mercury. When the finger is removed the mercury falls until it is about 760 mm above the level in the bowl, Fig. 31.6a. The pressure at X due to the weight of the column of mercury XY equals the atmospheric pressure on the surface of the mercury in the bowl. XY measures the atmospheric pressure in mm of mercury (mmHg).

Fig. 31.6

Y

mercury

760 mm

atmospheric pressure

to vacuum pump

air pressure

mercury

(a)

X

(b)

The *vertical* height of the column is unchanged if the tube is tilted. Would it be different with a wider tube? Why? The space above the mercury in the tube is a vacuum (except for a little mercury vapour). How could you test this?

The apparatus in Fig. 31.6b may be used to show that it is atmospheric pressure which holds up the column. When the air above the mercury in the bottle is pumped out, the column falls.

Aneroid barometer

An aneroid (no liquid) barometer consists of a partially evacuated, thin metal box with corrugated sides to increase its strength, Fig. 31.7. The box is pre-

pointer

chain

strong spring

pivot

hinge

Fig. 31.7

partial vacuum

corrugated metal box

vented from collapsing by a strong spring. If the atmospheric pressure increases, the box caves in slightly, if it decreases the spring pulls it out. A system of levers magnifies this movement and causes a chain to move a pointer over a scale.

Aneroid barometers are used as weather glasses, high pressure being associated with fine weather. They are also used as altimeters to measure the height of an aircraft since the pressure decreases the higher it goes.

Pressure, aviation and diving

Our bodies are designed to work at normal atmospheric pressure. At high altitudes breathing is difficult and modern aircraft have pressurized cabins in which the air pressure is increased sufficiently above that outside to safeguard the crew and passengers.

Ear 'popping' occurs when there are pressure changes, e.g. at aircraft take-off. It is due to the pressure difference between the air in the middle part of the ear and that in the outer ear. The eardrum becomes distorted. Swallowing helps to equalize the pressures.

If astronauts are not in pressurized space capsules they must rely on space suits for supplying a suitable atmosphere, Fig. 31.8. Otherwise blood and water in the body would boil and possibly explode (see p. 138).

A diver meets high pressures and different dangers. If he breathed air, extra nitrogen might dissolve in his blood and on returning to the surface he would suffer the painful and sometimes fatal condition called 'bends'. This is caused by the dissolved nitrogen forming bubbles in the blood. To prevent this he breathes a mixture of oxygen and helium. If he has been working in deep waters (e.g. 150 m) he is brought to the surface in a diving bell and kept

in a decompression chamber for up to several days while the pressure is slowly reduced.

Questions

1. (*a*) Figs. 31.9*a* and *b* show an open ended and a closed tube manometer connected (at different times) to the same gas cylinder.

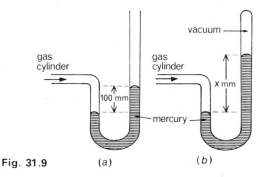

Fig. 31.9   (*a*)   (*b*)

The mercury barometer reads 760 mm. Assuming no loss in pressure from the gas cylinder, calculate (*i*) the pressure of gas in the cylinder, (*ii*) the height of the mercury in Fig. 31.9*b* (i.e. *x*).

(*b*) Draw a diagram of a manometer similar to that in (*i*) Fig. 31.9*a*, (*ii*) Fig. 31.9*b*, when it is connected to a gas supply at less than atmospheric pressure (760 mm of mercury).   (*W.M.*)

2. Fig. 31.10 shows a simple barometer.

Fig. 31.10

(*a*) What is the region A?
(*b*) What keeps the mercury in the tube?
(*c*) What is the value of the atmospheric pressure being shown by the barometer?
(*d*) What would happen to this reading if the barometer were taken up a high mountain? Give a reason.   (*E.M.*)

3. What would be the height of a water barometer if atmospheric pressure is 1.0×10^5 Pa and the density of water is 1.0×10^3 kg/m^3? (*Hint.* Use $p = 10\,hd$.)

4. Calculate the reduction in pressure indicated by a mercury barometer when it is raised through 1.0 km. Take the average density of air to be 1.3 kg/m^3 and the density of mercury to be 1.3×10^4 kg/m^3.   (*A.E.B.*)

Fig.
31.8

32 Pumps and pressure

Syringe

Fig. 32.1

The syringe is used by doctors to give injections and by gardeners to spray plants. It consists of a tight-fitting piston in a barrel, Fig. 32.1, and may be filled by putting the nozzle under the liquid and drawing back the piston. This reduces the air pressure in the barrel and atmospheric pressure forces the liquid up into it. Pushing down the piston drives liquid out of the nozzle.

Lift pump

From early times lift pumps were used to raise water from wells and many are preserved in villages today. They have two valves, one in the piston and one at the bottom of the barrel. The valves, which allow water to flow upwards only, are bits of leather weighted by metal discs that normally keep them closed.

The pump is primed by first pouring water on top of the piston to prevent air leaking past it. After a few strokes the pump fills with water as a result of the following action.

On the upstroke, Fig. 32.2a, valve A is closed and the pressure falls in the barrel below the piston. Atmospheric pressure acting on the surface of the

Fig. 32.2

water in the well then pushes water up the pipe through valve B. Also, water on top of the piston is lifted upwards and flows out of the spout.

On the downstroke, Fig. 32.2b, valve B closes by the pressure of water on it and valve A opens, allowing water to pass upwards into the barrel above the piston.

Atmospheric pressure can only support a column of water 10 m high and this is the maximum height through which water can be raised by a lift pump. In practice it is less because of leaks at the valves and piston.

Force pump

Force pumps can raise water more than 10 m if the pump itself is within 10 m of the water supply. They are used in modern caravans.

On the upstroke, Fig. 32.3, valve A closes and atmospheric pressure forces water up into the barrel of the pump through valve B.

Fig. 32.3

On the downstroke, valve B closes and water is forced through valve A into the reservoir C and also out of the spout D. The air in C is compressed and on the next upstroke it expands so keeping up the supply of water from D.

Bicycle pump

When the piston is pushed in, the air between it and the tyre valve is compressed. This pushes the rim of the plastic washer against the wall of the barrel to form an airtight seal, Fig. 32.4. Air is forced past

88

Fig. 32.4

Fig. 32.7

the tyre valve into the tyre when the pressure of the air between the plastic washer and the valve exceeds the pressure of the air in the tyre.

When the piston is withdrawn, the tyre valve is closed by the greater pressure in the tyre. Atmospheric pressure then forces air past the plastic washer, no longer pressed hard against the wall, into the barrel.

Vacuum pump

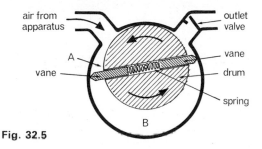

Fig. 32.5

The drum and vanes in Fig. 32.5 are rotated by an electric motor. The volume of space A increases and the pressure decreases so drawing air in from the apparatus to be evacuated. The air in space B is then compressed and forced out of the outlet valve. This happens every half rotation until hardly any air is left.

Siphon

Using a siphon is often the only way to empty a tank. To start the siphon, Fig. 32.6, it must be full of liquid and end A must be below the liquid level in the tank.

Fig. 32.6

Boyle's law

Changes in the volume of a gas due to pressure changes can be studied using the apparatus in Fig. 32.7. The volume V of air trapped in the glass tube is read off on the scale behind. The pressure is altered by pumping air from a foot pump into the space

above the oil reservoir. This forces more oil into the glass tube and increases the pressure p on the air in it; p is measured by the Bourdon gauge.

If p is doubled, V is halved. That is, V is *inversely proportional* to p.

$$V \propto \frac{1}{p} \quad \text{or} \quad V = \text{constant} \times \frac{1}{p}$$
$$\therefore \qquad pV = \text{constant}$$

If several pairs of readings $p_1 V_1$, $p_2 V_2$, etc. are taken, then $p_1 V_1 = p_2 V_2 = $ a constant.

Boyle's law states that the volume of a fixed mass of gas is inversely proportional to the pressure, if the temperature is unchanged.

Questions

1. Fig. 32.8*a* shows air enclosed in a cylinder by an airtight piston. In Fig. 32.8*b* the piston has been pushed in so that the air occupies one-third of the length of the cylinder that it previously occupied. What, if anything, has happened to (*a*) the number of molecules of air, (*b*) the volume of air, (*c*) the pressure of the air? (*E.A.*)

(*a*)   (*b*)

Fig. 32.8

2. If a certain quantity of gas has a volume of $30\,\text{cm}^3$ at a pressure of $1 \times 10^5\,\text{Pa}$, what is its volume when the pressure is (*a*) $2 \times 10^5\,\text{Pa}$, (*b*) $5 \times 10^5\,\text{Pa}$?

3. An enclosed mass of air occupies $4.0 \times 10^{-3}\,\text{m}^3$ at a pressure of $100\,\text{kPa}$; when the pressure is changed to $80\,\text{kPa}$ (at constant temperature) the volume of the air, in m^3, will be

    A 2.2×10^{-3} B 3.2×10^{-3} C 4.0×10^{-3} D 5.0×10^{-3}
    E 9.0×10^{-3} (*N.I.*)

4. A diver at the bottom of a lake releases an air bubble of volume $2\,\text{cm}^3$. As the bubble rises its volume increases until at the surface it is $4\,\text{cm}^3$. How deep is the lake if atmospheric pressure equals the pressure due to a column of water $10\,\text{m}$ high?

33 Floating, sinking and flying

A ship floats because it gets support from the water. Any object in a liquid, whether floating or submerged, is acted on by an upward force or *upthrust*. This makes it seem to weigh less than normal.

Archimedes' principle

In Fig. 33.1a the block hanging from the spring balance weighs 10 N in air. When it is completely immersed in water the reading becomes 6 N, Fig. 33.1b. The loss in weight of the block is $(10-6)\text{N} = 4\text{N}$: the upthrust of the water on it is therefore 4 N.

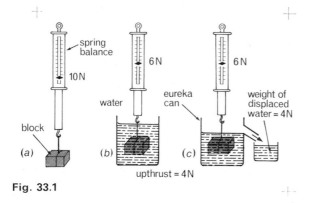

Fig. 33.1

If a can like that in Fig. 33.1c is used, full of water to the level of the spout, the water displaced (the overflow) can be collected and weighed. Its weight here is 4 N, the same as the upthrust. (Its volume is exactly equal to the volume of the block.) Experiments with other liquids and also with gases lead to the general conclusion called *Archimedes' principle*.

When a body is wholly or partly submerged in a fluid the upthrust equals the weight of fluid displaced (i.e. pushed aside).

A fluid means either a liquid or a gas. The case of gases will be dealt with later.

Experiment: relative densities

On page 58 we saw that

$$\text{relative density} = \frac{\text{mass of substance}}{\text{mass of same volume of water}}$$

But weight is proportional to mass, i.e. if a mass of 1 kg has weight 10 N, a mass of 2 kg has weight 2×10 N. We can therefore write

$$\text{relative density} = \frac{\text{weight of substance}}{\text{weight of same volume of water}}$$

(a) *Solids.* Using a suitable balance find the weight of a solid (e.g. an iron bolt, a glass stopper) in air and then in water. By Archimedes, the apparent loss in weight equals the weight of water displaced by the solid. The volume of this weight of water is the same as the volume of the solid. Hence

$$\text{relative density of solid} = \frac{\text{weight of solid}}{\text{apparent loss in weight of solid in water}}$$

Work out the relative density of the solid from this expression.

(b) *Liquids.* Weigh the solid used in (a) in the liquid (e.g. methylated spirit) whose relative density is to be found. As before, the apparent loss in weight of the solid equals the weight of liquid having the same volume as the solid. Therefore

$$\text{relative density of liquid}$$
$$= \frac{\text{weight of any volume of liquid}}{\text{weight of an equal volume of water}}$$
$$= \frac{\text{apparent loss in weight of solid in liquid}}{\text{apparent loss in weight of solid in water}}$$

Work out the relative density of the liquid.

Floating

A stone held below the surface of water sinks when released, a cork rises. The weight of the stone is

Fig. 33.2

(a) Stone sinks   (b) Cork rises   (c) Wood floats

greater than the upthrust on it (i.e. the weight of water displaced) and there is a net or resultant downward force on it, Fig. 33.2a. If the cork has the same volume as the stone, it will displace the same weight (and volume) of water. The upthrust on it is therefore the same as for the stone but it is greater than the weight of the cork. The resultant upward force on the cork makes it rise, Fig. 33.2b.

When a body floats in water the upthrust equals the weight of the body. The net force on the body is zero, Fig. 33.2c. This is a case of the *principle of flotation.*

A floating body displaces its own weight of fluid.

For example, a block of wood of weight 10 N displaces an amount of water (or any other liquid in which it floats) having weight 10 N (i.e. mass 1 kg).

Ships, submarines, balloons

(*a*) *Ships.* A floating ship displaces a weight of water equal to its own weight including that of the cargo. The load lines (called the Plimsoll mark) on the side of a ship show the levels to which it can legally be loaded under different conditions, Fig. 33.3. Why can it take a greater load in summer than in winter?

Fig. 33.3

(*b*) *Submarines.* A submarine sinks by taking water into its buoyancy tanks. Once submerged, the upthrust is unchanged but the weight of the submarine increases with the inflow of water and it sinks faster. To surface, compressed air is used to blow the water out of the tanks.

In the Cartesian diver, Fig. 33.4, pressure on the cork forces more water into the bulb. The diver's weight increases and he sinks. Decreasing the pressure causes him to rise.

Fig. 33.4

The Swedish warship *Wasa*, which sank in a squall in Stockholm Harbour over three hundred years ago, was refloated in 1961. Fig. 33.5a shows the ship emerging from the water. Fig. 33.5b shows it in dock with three of its four buoyancy tanks. The tanks, full of water, were attached to the partly submerged ship which was then raised by pumping the water out of the tanks. Can you explain why this happened?

Fig. 33.5a

Fig. 33.5b

(a)

(b)

Fig. 33.7

Fig. 33.6

(c) *Balloons.* A balloon filled with hydrogen weighs less than the weight of air it displaces. The upthrust is therefore greater than its weight and the resultant upwards force on the balloon causes it to rise.

Meteorological balloons carrying scientific instruments called *radiosondes* are sent into the upper atmosphere. A small radio transmitter sends signals back to earth which contain information about the temperature, pressure and humidity, Fig. 33.6. They are tracked by radar to give data on wind direction and speed.

Hydrometer

This is an instrument for measuring rapidly the relative density of a liquid, Fig. 33.7a. It is placed in the liquid and the scale read at the level of the liquid surface. The denser the liquid the higher it floats; the numbers on the scale increase downwards.

The large bulb gives the instrument buoyancy and the small weighted bulb makes it float upright. The narrow stem gives greater sensitivity, i.e. a small density change causes the instrument to float much higher or lower.

Hydrometers enable the state of a car battery to be checked, Fig. 33.7b. In a fully charged one the relative density of the acid should be about 1.25. Recharging is required when the reading is less than 1.18. Hydrometers are also used in breweries to measure the relative density of beer. The 'watering down' of milk and wine can be tested similarly.

Bernoulli's principle

The pressure is the same at all points on the same level in a fluid at rest; this is not so when the fluid is moving.

(a) *Liquids.* When a liquid flows through a uniform tube the pressure falls steadily, as shown by the three manometer tubes in Fig. 33.8a. In Fig. 33.8b

(a) (b)

Fig. 33.8

the pressure falls in the narrow part B but rises again in the wider part C. Since the same volume of liquid passes through B in a certain time as enters A, the liquid must be moving faster in B than in A.

Therefore a decrease of pressure occurs when the speed of the liquid increases. Conversely an increase of pressure accompanies a fall in speed. This effect, called Bernoulli's principle, will be explained later (p. 111) and is stated as follows.

When the speed of a fluid increases, the pressure in the fluid decreases and vice versa.

(b) *Gases.* Bernoulli effects in air streams can be shown as in Fig. 33.9a and b. In (a) the two sheets of paper come together when you blow *between* them and in (b) the paper rises when you blow *over* it. In both cases the pressure falls in the moving air stream.

Fig. 33.9

(c) *Applications.* As a fluid comes out of a jet its speed increases and its pressure decreases. This fact is used in a Bunsen burner, Fig. 33.10a, and in a carburettor. A spinning ball takes a curved path because it drags air round with it, thereby increasing the speed of the air flow on one side and reducing it on the other, Fig. 33.10b.

Fig. 33.10

An aircraft wing, called an *aerofoil*, is shaped so that the air has to travel farther and so faster over the top surface than underneath, Fig. 33.11. The resultant upward force on the wing provides 'lift' for the aircraft.

Fig. 33.11

Questions

1. A metal block is weighed (a) in air, (b) half-submerged in water, (c) fully submerged in water, (d) fully submerged in a strong salt solution.

The readings obtained, though not necessarily in the correct order, were 5 N, 8 N, 10 N and 6 N. Which reading was obtained for each weighing?

2. A glass block weighs 25 N. When wholly immersed in water, the block appears to weigh 15 N. The relative density of glass is therefore

A 0.4   B 0.6   C 1.67   D 2.5   E 10   (*E.A.*)

3. A lump of metal of weight 5.6 N is suspended on a thin cord and completely immersed in water; it then appears to weigh only 4.9 N. When similarly immersed in brine the apparent weight is 4.8 N. Calculate the densities of the metal and the brine.

(*S.*)

4. A block of wood of volume 50 cm³ and density 0.6 g/cm³ floats on water. What is (a) the mass of the block, (b) the mass of water displaced, (c) the volume immersed in the water? (Density of water = 1 g/cm³.)

5. (a) A swimmer dives off a raft in a pool. Does the raft rise or sink in the water? What happens to the water level in the pool? Give reasons for your answer.

(b) A car ferry has a uniform cross-sectional area of 1000 m² and floats in water of density 1000 kg/m³. How far will it sink if 10 cars each of mass 1000 kg are taken aboard?

6. (a) A test tube of mass 5 g, length 10 cm and uniform cross-sectional area 2 cm² is partly filled with lead shot and floats vertically in water with 5 cm of its length submerged, Fig. 33.12.

Fig. 33.12

Calculate (i) the volume of water displaced, (ii) the mass of water displaced, (iii) the combined mass of the test tube and lead shot, (iv) the mass of the lead shot, (v) the length of the test tube that would be submerged in a liquid of density 0.8 g/cm³.

(b) (i) State one reason why it would be better to have chosen a tube of smaller cross-section if this method is to be used to measure the densities of liquids. (ii) What name is given to the commercial form of this apparatus? (iii) Give one example of the use of the commercial form. (iv) Why is a definite temperature usually marked on the instrument?   (*E.M.*)

34 Further questions

Moments and levers

1. Fig. 34.1 shows a nail being removed from a piece of wood by a claw hammer.

Fig. 34.1

(a) (i) What physical principle or law is involved in the withdrawal of the nail?

(ii) The nail begins to move when a force of 100 N is applied at the end of the handle. What is the frictional resistance exerted on the nail by the wood?

(b) State *one* more example of a lever of the same type as the claw hammer. (*N.W.*)

2. A horizontal uniform metal bar PQ of weight 5.0 N and length 0.50 m is pivoted at P, as shown

Fig. 34.2

in Fig. 34.2. The bar is held stationary by the light string QR so that it makes an angle of 30° with the bar. Calculate the moment about P due to the weight of the bar and hence or otherwise calculate the tension in the string. (*J.M.B.*)

3. Two uniform strip lights each of weight 30 N are supported from a ceiling as in Fig. 34.3a, b. Find the values of T_1, T_2, T_3 and T_4.

Fig. 34.3

Centres of gravity

4. (a) What is meant by (i) the centre of gravity of a body, (ii) a couple?

A metal sheet of irregular shape is suspended so that it can swing freely about a fixed horizontal needle which passes through a hole P near its edge. Draw a diagram showing the sheet at an instant during the swing when the sheet is not at its rest position. Show on the diagram the direction and point of application of each force acting on the metal sheet. Draw a second diagram showing the forces on the sheet when it has stopped swinging. Explain why the sheet comes to rest in this position.

(b) In order to 'weigh' a boy in the laboratory, a uniform plank of wood AB = 3.0 m long, having a mass of 8.0 kg, is pivoted about a point 0.50 m from A. The boy stands 0.30 m from A and a mass of 2.0 kg is placed 0.50 m from B in order to balance the plank horizontally.

Sketch the arrangement, representing each force acting on the plank by an arrow showing the direction of the force. Indicate the value of each force. Calculate the mass of the boy. (Take the weight of 1 kg as 10 N.) (*J.M.B.*)

5. (a) (i) Define the *moment of a force about a point*.

(ii) State the *principle of moments*.

(b) A uniform plank PQ weighing 300 N and of length 3.0 m rests on two narrow supports C and D. C is 0.50 m from P and D is 1.0 m from Q.

(i) Draw a neat diagram of the arrangement; on this diagram draw arrows at the points where the forces act ON THE PLANK, clearly marking the distances. The arrows should show the directions of the forces. Label the known force with its value.

(ii) A weight W causes the plank to tip over when placed at one end, but does not do so when placed at the other end. At which end is it placed when it causes tipping? Give the reason for your answer.

(iii) What is the least value of W which will cause tipping when placed (a) at end P, (b) at end Q?

(iv) By hanging a bucket at Q and pouring water into it the plank can be made to balance about support D. How could this arrangement be used to check the value given for the weight of the plank? (*J.M.B./A.L./N.W.16+*)

Adding forces

6. The resultant of the two forces shown in Fig. 34.4 makes an angle of 30° with the force of 40 N. Determine, graphically or otherwise, the values of the resultant and of the force *P*. (*L.*)

Fig. 34.4

7. A string attached to two hooks A, B, supports a weight *W* attached at a point C. CA makes an angle with the vertical of 30° and CB an angle of 45°, Fig. 34.5.

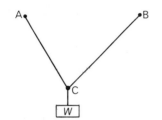

Fig. 34.5

If the tension in BC is 100 N, find, by drawing or calculation, the tension in AC and the weight *W*. (*O. and C.*)

8. What is meant by a *resultant* of two forces and by the *components* of a force?

What is the resultant of two equal forces, each of 20 N, if the direction of the two forces are at an angle of 60° to each other?

What is the component of a force of 20 N in a direction of 30° to the direction of the force if the two components are at right angles to each other? (*C.*)

Work, energy, power

9. Compressed air, a wound-up watch spring, a flywheel rotating on a fixed axle and a clock pendulum at maximum displacement.

The number of systems named above which possess p.e. is

   A 0   **B** 1   **C** 2   **D** 3   **E** 4   (*J.M.B.*)

10. A boy is lifting sandbags from the floor onto a shelf 1.6 m high. The pull of the earth on each sandbag is 10 N. The boy lifts 80 sandbags in 100 s.

(*a*) How much useful work was done in lifting the sandbags?

(*b*) What is the total p.e. when all the bags are on the shelf?

(*c*) What was the boy's useful power output?

(*d*) The actual power output was greater than answer (*c*). Suggest two possible reasons for this difference.

One sandbag fell from the shelf.

(*e*) What is its p.e. when it is halfway to the ground?

(*f*) What is its k.e. when it is halfway to the ground?

(*g*) What happens to its k.e. when it hits the ground? Give two possible answers.

Fig. 34.6

Fig. 34.6 shows the boy's arm when he is measuring the pull of the earth on a sandbag. He holds the balance still to take a reading.

(*h*) How much work is he doing as he checks the reading?

(*i*) Give a rough estimate (from the diagram) of the tension in the boy's biceps as he holds the balance. Explain how you arrived at this value. (*E.M.*)

Machines

11. Using a pulley system operating at an efficiency of 75% a man lifts a load of weight 1800 N using an effort of 400 N. Calculate the velocity ratio of the system. (*S.*)

12. A screw jack has a screw of pitch 5 mm and the effort applied at the end of the effort arm moves a distance of 1 m for one turn, Fig. 34.7. It needs an effort of 30 N to lift a load of 750 N.

(*a*) What is the M.A. of the screw jack?

(*b*) What is the V.R. of the screw jack?

Fig. 34.7

(c) Explain why the screw jack has a wide and heavy base.

(d) What benefit would be gained with a longer effort arm?

(e) What is the cause of low efficiency on a machine of this type?

(f) Calculate the percentage efficiency of the screw jack.

(g) The energy supplied to the screw jack is finally converted into two forms. What are these forms? Explain with reference to the low efficiency why one is much greater than the other.

(h) The efficiency of the screw jack is determined for a range of loads. Explain how this efficiency would be expected to vary from a very small load to the maximum possible load.   (O./S.R.16+)

Pressure in liquids

13. What is meant by the term *pressure*? Explain the fact that when someone uses his thumb to push a drawing pin into a block of wood, the pressure on the wood is greater than the pressure on the thumb.

Calculate the pressure on the thumb when the force exerted is 20 N and the top of the pin is square, the length of each side being 10 mm.   (C.)

14. The pressure of the liquid column XY in Fig. 34.8 supports the mass M on the light piston.

Fig. 34.8

(a) If the density of the liquid is 800 kg/m³ and a mass of 1 kg has a weight of 10 N, calculate the pressure at Y (in Pa) due to the column XY.

(b) What is (i) the pressure, (ii) the force on the lower surface of the piston if its area is 0.1 m²?

(c) Calculate the value of M.

(d) Would the value of M supported be affected if (i) tube XY were wider but with the same height of liquid, (ii) water of density 1000 kg/m³ replaced the liquid?

15. Two jars, A and B, each of uniform cross-section, are filled to the brim with liquids X and Y respectively. A has twice the area of cross-section of B, but is the same height as B. The density of liquid X is twice the density of liquid Y.

(a) Compare the mass of liquid X in A with that of liquid Y in B.

(b) Compare the pressure at the bottom of A with that at the bottom of B due to the liquids X and Y respectively.   (W.)

Atmospheric pressure

16. (a) A mercury barometer is shown in Fig. 34.9. Copy it and mark the mercury levels when the tube is tilted from position A to positions B and C.

Fig. 34.9

(b) How would the mercury height be affected if air got into the tube in position A?

(c) Why is mercury suitable as a liquid for use in a barometer?

17. Describe how you would set up a simple mercury barometer, pointing out precautions you would take to obtain a reasonably accurate form of instrument.

How would you test whether there is a vacuum above the mercury?

The air pressure at the base of a mountain is 75.0 cm of mercury and at the top is 60.0 cm of mercury. Given that the average density of air is 1.25 kg/m³ and the density of mercury is 1.36×10^4 kg/m³, calculate the height of the mountain.   (W.)

Pumps and pressure

18. Explain the action of a lift pump with the help of a labelled diagram.

19. The diagram, Fig. 34.10, shows the essential features of a bicycle pump connected to a tube.

Fig. 34.10

(a) When the handle has moved halfway outwards, will the valves be open or closed? Explain.

(b) Under what circumstances will valve 1 open?

(c) Explain why the 'dead space' sets a limit to the pressure the pump can cause.   (S.R.)

20. Fig. 34.11 shows a siphon tube, full of water, dipping into two containers each holding water.

Fig. 34.11

Copy and complete the diagram to show the water level in each container so that water will flow from A to B.   (*E.A.*)

21. Boyle's law refers to the product of the volume and pressure being constant.

(*a*) (*i*) To what does it apply? (*ii*) Under what condition?

(*b*) With the aid of a diagram describe an experiment to show that Boyle's law is obeyed.

Fig. 34.12

(*c*) If the piston in Fig. 34.12 moves down 8 cm, what is the new pressure?   (*A.L.*)

22. Fig. 34.13 illustrates a simple experiment in which a column of air is enclosed in a very narrow (capillary) bore tube by a thread of mercury 1 cm in length. The capillary bore is uniform in cross-section. With the tube in the vertical position illustrated in diagram A the length of the air column is 15 cm as indicated. When the tube is inverted, as in B, the length of the air column changes to x cm. The height of the column of mercury in a mercury barometer at the time of the experiment is 76 cm and the temperature remains constant.

(*a*) What is the pressure (in cm of mercury) in the tube when it is as shown in diagram A?

Fig. 34.13

(*b*) What is the pressure in the tube when it is as shown in diagram B?

(*c*) Calculate the value of x.
                     (*J.M.B./A.L./N.W.16+*)

23. The level of mercury in a perfect barometer stands at 75 cm above the level in the reservoir and is reduced to 70 cm by the introduction of a small quantity of air. Determine the volume of this air at atmospheric pressure if the tube is of uniform bore of cross-sectional area 2.0 cm^2 and its upper end is at a constant height of 80 cm above the external mercury level. You may assume that the external mercury level and the external temperature do not change.   (*L.*)

Floating, sinking and flying

24. A body of mass 2 kg is suspended from a spring balance, calibrated in newtons, which reads 17 N when the body is completely submerged in water. The intensity of the earth's gravitational field is 10 N/kg (i.e. the acceleration due to gravity is 10 m/s^2).

(*a*) What is the upthrust (in newtons) of the water on the body?

(*b*) What is the mass (in kg) of water displaced by the body?

(*c*) If the density of water is 1000 kg/m^3, what is the volume (in m^3) of water displaced?

(*d*) What is the density (in kg/m^3) of the material of which the body is made?
                     (*J.M.B./A.L./N.W.16+*)

25. A rectangular block of wood, mass 0.32 kg, measuring 10 cm × 10 cm × 5 cm, floats in a liquid of density 1600 kg/m^3 with its large face horizontal. What is the height in cm of the upper face of the block above the surface of the liquid?

A 0.4   **B** 2.0   **C** 2.5   **D** 3.0   **E** 4.8   (*N.I.*)

26. Describe and explain the design features of a common hydrometer. If it is intended to be used over the range of relative densities 0.70 to 1.00 indicate simply the appearance of its scale. State and explain what would happen if it was placed in a strong copper sulphate solution.

A balloon of volume 2000 m^3 is filled with hydrogen of density 0.09 kg/m^3. If the mass of the fabric is 100 kg and that of the pilot is 75 kg, what will be the greatest mass of equipment that can be carried when operating in air of density 1.25 kg/m^3?

How would this figure change if helium, which has twice the density of hydrogen under the same conditions, were to be used?   (*L.*)

35 Velocity and acceleration

Speed

If a car travels 300 km from Liverpool to London in 5 hours, its *average speed* is 300 km/5 h = 60 km/h. The speedometer would certainly not read 60 km/h for the whole journey but might vary considerably from this value. This is why we state the average speed. If a car could travel at a constant speed of 60 km/h for 5 hours, the distance covered would still be 300 km. It is *always* true that

$$\text{AVERAGE SPEED} = \frac{\text{DISTANCE MOVED}}{\text{TIME TAKEN}}$$

To find the *actual speed* at any instant we would need to know the distance moved in a very short interval of time. This can be done by multiflash photography. In Fig. 35.1 the golfer is photographed whilst a flashing lamp illuminates him 100 times a second. The speed of the club-head as it hits the ball is about 190 km/h.

Velocity

Speed is the distance travelled in unit time, *velocity is the distance travelled in unit time in a stated direction*. If two cars travel due north at 60 km/h, they have the same speed of 60 km/h and the same velocity of 60 km/h *due north*. If one travels north and the other south, their speeds are the same but not their velocities since their directions of motion are different. Speed is a scalar and velocity a vector quantity (see p. 75).

$$\text{VELOCITY} = \frac{\text{DISTANCE MOVED}}{\text{TIME TAKEN}} \text{ in a stated direction}$$

The *velocity* of a body is *uniform* or *constant* if it moves with a steady speed in a straight line. It is not uniform if it moves in a curved path. Why?

The units of speed and velocity are the same, e.g. km/h, m/s, and

$$60 \text{ km/h} = 60\,000 \text{ m}/3600 \text{ s} = 17 \text{ m/s}$$

Acceleration

When the velocity of a body changes we say it accelerates. If a car starting from rest and moving due north has velocity 2 m/s after 1 second, its velocity has increased by 2 m/s in 1 s and its acceleration is 2 m/s per second due north. We write this as 2 m/s². *Acceleration is the change of velocity in unit time.*

$$\text{ACCELERATION} = \frac{\text{CHANGE OF VELOCITY}}{\text{TIME TAKEN FOR CHANGE}}$$

Fig. 35.1

For a steady increase of velocity from 40 km/h to 70 km/h in 5 s

$$\text{acceleration} = \frac{(70-40)\,\text{km/h}}{5\,\text{s}} = 6\,\text{km/h per second}$$

Acceleration is also a vector and both its magnitude and direction should be stated. However, at present we will consider only motion in a straight line and so the magnitude of the velocity will equal the speed, and the magnitude of the acceleration will equal the change of speed in unit time.

The speedometer readings of a car accelerating on a straight road are shown below.

Time (s)	0	1	2	3	4	5	6
Speed (km/h)	0	5	10	15	20	25	30

The speed increases by 5 km/h every second and the acceleration is said to be *uniform*.

An acceleration is positive if the velocity increases and negative if it decreases. A negative acceleration is also called a *deceleration* or *retardation*.

Tickertape timer: tape charts

Fig. 35.2

A tickertape timer, Fig. 35.2, enables us to measure speeds and hence accelerations. It has a steel strip which vibrates 50 times a second and makes dots at 1/50 s intervals on the paper tape being pulled through it. 1/50 s is called a 'tick'.

The distance between successive dots equals the average speed of whatever is pulling the tape in, say, cm per 1/50 s, i.e., cm per tick. The 'tentick' (1/5 s) is also used as a unit of time. Since ticks and tenticks are small we drop the 'average' and just refer to the 'speed'.

Tape charts are made by sticking successive strips of tape, usually tentick lengths, side by side.

That in Fig. 35.3 represents a body moving with *uniform velocity* since equal distances have been moved in each tentick interval.

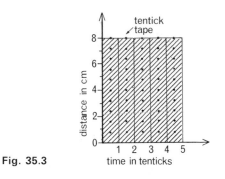

Fig. 35.3

The chart in Fig. 35.4 is for *uniform acceleration*: the 'steps' are of equal size showing that the speed increased by the same amount in every tentick (1/5 s). The acceleration (average) can be found from the chart as follows.

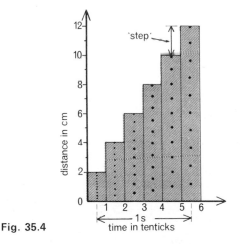

Fig. 35.4

The speed during the *first* tentick is 2 cm/$\frac{1}{5}$ s or 10 cm/s. During the *sixth* tentick it is 12 cm/$\frac{1}{5}$ s or 60 cm/s. And so during this interval of 5 tenticks, i.e. 1 second, the change of speed is $(60-10)$ cm/s = 50 cm/s.

$$\text{acceleration} = \frac{\text{change of speed}}{\text{time taken}}$$

$$= \frac{50\,\text{cm per s}}{1\,\text{s}}$$

$$= 50\,\text{cm per s per s}$$

$$= 50\,\text{cm/s}^2$$

Experiment: analysing motion

(a) tickertape

tickertape timer

runway

(b) trolley

Fig. 35.5

(a) *Your own motion.* Pull a 2 m length of tape through a tickertape timer as you walk away from it quickly, then slowly, then speeding up again and finally stopping, Fig. 35.5a.

Cut the tape into tentick lengths and make a tape chart. Write labels on it to show where you speeded up, slowed down, etc.

(b) *Trolley on a sloping runway.* Attach a length of tape to a trolley and release it at the top of a runway, Fig. 35.5b. The dots will be very crowded at the start—ignore them; but beyond cut the tape into tentick lengths.

Make a tape chart. Is the acceleration uniform? What is its average value?

Questions

1. What is the average speed in km/h of a runner who does 1500 m in 4 minutes?

2. If the radius of the earth is 6400 km, how many minutes does it take an astronaut in a space capsule, travelling at 8 km/s at a height of 160 km above the earth, to make one complete orbit? Take $\pi = 3$.

3. A train has a speed of 60 km/h. Its speed 5 s later is 70 km/h.
 (a) What is its acceleration in km/h per second?
 (b) What will its speed be after another 2 s if the acceleration remains the same?
 (c) How long will it take to reach 105 km/h at this acceleration?

4. Each strip in the tape chart of Fig. 35.6 is for a time interval of 1 tentick.

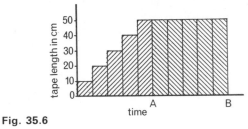

Fig. 35.6

(a) If the timer makes 50 dots per second, what time intervals are represented by OA and AB?
 (b) What is the acceleration between O and A in (i) cm/tentick^2, (ii) cm/s per tentick, (iii) cm/s^2?
 (c) What is the acceleration between A and B?

5. An aircraft travelling at 600 km/h accelerates steadily at 10 km/h per second. Taking the speed of sound as 1100 km/h at the aircraft's altitude, how long will it take to reach the 'sound barrier'?

6. The tape in Fig. 35.7 was pulled through a timer by a trolley travelling down a runway. It was marked off in tentick lengths.
 (a) What can you say about the trolley's motion?
 (b) Find its acceleration in cm/s^2.

Fig. 35.7

7 cm
2 cm
15 cm
26 cm

7. A car increases its speed steadily from 30 km/h to 60 km/h in 1 minute.
 (a) What is its average speed during this time in (i) km/h, (ii) km/min, (iii) m/s?
 (b) How far does it travel (in km) whilst increasing its speed?
 (c) What is its acceleration in (i) km/h per minute and (ii) km/min^2?

8. A train is travelling at 72 km/h.
 (a) What is its speed in m/s?
 (b) How far does it travel in 1 minute?
 (c) If the brakes are applied and it decelerates steadily to rest, what is its average speed in m/s during the deceleration?
 (d) How far does it travel (in m) before stopping if it takes 20 s to come to a halt?

36 Equations of motion

Equations for uniform acceleration

Problems on bodies moving with *uniform acceleration* can often be solved quickly using the equations of motion.

First equation. If a body is moving with uniform acceleration a and its velocity increases from u to v in time t, then

$$a = \frac{\text{change of velocity}}{\text{time taken}} = \frac{v-u}{t}$$

$$\therefore \quad at = v - u$$

or $\quad v = u + at \qquad\qquad\qquad (1)$

Note that the initial velocity u and the final velocity v refer to the start and the finish of the *timing* and do not necessarily mean the start and finish of the motion.

Second equation. The velocity of a body moving with uniform acceleration increases steadily. Its average velocity therefore equals half the sum of its initial and final velocities, that is,

$$\text{average velocity} = \frac{u+v}{2}$$

From (1) $\qquad\qquad v = u + at$

$$\therefore \quad \text{average velocity} = \frac{u+u+at}{2} = \frac{2u+at}{2}$$

$$= u + \tfrac{1}{2}at$$

If s is the distance moved in time t, then since average velocity = distance/time = s/t,

$$\frac{s}{t} = u + \tfrac{1}{2}at$$

$$\therefore \quad s = ut + \tfrac{1}{2}at^2 \qquad\qquad (2)$$

Third equation. This is obtained by eliminating t from equations (1) and (2). We have

$$v = u + at$$

$$\therefore \quad v^2 = u^2 + 2uat + a^2t^2$$

$$= u^2 + 2a(ut + \tfrac{1}{2}at^2)$$

But $\qquad s = ut + \tfrac{1}{2}at^2$

$$\therefore \quad v^2 = u^2 + 2as \qquad\qquad (3)$$

If we know any *three* of u, v, a, s and t, the others can be found from the equations.

Worked example

A cyclist starts from rest and accelerates at $1\,\text{m/s}^2$ for 20 seconds. He then travels at a constant speed for 1 minute and finally decelerates at $2\,\text{m/s}^2$ until he stops. Find his maximum speed in km/h and the total distance covered in metres.

First stage

$u = 0 \quad a = 1\,\text{m/s}^2 \quad t = 20\,\text{s}$

We have $v = u + at = 0 + 1 \times 20 = 20\,\text{m/s}$

$$= \frac{20}{1000} \times 60 \times 60 = 72\,\text{km/h}$$

The distance s moved in the first stage is given by

$$s = ut + \tfrac{1}{2}at^2 = 0 \times 20 + \tfrac{1}{2} \times 1 \times 20^2 = 200\,\text{m}$$

Second stage

$u = 20\,\text{m/s (constant)} \quad t = 60\,\text{s}$

Distance moved = speed × time = $20 \times 60 = 1200\,\text{m}$

Third stage

$u = 20\,\text{m/s} \quad v = 0 \quad a = -2\,\text{m/s}^2$ (a deceleration)

We have $\quad v^2 = u^2 + 2as$

$$\therefore \quad s = \frac{v^2 - u^2}{2a} = \frac{0 - (20)^2}{2 \times (-2)} = \frac{-400}{-4} = 100\,\text{m}$$

Answers

Maximum speed = 72 km/h

Total distance moved = $200 + 1200 + 100 = 1500\,\text{m}$

Velocity-time graphs

If the velocity of a body is plotted against the time, the graph obtained is a velocity-time graph. It provides another way of solving motion problems. Tape charts are crude velocity-time graphs which show the velocity changing in jumps rather than smoothly, as occurs in practice.

(a) *The area under a velocity-time graph measures the distance travelled.*

In Fig. 36.1 AB is the velocity-time graph for a body moving with a *uniform velocity* of 20 m/s. Since distance = average velocity × time, after 5 s it will have moved $20\,\text{m/s} \times 5\,\text{s} = 100\,\text{m}$. This is the shaded area under the graph, i.e. rectangle OABC.

Fig. 36.1

In Fig. 36.2, PQ is the velocity-time graph for a body moving with *uniform acceleration*. At the start of the timing the velocity is 20 m/s but it increases steadily to 40 m/s after 5 s. If the distance covered equals the area under PQ, i.e. the shaded area OPQS, then

$$\text{distance} = \text{area of rectangle OPRS} +$$
$$\text{area of triangle PQR}$$
$$= OP \times OS + \tfrac{1}{2} \times PR \times QR$$
$$(\text{area of a triangle} = \tfrac{1}{2} \text{ base} \times \text{height})$$
$$= 20 \,\text{m/s} \times 5 \,\text{s} + \tfrac{1}{2} \times 5 \,\text{s} \times 20 \,\text{m/s}$$
$$= 100 + 50 = 150 \,\text{m}$$

We can check this using $s = ut + \tfrac{1}{2}at^2$. We have $u = 20 \,\text{m/s}$, $t = 5 \,\text{s}$, $a = (v - u)/t = (40 - 20)/5 = 4 \,\text{m/s}^2$. Hence

$$s = 20 \times 5 + \tfrac{1}{2} \times 4 \times 5^2 = 100 + 50 = 150 \,\text{m}$$

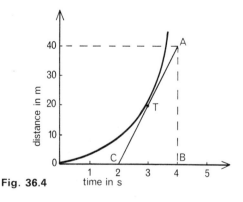

Fig. 36.2

Notes. 1. When calculating the area from the graph the unit of time must be the same on both axes.
2. This rule for finding distances travelled is true even if the acceleration is not uniform.

(b) *The slope or gradient of a velocity-time graph represents the acceleration of the body.*

In Fig. 36.1 the slope of AB is zero, as is the acceleration. In Fig. 36.2 the slope of PQ is QR/PR = 20/5 = 4: the acceleration is 4 m/s².

Distance-time graphs

Fig. 36.3

A body travelling with uniform velocity covers equal distances in equal times. Its distance-time graph is a straight line, like OL in Fig. 36.3 for a velocity of 10 m/s. The slope of the graph = LM/OM = 40/4 = 10, which is the value of the velocity. The following statement is true in general.

The slope or gradient of a distance-time graph represents the velocity of the body.

When the velocity of the body is changing, the slope of the distance-time graph varies, Fig. 36.4, and at any point equals the slope of the tangent. For example, the slope of the tangent at T is AB/BC = 40/2 = 20. The velocity at the instant corresponding to T is therefore 20 m/s.

Fig. 36.4

Questions

1. A body starts from rest and reaches a speed of 5 m/s after travelling with uniform acceleration in a straight line for 2 s. Calculate the acceleration of the body. (*E.A.*)

2. A body starts from rest and moves with a uniform acceleration of 2 m/s² in a straight line.
   (*a*) What is its velocity after 5 s?
   (*b*) How far has it travelled in this time?
   (*c*) After how long will the body be 100 m from its starting point? (*J.M.B./A.L./N.W.16+*)

Fig. 36.5

(a)

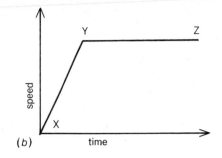

(b)

3. Fig. 36.5a shows the distance-time graph for a moving object and Fig. 36.5b shows the speed-time graph for another moving object.

Describe the motion, if any, of the objects in the regions (a) UV, (b) VW, (c) XY, (d) YZ.   (E.A.)

4. The graph in Fig. 36.6 represents the distance travelled by a car plotted against time.

Fig. 36.6

(a) How far has the car travelled at the end of 5 seconds?
(b) What is the speed of the car during the first 5 seconds?
(c) What has happened to the car after A?
(d) Plot a graph showing the speed of the car plotted against time during the first 5 seconds.   (Met.)

5. Fig. 36.7 shows an uncompleted velocity-time graph for a boy running a distance of 100 m.

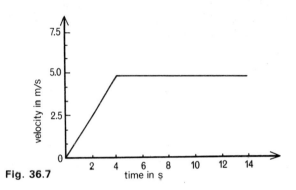

Fig. 36.7

(a) What is his acceleration during the first 4 seconds?
(b) How far does the boy travel during (i) the first 4 seconds, (ii) the next 9 seconds?
(c) Copy and complete the graph showing clearly at what time he has covered the distance of 100 m. Assume his speed remains constant at the value shown by the horizontal portion of the graph.

37 Falling bodies

In air, a coin falls faster than a bit of paper. In a vacuum they fall at the same rate as may be shown with the apparatus of Fig. 37.1. The difference is due to *air resistance* being greater to light bodies than to heavy ones—even more so if the light bodies have a larger surface area.

However, heavy bodies, whatever their size, are only slightly affected by air resistance. There is a story, untrue we now think, that in the sixteenth century the Italian scientist Galileo dropped a small iron ball and a large cannon ball ten times heavier, from the top of the Leaning Tower of Pisa, Fig. 37.2. And we are told, to the surprise of onlookers who expected the cannon ball to arrive first, they reached the ground almost simultaneously.

Experiment: motion of a falling body

Arrange things as in Fig. 37.3 and investigate the motion of a 100 g mass falling from a height of about 2 m.

Fig. 37.1

rubber stopper

Perspex or Pyrex tube

paper

coin

1.5 m

pressure tubing

to vacuum pump

screw clip

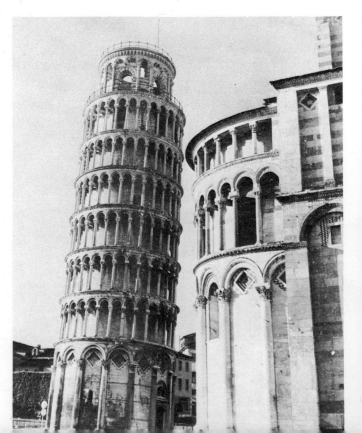

Fig. 37.2

104

Fig. 37.3

timer

6–12 V
a.c.

tickertape

100 g mass

electromagnet

ball
bearing

electric
stop clock

two-way
switch

EXT

COM +

CLOCK
OPERATING

12 V a.c.

magnet

adjustable
terminal

hinge

trap–door of
impact switch

Fig. 37.4

Construct a tape chart using *one tick* lengths. The dots at the start will be too close together but choose as dot '0' the first one you can see clearly. What does the tape chart tell you about the motion of the falling mass?

Acceleration due to gravity

All bodies falling freely under the force of gravity do so with *uniform acceleration* if air resistance is negligible (i.e. the 'steps' in the previous tape chart should all be equal).

This acceleration, called the *acceleration due to gravity*, is denoted by the italic letter g. Its value varies over the earth. In Britain it is about 9.8 m/s^2 or near enough 10 m/s^2. The velocity of a free falling body therefore increases by 10 m/s every second. A ball thrown straight upwards with a velocity of 30 m/s decelerates by 10 m/s every second and reaches its highest point after 3 s.

In calculations using the equations of motion, g replaces a. It is given a positive sign for falling bodies (i.e. $a = +10$ m/s^2) and a negative sign for rising bodies since they are decelerating (i.e. $a = -10$ m/s^2).

Measuring g

Using the arrangement in Fig. 37.4 the time for a steel ball-bearing to fall a known distance is measured by an electric stop clock.

When the two-way switch is changed to the 'down' position, the electromagnet releases the ball and simultaneously the clock starts. At the end of its fall the ball opens the 'trap-door' on the impact switch and the clock stops.

The result is found from $s = ut + \frac{1}{2}at^2$, where s is the distance fallen (in m), t is the time taken (in s), $u = 0$ (the ball starts from rest) and $a = g$ (in m/s^2). Hence

$$s = \tfrac{1}{2}gt^2 \quad \text{or} \quad g = 2s/t^2$$

Air resistance is negligible for a dense object such as a steel ball-bearing.

Worked example

A ball is thrown vertically upwards with an initial velocity of 30 m/s. Find (a) its maximum height, (b) the time taken to return to its starting point. Neglect air resistance and take $g = 10$ m/s^2.

(a) We have $u = 30$ m/s, $a = -10$ m/s^2 (a deceleration) and $v = 0$ since the ball is momentarily at rest at its highest point. Substituting in

$$v^2 = u^2 + 2as$$
$$\therefore \quad 0 = 30^2 + 2(-10)s \quad \text{or} \quad -900 = -20s$$
$$\therefore \quad s = \frac{-900}{-20} = 45 \text{ m}$$

(b) If t is the time to reach the highest point, we have from

$$v = u + at$$
$$\therefore \quad 0 = 30 + (-10)t \quad \text{or} \quad -30 = -10t$$
$$\therefore \quad t = \frac{-30}{-10} = 3 \text{ s}$$

The downward trip takes exactly the same time as the upward one and so the answer is 6 s.

Fig. 37.5

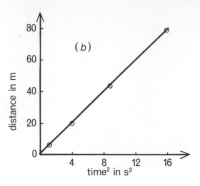

Distance-time graphs

For a body falling freely from rest we have

$$s = \tfrac{1}{2}gt^2$$

A graph of s against t is shown in Fig. 37.5a and for s against t^2 in Fig. 37.5b. The latter is a straight line through the origin since $s \propto t^2$ (g being constant at one place).

Projectiles

The photograph in Fig. 37.6 was taken whilst a lamp emitted regular flashes of light. One ball was *dropped* from rest and the other, a 'projectile', was *thrown sideways* at the same time. Their vertical accelerations (due to gravity) are equal, showing that a projectile falls like a body which is dropped from rest. Its horizontal velocity does not affect its vertical motion.

The horizontal and vertical motions of a body are independent and can be treated separately.

For example if a ball is *thrown* horizontally from the top of a cliff and takes 3 s to reach the beach

Fig. 37.6

below we can calculate the height of the cliff by considering the vertical motion only. We have $u = 0$ (since the ball has no vertical velocity initially), $a = g = +10 \, \text{m/s}^2$ and $t = 3 \, \text{s}$. The height s of the cliff is given by $s = ut + \tfrac{1}{2}at^2 = 0 \times 3 + \tfrac{1}{2}(+10)3^2 = 45 \, \text{m}$.

Questions

1. A stone falls from rest from the top of a high tower. Ignoring air resistance and taking $g = 10 \, \text{m/s}^2$
   (*a*) what is its velocity after (*i*) 1 s, (*ii*) 2 s, (*iii*) 3 s, (*iv*) 5 s?
   (*b*) how far has it fallen after (*i*) 1 s, (*ii*) 2 s, (*iii*) 3 s, (*iv*) 5 s?

2. A body falls from a cliff 125 m high. Find the time of fall. How far did the body fall in half this time? (Take the acceleration due to gravity as $10 \, \text{m/s}^2$.)   (*E.A.*)

3. A mass is projected upwards with a velocity of 10 m/s. If the acceleration due to gravity is $10 \, \text{m/s}^2$, what is the maximum height reached in metres?

   A 1   **B** 5   **C** 10   **D** 20   **E** 100   (*N.I.*)

4. An object is dropped from a helicopter at a height of 45 m above the ground.
   (*a*) If the helicopter is at rest, how long does the object take to reach the ground and what is its velocity on arrival?
   (*b*) If the helicopter is falling with a velocity of 1 m/s when the object is released, what will be the final velocity of the object? ($g = 10 \, \text{m/s}^2$.)

5. An object is released from an aircraft travelling horizontally with a constant velocity of 200 m/s at a height of 500 m. Ignoring air resistance and taking $g = 10 \, \text{m/s}^2$ find
   (*a*) how long it takes the object to reach the ground,
   (*b*) the horizontal distance covered by the object between leaving the aircraft and reaching the ground.

6. A gun pointing vertically upwards is fired from an open car B moving with uniform velocity. When the bullet returns to the level of the gun, car B has travelled to C and another car A has reached the position occupied by B when the gun was fired, Fig. 37.7. Are the occupants of A or B in danger?

Fig. 37.7

38 Newton's laws of motion

First law

Friction and air resistance cause a car to come to rest when the engine is switched off. If these forces were absent we believe that a body, once set in motion, would go on moving forever with a constant speed in a straight line. That is, force is not needed to keep a body moving with uniform velocity so long as no opposing forces act on it.

This idea was proposed by Galileo and is summed up in Newton's first law.

A body stays at rest, or if moving it continues to move with uniform velocity, unless an external force makes it behave differently.

It seems that the question we should ask about a moving body is not 'what keeps it moving' but 'what changes or stops its motion'. The smaller the external forces opposing a moving body, the smaller is the force needed to keep it moving with uniform velocity. Friction is much reduced for a hovercraft floating on a cushion of air, Fig. 38.1.

Fig. 38.1

Mass and inertia

The first law is another way of saying that all matter has a built-in opposition to being moved if it is at rest or, if it is moving, to having its motion changed. This property of matter is called *inertia* (from the Latin word for laziness).

Its effect is evident on the occupants of a car which stops suddenly; they lurch forward in an attempt to continue moving. The reluctance of a stationary object to move can be shown by placing a large coin on a piece of card on your finger, Fig. 38.2. If the card is flicked *sharply* the coin stays where it is while the card flies off.

Fig. 38.2

coin card

The larger the mass of a body the greater is its inertia, i.e. the more difficult is it to move when at rest and to stop when in motion. Because of this we consider that *the mass of a body measures its inertia*. This is a better definition of mass than the one given earlier (p. 56) in which it was stated to be the 'amount of matter' in a body.

Experiment: effect of force and mass on acceleration

The apparatus consists of a trolley to which a force is applied by a stretched length of elastic, Fig. 38.3. The velocity of the trolley is found from a timer.

tickertape timer

tape

stretched elastic

book

runway

trolley

Fig. 38.3

First compensate the runway for friction by raising one end until the trolley runs down with uniform velocity when given a push. The dots on the tape should be equally spaced. There is now no resultant force on the trolley and any acceleration produced later will be due only to the force caused by the stretched elastic.

(*a*) *Force and acceleration* (*mass constant*). Fix one end of an elastic to the rod at the back of the trolley and stretch it until the other end is level with the front of the trolley. Before attaching a tape, practise pulling the trolley down the runway, keeping the same stretch on the elastic. After a few trials you should be able to produce a steady accelerating force. Now do it with a tape.

Repeat with fresh tapes using first two and then three *identical* elastics, stretched side by side by the same amount, to give two and three units of force.

Make a tape chart for each force and use it to find the acceleration produced in cm/tentick^2 (see p. 99). Ignore the start of the tape (where the dots are too close) and the end (where the force may not be steady). Does a steady force cause a steady acceleration? Put the results in a table. Do they suggest any relationship between *a* and *F*?

Force (F) (no. of elastics)	1	2	3
Acceleration (a) (cm/tentick^2)			

(*b*) *Mass and acceleration* (*force constant*). Do the experiment as in (*a*) using two elastics (i.e. constant *F*) to accelerate first one trolley, then two (stacked one above the other) and finally three. Check the friction compensation of the runway each time.

Find the accelerations from the tape charts and tabulate the results. Do they suggest any relationship between *a* and *m*?

Mass (m) (no. of trolleys)	1	2	3
Acceleration (a) (cm/tentick^2)			

Second law

The previous experiment should show roughly that the acceleration *a* is

(*i*) directly proportional to the applied force *F* for a fixed mass, i.e. $a \propto F$, and

(ii) inversely proportional to the mass m for a fixed force, i.e. $a \propto 1/m$.

Combining the results into one equation, we get

$$a \propto F/m \quad \text{or} \quad F \propto ma.$$

Therefore $\qquad F = kma$

where k is the constant of proportionality.

One newton is defined as the force which gives a mass of 1 kg an acceleration of 1 m/s².

Hence if $m = 1$ kg and $a = 1$ m/s² then $F = 1$ N. Substituting in $F = kma$ we get $k = 1$ and so we can write

$$F = ma$$

This is Newton's second law of motion. When using it two points should be noted. First, F is the resultant (or unbalanced) force causing the acceleration a. Second, F must be in newtons, m in kilograms and a in metres per second squared, otherwise k is not 1.

Worked examples

1. A block of mass 2 kg is pushed along a table with a constant velocity by a force of 5 N. When the push is increased to 9 N what is (a) the resultant force, (b) the acceleration?

When the block moves with constant velocity the forces acting on it are balanced. The force of friction opposing its motion must therefore be 5 N.

(a) When the push is increased to 9 N the resultant (unbalanced) force F on the block is $(9-5)N = 4$ N (since the frictional force is still 5 N).

(b) The acceleration a is obtained from $F = ma$ where $F = 4$ N and $m = 2$ kg.

$$\therefore \ a = F/m = 4/2 = 2 \text{ m/s}^2$$

2. A car of mass 1200 kg travelling at 72 km/h is brought to rest in 4 s. Find the (a) average deceleration, (b) average braking force, (c) distance moved during the deceleration.

(a) The deceleration is found from $v = u + at$ where $v = 0$, $u = 72 \text{ km/h} = \dfrac{72 \times 1000}{60 \times 60} = 20 \text{ m/s}$ and $t = 4$ s. Hence

$$0 = 20 + a \times 4 \quad \text{or} \quad -20 = 4a$$
$$\therefore \ a = -20/4 = -5 \text{ m/s}^2$$

(b) The average braking force F is given by $F = ma$ where $m = 1200$ kg and $a = -5$ m/s². Therefore

$$F = 1200 \times (-5) = -6000 \text{ N}$$

(c) To find the distance moved s we use $s = ut + \frac{1}{2}at^2$

$$\therefore \ s = 20 \times 4 + \tfrac{1}{2} \times (-5) \times (4^2)$$
$$= 80 - 40 = 40 \text{ m}$$

Gravitational field

The force of gravity acts through space and can cause a body, not in contact with the earth, to fall to the ground. It is an invisible, action-at-a-distance force. We try to 'explain' its existence by saying that the earth is surrounded by a *gravitational field* which exerts a force on any body in the field. Later, magnetic and electric fields will be considered.

The strength of a gravitational field is defined as the force acting on unit mass in the field.

Measurement shows that on the earth's surface a mass of 1 kg experiences a force of 9.8 N, i.e. its weight is 9.8 N. The strength of the earth's field is therefore 9.8 N/kg (near enough 10 N/kg). It is denoted by g, the letter also used to denote the acceleration due to gravity. Hence

$$g = 9.8 \text{ N/kg} = 9.8 \text{ m/s}^2$$

We now have two ways of regarding g. When considering bodies *falling freely* we can think of it as an acceleration of 9.8 m/s², but when a body of known mass is *at rest* and we wish to know the force of gravity (in N) acting on it we think of g as the earth's gravitational field strength of 9.8 N/kg.

Third law

If a body A exerts a force on body B, then body B exerts an equal but opposite force on body A.

The law states that forces never occur singly but always in pairs as a result of the action between two bodies. For example, when you step forward from rest your foot pushes backwards on the earth and the earth exerts an equal and opposite force forward on you. Two bodies and two forces are involved. The small force you exert on the large mass of the earth gives no noticeable acceleration to the earth but the equal force it exerts on your very much smaller mass causes you to accelerate.

Note that the equal and opposite forces *do not act on the same body*; if they did, there could never be any resultant forces and acceleration would be impossible.

109

An appreciation of the third law and the effect of friction is desirable when stepping from a rowing boat, Fig. 38.4. You push backwards on the boat

Fig. 38.4

and, although the boat pushes you forwards with an equal force, it is itself now moving backwards (because friction with the water is slight), and this reduces your forwards motion by the same amount—and you might fall in!

Fluid friction: terminal velocity

Fluid friction is the opposition to an object when it moves in a liquid or gas.

In air, fluid friction is negligible for small dense objects, e.g. ball-bearings. And as we have seen, these fall with a constant acceleration of $9.8 \, \text{m/s}^2$. It is appreciable however for objects that are light, e.g. raindrops, or have a large surface area, e.g. parachutes or the 'Red Devils' sky divers in free fall, Fig. 38.5. In these cases, as the falling object speeds up, air friction increases and reduces its acceleration. Eventually the upward frictional force equals the weight of the object acting downwards. The resultant force is then zero and the object falls with a constant velocity called its *terminal velocity*.

Objects moving in viscous liquids, e.g. motor oil, behave similarly.

Fig. 38.5

Explanation of Bernoulli's principle

In Fig. 33.8b (p. 93) the liquid speeds up going from the wide part A of the tube to the narrower part B, i.e. it is accelerated. Therefore, since $F=ma$, the force at A, and so also the pressure at A, must be greater than the force and pressure at B. Between B and C the liquid slows down due to the pressure at C being greater than that at B.

Questions

1. Which one of the diagrams in Fig. 38.6 shows the arrangement of forces which gives the block M the greatest acceleration?

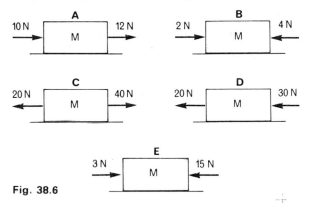

Fig. 38.6

2. In Fig. 38.7 if P is a force of 20 N and the object moves with *constant velocity* what is the value of the opposing force F?

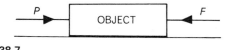

Fig. 38.7

3. (*a*) What resultant force produces an acceleration of $5\,\mathrm{m/s^2}$ in a car of mass 1000 kg?

(*b*) What acceleration is produced in a mass of 2 kg by a resultant force of 30 N?

4. A car of mass 500 kg accelerates steadily from rest to 40 m/s in 20 s.

(*a*) What is its acceleration?

(*b*) What resultant force produces this acceleration?

(*c*) The actual force will be greater. Why?

5. A block of mass 500 g is pulled from rest on a horizontal frictionless bench by a steady force F and travels 8 m in 2 s. Find (*a*) the acceleration, (*b*) the value of F.

6. Starting from rest on a level road a boy can reach a speed of 5 m/s in 10 s on his bicycle. Find (*i*) the acceleration, (*ii*) the average speed during the 10 s and (*iii*) the distance he travels in 10 s.

Eventually, even though he is still pedalling as fast as he can, he stops accelerating and his speed reaches a maximum value. Explain in terms of the forces acting why this happens.

7. A trailer of mass 1000 kg is towed by means of a rope attached to a car moving at a steady speed along a level road. The tension in the rope is 400 N. Why is it not zero?

The car starts to accelerate steadily. If the tension in the rope is now 1650 N, with what acceleration is the trailer moving?

(*O. and C.*)

8. What does an astronaut of mass 100 kg weigh (*a*) on earth where the gravitational field strength is 10 N/kg, (*b*) on the moon where the gravitational field strength is 1.7 N/kg?

9. Fig. 38.8 shows the forces acting on a raindrop which is falling to the ground.

Fig. 38.8

(*a*) (*i*) A is the force which causes the raindrop to fall. What is this force called? (*ii*) B is the total force opposing the motion of the drop. State *one* possible cause of this force.

(*b*) What happens to the raindrop when force $A =$ force B?

111

39 Momentum

Momentum is a useful quantity to consider when bodies are involved in collisions and explosions. It is defined as the mass of the body multiplied by its velocity and is measured in *kilogram metre per second* (kg m/s).

$$\text{MOMENTUM} = \text{MASS} \times \text{VELOCITY}$$

A 2 kg mass moving at 10 m/s has momentum 20 kg m/s, the same as the momentum of a 5 kg mass moving at 4 m/s.

Experiment: collisions and momentum

In an *inelastic* collision the colliding bodies stay together after colliding. One occurs when some putty hits the floor without bouncing. In an *elastic* collision the bodies separate afterwards, as happens when a rubber ball bounces.

(*a*) *Inelastic collisions.* Friction-compensate a runway as before (p. 108). Place one trolley at rest half-way down the runway and another at the top with a length of tickertape from it passing through a timer, Fig. 39.1. Each trolley should have a strip of Velcro (from haberdashery departments) fitted so that it 'sticks' to the other on collision.

Give the top trolley a good push. It will move forward with uniform velocity and should hit the second trolley so that they travel on as one.

From the tape find the velocity of the moving trolley before the collision and the common velocity of both trolleys after the collision (in cm/tentick say).

Repeat the experiment with another trolley stacked on top of the one to be pushed so that two are moving before the collision and three after.

Copy and complete the table of results.

BEFORE COLLISION (m_2 at rest)		
Mass m_1 (no. of trolleys)	*Velocity* v (cm/tentick)	*Momentum* $m_1 v$
1		
2		

AFTER COLLISION (m_1 and m_2 together)		
Mass $m_1 + m_2$ (no. of trolleys)	*Velocity* v_1 (cm/tentick)	*Momentum* $(m_1 + m_2)v_1$
2		
3		

(*b*) *Elastic collisions.* Repeat (*a*) but have the buffer rod sticking out on one trolley, Fig. 39.2. After colliding the trolleys move separately. Each needs its own tape which should be passed under a *separate* carbon disc on the *same* timer.

tickertape timer trolley

tape

book

runway

Velcro

Fig. 39.1

Fig. 39.2

Find the velocities from the tapes before and after the collision. Copy and complete the table of results.

BEFORE COLLISION (m_2 at rest)			AFTER COLLISION (m_1 and m_2 separate)						
m_1	v	$m_1 v$	m_1	v_1	$m_1 v_1$	m_2	v_2	$m_2 v_2$	$m_1 v_1 + m_2 v_2$
1			1		1				
2			2		1				

Do the results suggest any connection between the momentum before the collision and after it?

Conservation of momentum

When two or more bodies act on one another, as in a collision, the total momentum of the bodies remains constant, provided no external forces act (e.g. friction).

This statement is called the *principle of conservation of momentum*. Experiments like those above show that it is true for all types of collisions.

As an example, suppose a truck of mass 60 kg moving with velocity 3 m/s collides and couples with a stationary truck of mass 30 kg, Fig. 39.3a. The two move off together with the same velocity v which we can find as follows, Fig. 39.3b.

Fig. 39.3

Total momentum before $= (60 \times 3 + 30 \times 0)$ kg m/s
$$= 180 \text{ kg m/s}$$
Total momentum after $= (60 + 30)v$ kg m/s
$$= 90v \text{ kg m/s}$$

Since momentum is not lost

$$90v = 180 \quad \text{or} \quad v = 2 \text{ m/s}$$

Explosions

Momentum, like velocity, is a vector since it has both magnitude and direction. Vectors cannot be added by ordinary addition unless they act in the same direction. If they act in exactly opposite directions, e.g. east and west, the smaller subtracts from the greater, or if the same they cancel out.

Momentum is conserved in an explosion such as occurs when a rifle is fired. Before firing, the total momentum is zero since both rifle and bullet are at rest. During the firing the rifle and bullet receive *equal* but *opposite* amounts of momentum so that the *total* momentum after firing is zero. For example a bullet of mass 0.01 kg fired from a rifle with a speed of 300 m/s has a forward momentum of $0.01 \times 300 = 3$ kg m/s. If the rifle has mass $m = 6$ kg, its backward momentum will also be 3 kg m/s, i.e. it recoils (kicks back) with a velocity v such that $mv = 3$ kg m/s. But $m = 6$ kg and so $v = 0.5$ m/s.

Rockets and jets

If you release an inflated balloon with its neck open, it flies off in the opposite direction to that of the escaping air. In Fig. 39.4 the air has momentum to the left and the balloon moves to the right with equal momentum.

Fig. 39.4

Fig. 39.5

This is the principle of rockets and jet engines. In both, a high-velocity stream of hot gas is produced by burning fuel and leaves the exhaust with large momentum. The rocket or jet engine itself acquires an equal forward momentum. Space rockets, Fig. 39.5, carry their own oxygen supply; jet engines use the surrounding air.

Force and momentum

If a steady force F acting on a body of mass m, increases its velocity from u to v in time t, the acceleration a is given by

$$a = (v - u)/t \quad (\text{from } v = u + at)$$

Substituting for a in $F = ma$,

$$F = \frac{m(v-u)}{t} = \frac{mv - mu}{t}$$

mv is the final momentum and mu the initial momentum. Therefore

$$\text{force} = \frac{\text{change of momentum}}{\text{time}} = \frac{\text{rate of change of}}{\text{momentum}}$$

This is another version of the second law of motion. For some problems it is more useful than $F = ma$.

Questions

1. What is the momentum in kg m/s of a 10 kg truck travelling at (a) 5 m/s, (b) 20 cm/s, (c) 36 km/h?

2. A ball X mass 1 kg travelling at 2 m/s has a head-on collision with an identical ball Y at rest. X stops and Y moves off. What is Y's velocity?

3. A boy with mass 50 kg running at 5 m/s jumps on to a 20 kg trolley travelling in the same direction at 1.5 m/s. What is their common velocity?

4. A 50 kg girl jumps out of a rowing boat of mass 300 kg on to the bank with a horizontal velocity of 3 m/s. With what velocity does the boat begin to move backwards?

40 K.E. and P.E.

Energy and its different forms were discussed earlier (p. 76). Here we will consider kinetic energy (k.e.) and potential energy (p.e.) in more detail.

Kinetic energy

Kinetic energy is the energy a body has because of its motion.

We can obtain an expression for k.e. Suppose a body of mass m starts from rest and is acted on by a steady force F which gives it a uniform acceleration a. If the velocity of the body is v when it has travelled a distance s, then, using $v^2 = u^2 + 2as$, we get, since $u = 0$,

$$v^2 = 2as \quad \text{or} \quad a = v^2/2s$$

Fig. 40.1

Substituting in $F = ma$

$$F = m\left(\frac{v^2}{2s}\right) \quad \text{or} \quad Fs = \tfrac{1}{2}mv^2$$

Fs is the work done on the body to give it velocity v and therefore equals its k.e. Hence

$$\text{KINETIC ENERGY} = \tfrac{1}{2}mv^2$$

If m is in kg and v in m/s, then k.e. is in J. For example, a cricket ball of mass 0.2 kg (200 g) moving with velocity 20 m/s has k.e. $= \tfrac{1}{2}mv^2 = \tfrac{1}{2} \times 0.2 \times (20)^2 = 0.1 \times 400 = 40$ J.

Since k.e. depends on v^2, a vehicle, such as a High Speed Train, Fig. 40.1, travelling at 200 km/h (125 m.p.h.), has four times the k.e. it has at 100 km/h.

Fig. 40.2

Potential energy

Potential energy is the energy a body has because of its position or condition.

A body above the earth's surface is considered to have an amount of gravitational p.e. equal to the work that has been done against gravity by the force used to raise it. To lift a body of mass m through a *vertical* height h at a place where the earth's gravitational field strength is g, needs a force equal and opposite to the weight mg of the body. Hence

$$\text{work done by force} = \text{force} \times \text{vertical height}$$
$$= mg \times h$$
$$\therefore \quad \text{POTENTIAL ENERGY} = mgh$$

When m is in kg, g in N/kg (or m/s²) and h in m, the p.e. is in J. For example, if $g = 10$ N/kg, the p.e. gained by a 0.1 kg (100 g) mass raised vertically by 1 m is $0.1 \text{ kg} \times 10 \text{ N/kg} \times 1 \text{ m} = 1 \text{ N m} = 1 \text{ J}$.

Experiment: change of p.e. to k.e.

Friction-compensate a runway and arrange the apparatus as in Fig. 40.2 with the bottom of the 0.1 kg (100 g) mass 0.5 m from the floor.

Start the timer and release the trolley. It will accelerate until the falling mass reaches the floor; after that it moves with *constant* velocity v.

From the tickertape measure v in m/s (50 ticks = 1 s). Find the mass of the trolley in kg. Work out:

116

k.e. gained by trolley and 0.1 kg mass =   J
p.e. lost by 0.1 kg mass =   J

Compare and comment on the results.

Conservation of energy

A mass m at height h above the ground has p.e. = mgh, Fig. 40.3. When it falls, its velocity increases and it gains k.e. at the expense of its p.e. If it starts

Fig. 40.3

from rest and air resistance is negligible, its velocity v on reaching the ground is given by

$$v^2 = u^2 + 2as = 0 + 2gh = 2gh$$

Also, as it reaches the ground, its

$$\text{k.e.} = \tfrac{1}{2}mv^2 = \tfrac{1}{2}m \times 2gh = mgh$$
$$\therefore \quad \text{loss of p.e.} = \text{gain of k.e.}$$

This is an example of the *principle of conservation of energy*.

Energy may be changed from one form to another but it cannot be destroyed.

In a pendulum k.e. and p.e. are interchanged continually. The energy of the bob is all p.e. at the end

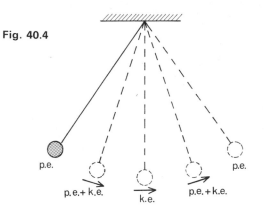

Fig. 40.4

of the swing and all k.e. as it passes through its central position. In other positions it has both p.e. and k.e., Fig. 40.4. Eventually all the energy is changed to heat as a result of overcoming air resistance.

Elastic and inelastic collisions

In everyday life we try to avoid having collisions because of the damage they cause. In atomic physics they are often purposely arranged and can provide information about atoms. Fig. 40.5 is a photograph

Fig. 40.5

of an alpha particle colliding with a helium atom in a cloud chamber.

Two useful quantities to keep track of in a collision are momentum and k.e. *Momentum is never lost in any collision. In an elastic collision k.e. is conserved* but it is not in an inelastic (no bounce) one.

For example, suppose a 4 kg truck travelling at 6 m/s has a head-on collision with a stationary truck of mass 2 kg and that they become coupled and move off together. By considering momentum and k.e. we can find (a) the velocity v of the coupled trucks and (b) if the collision is elastic.

(a) Momentum before $= 4 \times 6 + 2 \times 0 = 24$ kg m/s
Momentum after $= (4 + 2)v = 6v$ kg m/s

By the principle of conservation of momentum
$$6v = 24 \qquad \therefore \quad v = 4 \text{ m/s}$$

(b) k.e. before $= \frac{1}{2} \times 4 \times 6^2 = 72$ J (from k.e. $= \frac{1}{2}mv^2$)
k.e. after $= \frac{1}{2} \times 6 \times 4^2 = 48$ J

The collision is inelastic and the k.e. 'lost' (24 J) in the collision becomes heat and sound energy.

Questions

1. Calculate the k.e. of
(a) a 1 kg trolley travelling at 2 m/s,
(b) a 2 g (0.002 kg) bullet travelling at 400 m/s,
(c) a 500 kg minicar travelling at 72 km/h.

2. A 100 g steel ball falls from a height of 1.8 m on to a plate and rebounds to a height of 1.25 m. Find
(a) the p.e. of the ball before the fall ($g = 10$ m/s^2),
(b) its k.e. as it hits the plate,
(c) its velocity on hitting the plate,
(d) its k.e. as it leaves the plate on the rebound,
(e) its velocity of rebound.

3. A body of mass 5 kg falls from rest and has a k.e. of 1000 J just before touching the ground. Assuming there is no friction and using a value of 10 m/s^2 for the acceleration due to gravity, calculate
(a) (i) the loss in p.e. during the fall, (ii) the height from which the body has fallen.
(b) Name an important principle which applies in this situation.   (J.M.B./A.L./N.W.16+)

4. At what height above the ground must a mass of 5 kg be to have a p.e. equal in value to the k.e. possessed by a mass of 5 kg moving with a velocity of 10 m/s? (Assume $g = 10$ m/s^2.)
A 1 m B 5 m C 10 m D 50 m E 100 m   (J.M.B.)

5. A trolley of mass 3 kg moving with a constant velocity of 4 m/s collided with a stationary trolley of mass 1 kg. After the collision the two trolleys moved together with a constant velocity of 3 m/s. Show that (i) these results satisfy the law of conservation of linear momentum; (ii) the kinetic energies of the trolleys before and after the collision are not the same and account for the difference in kinetic energy.   (A.E.B.)

41 Circular and relative motion

Fig. 41.1

Circular motion

There are many examples of bodies moving in circular paths—chair-o-planes at a fun fair, clothes in a spin drier, the planets going round the sun and the moon circling the earth. 'Throwing the hammer' is a sport practised at Highland Games in Scotland, Fig. 41.1, in which the hammer is whirled round and round before it is released. When a car turns a corner it may follow an arc of a circle.

Centripetal force

In Fig. 41.2 a ball attached to a string is being whirled round in a horizontal circle. Its direction of motion is constantly changing. At A it is along the tangent at A; shortly afterwards, at B, it is along the tangent at B and so on.

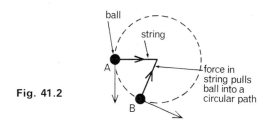

Fig. 41.2

Velocity has both size and direction; speed has only size. Velocity is speed in a stated direction and if the direction of a moving body changes, even if its speed does not, then its velocity has changed. A change of velocity is an acceleration and so during its whirling motion the ball is accelerating.

It follows from Newton's first law of motion that *if we consider a body moving in a circle to be accelerating* then there must be a force acting on it to cause the acceleration. In the case of the whirling ball it is reasonable to say the force is provided by the string pulling inwards on the ball. Like the acceleration, the force acts towards the centre of the circle and keeps the body at a fixed distance from the centre. If the ball is swung round faster or has a greater mass, a larger force is needed. Should the

force be greater than the string can bear, the string breaks and the ball flies off along a tangent.

The force which acts *towards the centre* and keeps a body in a circular path, is called the *centripetal force* (centre-seeking force). Whenever a body moves in a circle (or circular arc) there must be a centripetal force acting on it. In throwing the hammer it is the pull of the athlete's arms acting on the hammer towards the centre of the whirling path. When a car rounds a bend a frictional force is exerted inwards by the road on the car's tyres.

Universal gravitation

Newton proposed that all objects in the universe attract each other with a force he called *gravitation*. He suggested that the gravitational attraction of the sun for the planets was the centripetal force which kept the planets in near-circular orbits round the sun. The gravitational attraction between two ordinary objects, e.g. two 1 kg masses 1 m apart, is extremely small and difficult to detect. The greater the masses of the objects and the smaller their separation, the more do they attract.

Newton regarded *gravity* as the gravitational attraction of the earth for nearby objects. He saw it as being responsible for holding the moon in its orbit round the earth.

Satellite motion

To put an artificial satellite in orbit at a certain height above the earth it must enter the orbit at the correct speed. If it does not, the force of gravity, which decreases with height, will not be equal to the centripetal force needed for the orbit.

This can be seen by imagining a shell fired horizontally from the top of a very high mountain, Fig. 41.3. If gravity did not pull it towards the centre of the earth it would continue to travel horizontally, taking path A. In practice it might take path B. A second shell fired faster might take path C and travel farther. If a third shell is fired even faster, it might never catch up with the rate at which the earth's surface is falling away. It would remain at the same height above the earth (path D) and return to the mountain top, behaving like a satellite.

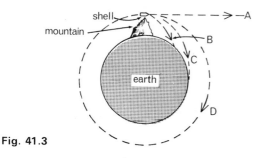

Fig. 41.3

How might a fourth shell behave if fired faster than the speed needed for orbit D?

Relative velocity

Suppose a Jaguar travelling on a straight road at 80 km/h passes a Mini going in the same direction at 50 km/h, Fig. 41.4a. The velocity of the Jaguar

Fig. 41.4

relative to the Mini is $(80-50)=30$ km/h, i.e. it is just as if the Mini were at rest and the Jaguar travelling at 30 km/h. We have, in effect, applied the Mini's velocity reversed to both cars, Fig. 41.4b. In general we can say

The velocity of A relative to B is found by adding the velocity of B reversed to the velocity of A.

Using this rule, if the cars are travelling in opposite directions, their relative velocity is $(80+50)=$ 130 km/h.

When the velocities are not in the same straight line, they must be added by the *parallelogram law* (p. 74) since velocities are vectors and their directions as well as their magnitudes must be considered.

Fig. 41.5

For example, suppose cyclist A is approaching a crossroads with a velocity $v_A = 6$ km/h due south and cyclist B is approaching it with a velocity $v_B = 8$ km/h due east, Fig. 41.5a. The velocity of A relative to B is the resultant of v_B reversed and v_A. It is represented in magnitude and direction by the diagonal OQ of the parallelogram in Fig. 41.5b. A scale drawing or a calculation using Pythagoras' theorem shows that to B, A seems to be approaching at 10 km/h from a direction 37° north of east.

Questions

1. An apple is whirled round in a horizontal circle on the end of a string which is tied to the stalk. It is whirled faster and faster and at a certain speed the apple is torn from the stalk. Why?

2. What provides the centripetal force for
(a) a *coin* placed on a rotating turntable
(b) a *space capsule* circling the earth?

3. Two bodies are moving in the same straight line with velocities of 4 m/s and 5 m/s in *opposite* directions. The magnitude of their relative velocity may be found by

A adding the numerical values
B subtracting the numerical values
C dividing the larger value by the smaller
D dividing the smaller by the larger
E multiplying the one value by the other.   (*O./S.R.16+*)

4. An aircraft is flying due north at 300 km/h in a wind of 100 km/h blowing from the west. Find the resultant velocity of the aircraft.

5. A ship can sail at 20 km/h in still water. Find the course which must be steered for the ship to travel due north when there is a current of 7 km/h running due east.
How long will it take the ship to travel 100 km?   (*E.A.*)

119

42 Further questions

Velocity and acceleration: equations of motion

1. (a) A body travelling with uniform velocity covers a distance of 840 m in 1 minute. What is its velocity in m/s?

(b) If the body begins to accelerate uniformly at $0.2 \, \text{m/s}^2$, what will be its velocity after a *further* minute?

(c) How far will the body have travelled from the instant at which it began to accelerate?

(d) If the body is then retarded uniformly and comes to rest in a *further* distance of 338 m, what is the value of the retardation?

(J.M.B./A.L./N.W.16+)

2. The distance from the starting point of a steel ball which starts from rest and rolls with uniform acceleration down an inclined plane is noted at one second intervals. The data are shown in the table.

Time in s	0	1	2	3	4
Distance in cm	0	2	8	18	32

The speed at the end of the fourth second in cm/s is

A 8   **B** 14   **C** 16   **D** 32   **E** 64

(N.I.)

3. (a) Define the terms 'velocity' and 'acceleration'. Choose *one* of these terms and explain what is meant when the quantity is said to be 'uniform'.

(b) A car runs at a constant speed of 15 m/s for 300 s and then accelerates uniformly to a speed of 25 m/s over a period of 20 s. This speed is maintained for 300 s before the car is brought to rest with uniform deceleration in 30 s.

Draw a velocity-time graph to represent the journey described above.

From the graph find

(i) the acceleration while the velocity changes from 15 m/s to 25 m/s,

(ii) the total distance travelled in the time described,

(iii) the average speed over the time described.

(J.M.B.)

Falling bodies

4. A stone is projected vertically upwards with an initial velocity of 90 m/s and at the same instant another stone is allowed to fall from rest from a height of 405 m. At what distance from the ground will the stones pass? ($g = 10 \, \text{m/s}^2$: air resistance may be neglected.) *(N.I.)*

5. A stone is projected vertically upwards from the ground and is observed to pass a point situated at a height H above ground level at 4 s and again at 5 s after projection. Assuming that air resistance is negligible, determine:

(i) the velocity of projection of the stone

(ii) the height H

(iii) the velocity of the stone when at height H. Take $g = 10 \, \text{m/s}^2$. *(L.)*

6. A man drops, without throwing, an iron ball from the top of a tower and it takes 1.5 s to reach the ground. Which one of the following actions will result in a similar ball taking more than 1.5 s to reach the ground?

A The ball is thrown downwards from the top of a shorter tower.

B The ball is thrown horizontally with a speed of 10 m/s from the top of a shorter tower.

C The ball is thrown horizontally with a speed of 10 m/s from the top of the same tower.

D The ball is thrown upwards at an angle of 10° to the horizontal from the top of the same tower.

E The ball is thrown downwards at an angle of 10° to the horizontal from the top of the same tower. *(O./S.R.16+)*

Newton's laws of motion

7. If the forces acting on a moving body cancel each other out (i.e. are in equilibrium) the body will

A move in a straight line at a steady speed

B slow down to a steady slower speed

C speed up to a steady faster speed

D be brought to a state of rest. *(W.M.)*

8. (a) Define the newton.

Describe an experiment to investigate the relationship between the force applied to a trolley and the acceleration produced in the trolley.

(b) The reading on the speedometer of a car of mass 500 kg is 18 km/h when the brakes are applied. The car is brought to rest in 10 m. Find (i) the average retardation, (ii) the average braking force.   (*J.M.B.*)

9. What is meant by *acceleration*? What evidence have you for believing that a moving body will proceed at a constant speed in a straight line indefinitely unless it is acted on by a resultant force?

A cyclist of mass 50 kg riding a cycle of mass 10 kg raises his speed from 2 m/s to 5 m/s by accelerating uniformly for 6 s while travelling due north along a horizontal road. What horizontal force is exerted on the machine by the road, and in which direction? Does the cyclist exert any force on the machine and, if so, in what direction?

How far does he travel in the 6 s?   (*O. and C.*)

Momentum: K.E. and P.E.

10. Fig. 42.1 shows a truck of mass 3 kg moving at 10 m/s along a horizontal track about to collide with another stationary truck of mass 2 kg. After the collision, the trucks link and move together. The speed of the trucks immediately after the collision is

   A 1 m/s   **B** 2 m/s   **C** 6 m/s   **D** 6.67 m/s
   E 10 m/s   (*O./S.R.16*+)

Fig. 42.1

11. A body of mass 20 kg, moving with uniform acceleration, has an initial momentum of 200 kg m/s and after 10 s the momentum is 300 kg m/s. What is the acceleration of the body?

   A 0.5 m/s^2 **B** 5 m/s^2 **C** 25 m/s^2
   D 50 m/s^2 **E** 100 m/s^2 (*J.M.B.*)

12. A small steel ball of mass 80 g is released from rest at a height of 1.25 m above a rigid horizontal metal plate. After the rebound the ball rises vertically to a height of 1.00 m above the plate. Calculate (a) the velocity of the ball just before impact, (b) the momentum of the ball just before impact, (c) the kinetic energy of the ball just before impact, (d) the loss of energy on impact. Give reasons for this loss of energy. ($g = 10$ m/s^2)   (*S.*)

13. Fig. 42.2 shows a trolley A, of mass 3 kg with light frictionless wheels, which is held at rest on a smooth inclined plane. When it is released its centre of mass is lowered through a *vertical* distance of 1.25 m while it is accelerating down the slope. It then collides with a second similar trolley B of mass 2 kg which is at rest on a horizontal plane. After the collision the two trolleys travel forward as a single body.

Fig. 42.2

(a) Calculate the speed of A immediately before the collision.

(b) Use the principle of conservation of momentum to find the common speed of the two trolleys after the collision.

(c) Calculate the kinetic energy of A just *before* the collision and the kinetic energy of the two trolleys *after* the collision.

(d) Explain why the kinetic energies before and after the collision are different. ($g = 10$ m/s^2)   (*O.*)

Circular and relative motion

14. A stone of mass 0.5 kg is held in a sling and whirled round in a horizontal circle at a constant speed.

(a) In what direction is the stone being accelerated at each point of its circular path?

(b) If the value of this acceleration of the stone is 25 m/s^2, what is the value of the horizontal force acting on the stone?   (*J.M.B./A.L./N.W.16*+)

15. An aircraft flies horizontally at a constant airspeed of 360 km/h and in a straight line from a point A to a point B 120 km due east of A. There is an 80 km/h wind blowing from the north. Find by drawing or calculation (a) the time taken by the aircraft to fly from A to B, (b) the direction in which the aircraft points on the flight. Illustrate your answer by a diagram.   (*O. and C.*)

43 Thermometers

The temperature of a body tells us how hot it is and is measured by a thermometer, usually in *degrees Celsius* (°C). There are different kinds of thermometers, each type being more suitable than another for a certain job. The one in Fig. 43.1 is being used to find the temperature of a furnace.

Liquid-in-glass thermometer

In this type the liquid in a glass bulb expands up a capillary tube when the bulb is heated. The liquid must be easily seen, expand (or contract) rapidly and by a large amount over a wide range of temperature. It must not stick to the inside of the tube or the reading will be low when the temperature is falling.

Mercury and coloured alcohol are in common use. Mercury freezes at $-39\,°C$ and boils at $357\,°C$; alcohol freezes at $-115\,°C$ and boils at $78\,°C$ and is therefore more suitable for low temperatures.

Scale of temperature

A scale and unit of temperature are obtained by choosing two temperatures, called the *fixed points*, and dividing the range between them into a number of equal divisions or *degrees*.

On the Celsius scale (named after the Swedish scientist who suggested it), *the lower fixed point is the temperature of pure melting ice* and is taken as

$0\,°C$. Impurities in the ice would lower its melting point (p. 138).

The upper fixed point is the temperature of the steam above water boiling at normal atmospheric pressure of 760 mmHg and is taken as 100 °C. The temperature of the boiling water itself is not used because any impurities in the water raise its boiling point; the temperature of the steam is not affected, however (p. 138).

Fig. 43.2

Methods of finding the fixed points are shown in Fig. 43.2a, b. When they have been marked on the thermometer, the distance between them is divided into 100 equal degrees, Fig. 43.3. The thermometer

Fig. 43.1

now has a scale, i.e. it has been calibrated or graduated.

Fig. 43.3

Clinical thermometer

This is a special type of mercury-in-glass thermometer used by doctors and nurses. Its scale only extends over a few degrees on either side of the normal body temperature of 37 °C, Fig. 43.4.

Fig. 43.4

The tube has a constriction (i.e. a narrower part) just beyond the bulb. When the thermometer is placed under the tongue the mercury expands, forcing its way past the constriction. When the thermometer is removed (after 1 minute) from the mouth, the mercury in the bulb cools and contracts, breaking the mercury thread at the constriction. The mercury beyond the constriction stays in the tube and shows the body temperature. After use the mercury is returned to the bulb—by a flick of the wrist.

Thermocouple thermometer

A thermocouple consists of two wires of different materials, e.g. copper and iron, joined together, Fig. 43.5. When one junction is at a higher temperature than the other an electric current flows and produces a deflection on a galvanometer (a sensitive ammeter) which depends on the temperature difference.

Thermocouples are used in industry to measure a wide range of temperatures up to about 1500 °C (Fig. 43.1), especially changing ones.

Fig. 43.5

Heat and temperature

It is important not to confuse the temperature of a body with the heat energy that can be obtained from it. For example, a red-hot spark from a fire is at a higher temperature than the boiling water in a saucepan. If the spark landed in the water, heat would pass from it to the water even though much more heat-energy could be supplied by the water.

Temperature decides the direction in which heat flows just as pressure does in liquid flow. Heat flows naturally from a body at a higher temperature to one at a lower temperature. A liquid flows of its own accord from a higher pressure to a lower one.

Questions

1. 1530 °C   120 °C   55 °C   37 °C   19 °C·   0 °C   −12 °C   −50 °C

From the above list of temperatures choose the most likely value for *each* of the following:
(*a*) melting point of iron, (*b*) the temperature of a room that is comfortably warm, (*c*) the melting point of pure ice at normal pressure, (*d*) the lowest outdoor temperature recorded in London in winter, (*e*) the normal body temperature of a healthy person.   (*Mddx.*)

2. In order to make a mercury thermometer which will measure smaller changes in temperature accurately

A decrease the volume of the mercury bulb
B put the degree markings farther apart
C decrease the diameter of the capillary tube
D put the degree markings closer together
E leave the capillary tube open to the air.   (*W.Y.*)

3. A simple thermometer has a stem and a bulb containing a liquid. Which one of the following will help the thermometer to rapidly register a new temperature?

A a large bulb   B a long stem
C a thick-walled bulb   D a liquid of high density
E a thin-walled bulb   (*O./S.R.16+.*)

4. Why does a clinical thermometer (*a*) have a constriction just above the bulb, (*b*) cover only a narrow range of temperature, (*c*) have a very fine bore?   (*E.A.*)

44 Expansion of solids and liquids

In general, when matter is heated it expands and when cooled it contracts. If the changes are resisted large forces are created which are sometimes useful but at other times are a nuisance.

According to the kinetic theory (p. 62) the molecules of solids and liquids are in constant vibration. When heated they vibrate faster and force each other a little farther apart. Expansion results.

Uses of expansion

(a) *Shrink fitting*. In Fig. 44.1 the axle is being shrunk by cooling in liquid nitrogen at $-196\,°C$ until the gear wheel can be slipped on to it. On regaining normal temperature the axle expands to give a very tight fit.

(b) *Riveting metal plates*. A white-hot rivet is placed in the rivet hole and its end hammered flat. On

Fig. 44.2

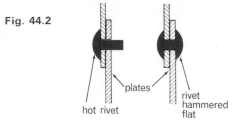

cooling it contracts and pulls the plates together, Fig. 44.2. Steel plates are riveted in shipbuilding.

Fig. 44.1

Fig. 44.3

Precautions against expansion

(a) *Railway lines.* Previously gaps were left between the lengths of rail to allow for expansion in summer. They caused a 'clickety-click' sound as the train passed over them.

Today rails are welded into lengths of about 1 km and are held by concrete sleepers that can withstand the large forces created, without buckling. Also, at the joints the ends are tapered and overlap, Fig. 44.3. This gives a smoother journey and allows some expansion near the ends of each length of rail.

(b) *Bridges.* One end is fixed and the other rests on rollers which permit movement.

Bimetallic strip

If equal lengths of two different metals, e.g. copper and iron, are riveted together so that they cannot move separately, they form a bimetallic strip, Fig. 44.4a. When heated, copper expands more than

Fig. 44.4

(a) Before heating

(b) After heating

iron and to allow this, the strip bends with copper on the outside, Fig. 44.4b. If they had expanded equally the strip would have stayed straight.

Bimetallic strips have many uses.

(a) *Fire alarm*, Fig. 44.5a. Heat from the fire makes the bimetallic strip bend and complete the electrical circuit, so ringing the alarm bell.

It is also used in this way to work the flashing direction indicator lamps in a car, being warmed by an electric heating coil wound round it.

Fig. 44.5

(b) *Thermostat.* A thermostat keeps the temperature of a room or an appliance constant. The one in Fig. 44.5b uses a bimetallic strip in the electrical heating circuit of, for example, an electric iron.

When the iron reaches the required temperature the strip bends down, breaks the circuit at the contacts and switches off the heater. After cooling a little the strip remakes contact and turns the heater on again. A near-steady temperature results.

125

If the control knob is screwed down, the strip has to bend more to break the heating circuit and this needs a higher temperature.

Gas oven thermostat

Use is made of the fact that Invar, an alloy of steel and nickel, has a very small expansion.

Fig. 44.6

The arrangement is shown in Fig. 44.6. As the temperature of the oven rises the brass tube expands to the left pulling the Invar rod with it. Since the expansion of the Invar is negligible, the gas supply through the valve to the burners is reduced. The control knob alters the original position of the valve and selects the steady temperature reached.

Linear expansivity

An engineer has to allow for the linear (lengthways) expansion of a bridge when designing it. The expansion can be calculated if he knows (*i*) the length of the bridge, (*ii*) the range of temperature it will experience and (*iii*) the *linear expansivity* of the material to be used.

The linear expansivity (previously the coefficient of linear expansion) *of a substance is the increase in length of unit length per degree rise in temperature.*

The linear expansivity of a material is found by experiment. For steel it is 0.000 012 per °C. This means that 1 m will become 1.000 012 m for a temperature rise of 1 °C. A steel bridge 100 m long will expand by 0.000 012 × 100 m for each 1 °C rise in temperature. If the maximum temperature *change* expected is 60 °C (e.g. from −15 °C to +45 °C), the

expansion will be 0.000 012 × 100 × 60 = 0.072 m = 7.2 cm. In general,

$$\text{EXPANSION} = \text{LINEAR EXPANSIVITY} \times \text{ORIGINAL LENGTH} \times \text{TEMPERATURE RISE}$$

Measurement of linear expansivity

Rewriting the above expression we get

$$\frac{\text{linear}}{\text{expansivity}} = \frac{\text{expansion}}{(\text{original length}) \times (\text{temp. rise})}$$

To find the linear expansivity of a material we must therefore measure the expansion of a known length for a known temperature rise.

Fig. 44.7

One form of apparatus is shown in Fig. 44.7. The original length of a rod of the material (about 50 cm) is measured with a metre rule. It is placed in the steam jacket with one end against the stop. The micrometer is adjusted until it just touches the other end. The reading is taken, as is the temperature of the rod.

The micrometer is unscrewed and steam passed through the jacket for several minutes. It is screwed up again and the new reading noted. This is repeated shortly afterwards to ensure it has not changed, showing that the rod is at the steam temperature—which is also taken. The difference in the micrometer readings equals the expansion of the rod. The linear expansivity can then be calculated.

Unusual expansion of water

As water is cooled to 4 °C it contracts, as we would expect. However between 4 °C and 0 °C it expands, surprisingly. *Water therefore has a maximum density at 4 °C.*

At 0 °C, when it freezes, a considerable expansion occurs and every 100 cm³ of water becomes 109 cm³ of ice—which accounts for the bursting of water pipes in very cold weather.

These changes are represented in Fig. 44.8.

Fig. 44.8

The unusual expansion of water between 4 °C and 0 °C explains why fish survive in a frozen pond. The water at the top of the pond cools first, contracts and being denser sinks to the bottom. Warmer less dense water rises to the surface to be cooled. When all the water is at 4 °C the circulation stops. If the temperature of the surface water falls below 4 °C, it becomes less dense and *remains at the top*, eventually forming a layer of ice at 0 °C. Temperatures in the pond are then as in Fig. 44.9.

Fig. 44.9

The expansion of water between 4 °C and 0 °C is due to the breaking up below 4 °C of the groups which water molecules form above 4 °C. The new arrangement requires a larger volume and more than cancels out the contraction due to the fall in temperature.

Questions

1. Explain why (*a*) the metal lid on a glass jam jar can be unscrewed easily if the jar is inverted for a few seconds with the *lid* in very hot water, (*b*) furniture may creak at night after a warm day, (*c*) concrete roads are laid in sections with pitch between them.

2. A bimetallic strip is made from aluminium and copper. When heated it bends in the direction shown in Fig. 44.10.

Fig. 44.10

Which metal expands more for the same rise in temperature? Draw a diagram to show how the bimetallic strip would appear if it were cooled to below room temperature.

3. How does the bimetallic thermometer in Fig. 44.11 work?

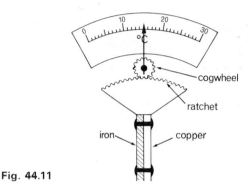

Fig. 44.11

4. The linear expansivities of some common substances are given below.

Aluminium	0.000 03 per °C	Glass	0.000 009 per °C
Concrete	0.000 01 per °C	Platinum	0.000 009 per °C
Copper	0.000 02 per °C	Steel	0.000 01 per °C

(*a*) Rods of aluminium, copper and steel are the same length at a temperature of 0 °C. Which will be the longest at 300 °C?

(*b*) If the aluminium rod is 1 m long at 0 °C, what will be its length at 300 °C?

(*c*) Why is steel a suitable material for reinforcing concrete?

(*d*) Which of the substances listed above would be most suitable for carrying a current of electricity through the walls of a glass vessel?

(*e*) How might a steel cylinder liner be fitted tightly inside a cylinder block made of aluminium?

5. Using the values for linear expansivities in Qn. 4, calculate the expansion of

(*a*) 100 m of copper pipe heated through 50 °C.

(*b*) 50 cm of steel pipe heated through 80 °C.

(*c*) 200 m of aluminium pipe heated from 10 °C to 60 °C.

6. A steel rod, 2 m long, expands by 1 mm when heated through 50 °C. By how much will a second steel rod, 1 m long, expand when heated through 25 °C?

A $\frac{1}{8}$ mm B $\frac{1}{4}$ mm C $\frac{1}{2}$ mm D 1 mm E 2 mm   (*E.A.*)

7. If a copper rod is 1 m long at 20 °C and 1.0016 m long at 100 °C what is the linear expansivity of copper?

At what temperature will the rod be 1.0020 m long? (*A.L.*)

8. When a particular substance at a certain temperature is heated, it expands. When the same substance at the same temperature is cooled, it also expands. (*a*) What is the substance? (*b*) What is the temperature? (*E.M.*)

45 The gas laws

When a gas is heated, as air is in a jet engine, its *pressure* as well as its *volume* may change. To study the effect of temperature on these two quantities we must keep one fixed while the other is changed.

Experiment: effect on volume of temperature (pressure constant)—Charles' law

Fig. 45.1

Arrange the apparatus as in Fig. 45.1. The index of concentrated sulphuric acid traps the air column to be investigated and also dries it. Adjust the capillary tube so that the bottom of the air column is opposite a convenient mark on the ruler.

Note the length of the air column (to the *lower* end of the index) at different temperatures. Put the results in a table but before taking a reading, stop heating and stir well to make sure that the air has reached the temperature of the water.

Plot a graph of volume (in cm, since the length of the air column is a measure of it) on the *y*-axis and temperature (in °C) on the *x*-axis.

The pressure of (and on) the air column is constant and equals atmospheric pressure plus the pressure of the acid index.

Experiment: effect on pressure of temperature (volume constant)—the Pressure law

The apparatus is shown in Fig. 45.2. The rubber tubing from the flask to the pressure gauge should be as short as possible. The flask must be in water

Fig. 45.2

almost to the top of its neck and be securely clamped to keep it off the bottom of the can.

Record the pressure over a wide range of temperatures. Tabulate the results but before taking a reading, stop heating, stir and allow time for the gauge reading to become steady; the air in the flask will then be at the temperature of the water.

Plot a graph of pressure on the *y*-axis and temperature on the *x*-axis.

Absolute zero

The volume-temperature and pressure-temperature graphs for a gas (obtained by experiments like the above) are straight lines, Fig. 45.3*a, b*. They show that gases expand *uniformly* with temperature as measured on a mercury thermometer, i.e. equal temperature increases cause equal volume or pressure increases.

The graphs do not pass through the Celsius temperature origin (0 °C). If they are produced backwards they cut the temperature axis at about −273 °C. This temperature is called *absolute zero* because we believe it is the lowest temperature possible. It is the zero of the *absolute* or *Kelvin scale of temperature*.

Degrees on this scale are called *kelvins* and are denoted by K. They are exactly the same size as Celsius degrees, i.e. 1 °C = 1 K. Since −273 °C = 0 K, conversions from °C to K are made by adding 273. For example

$$0\,^{\circ}\text{C} = 273\,\text{K}$$
$$15\,^{\circ}\text{C} = 273 + 15 = 288\,\text{K}$$
$$100\,^{\circ}\text{C} = 273 + 100 = 373\,\text{K}$$

(a)

(b)

Fig. 45.3

Fig. 45.4

Kelvin or absolute temperatures are represented by the letter T and if t stands for a Celsius scale temperature then, in general

$$T = 273 + t$$

Near absolute zero strange things occur. Liquid helium becomes a 'superfluid'. It cannot be kept in an open vessel because it flows up the inside of the vessel, over the edge and down the outside. Some metals and compounds become 'superconductors' of electricity and a current once started in them flows for ever without a battery. Electromagnets with coils of superconducting wires are being developed for use in industry and research, Fig. 45.4.

The gas laws

Using absolute temperatures the gas laws can be stated in a convenient form for calculations.

(a) Charles law. In Fig. 45.3a the volume-temperature graph does pass through the origin if temperatures are measured on the Kelvin scale. That is, if we take 0 K as the origin. We can then say that the volume V is directly proportional to the absolute temperature T, i.e. doubling T doubles V, etc. Therefore

$$V \propto T \quad \text{or} \quad V = \text{constant} \times T \qquad (1)$$
$$\text{or} \quad V/T = \text{constant}$$

Charles' law may be stated as follows.

The volume of a fixed mass of gas is directly proportional to its absolute temperature if the pressure is kept constant.

(b) *Pressure law.* From Fig. 45.3b we can say similarly for the pressure p that

$$p \propto T \quad \text{or} \quad p = \text{constant} \times T$$
$$\text{or} \quad p/T = \text{constant} \tag{2}$$

The Pressure law may be stated as follows.

The pressure of a fixed mass of gas is directly proportional to its absolute temperature if the volume is kept constant.

(c) *Boyle's law.* Previously (p. 89) we found for a fixed mass of gas at constant temperature, that

$$pV = \text{constant} \tag{3}$$

These three equations can be combined giving

$$\frac{pV}{T} = \text{constant}$$

It is useful for cases in which p, V and T all change from say, p_1, V_1 and T_1 to p_2, V_2 and T_2, then

$$\frac{p_1 V_1}{T_1} = \frac{p_2 V_2}{T_2} \tag{4}$$

Worked example

A cycle pump contains $50\,\text{cm}^3$ of air at $17\,^\circ\text{C}$ and a pressure of 1.0 atmosphere. Find the pressure when the air is compressed to $10\,\text{cm}^3$ and its temperature rises to $27\,^\circ\text{C}$.

We have,

$p_1 = 1.0$ atmosphere $p_2 = ?$
$V_1 = 50\,\text{cm}^3$ $V_2 = 10\,\text{cm}^3$
$T_1 = 273 + 17 = 290\,\text{K}$ $T_2 = 273 + 27 = 300\,\text{K}$

From equation (4) above we get

$$p_2 = p_1 \times \frac{V_1}{V_2} \times \frac{T_2}{T_1}$$

Replacing

$$p_2 = 1 \times \frac{50}{10} \times \frac{300}{290} = 5.2 \text{ atmosphere}$$

Notes. 1. All temperatures must be in K.
2. Any units can be used for p and V so long as they are the same on both sides of the equation.
3. In some calculations the volume of the gas has to be found at s.t.p. (standard temperature and pressure). This is $0\,^\circ\text{C}$ and $760\,\text{mmHg}$ pressure.

Gases and the kinetic theory

The kinetic theory can explain the behaviour of gases.

(a) *Cause of gas pressure.* The pressure exerted by a gas is due to the molecules bombarding the walls of the container.

Fig. 45.5

(b) *Boyle's law.* If the volume of a fixed mass of gas is halved by halving the volume of the container, Fig. 45.5, the number of molecules per cm^3 will be doubled. There will be twice as many collisions per second with the walls, i.e. the pressure is doubled. This is Boyle's law.

(c) *Temperature.* When a gas is heated and its temperature rises, the average speed of its molecules increases. If the volume of the gas is to remain constant, its pressure increases due to more frequent and more violent collisions of the molecules with the walls. If the pressure of the gas is to remain constant, the volume must increase so that the number of collisions does not.

(d) *Absolute zero.* This is the temperature at which the molecules have their lowest possible kinetic energy.

Questions

1. A gas of volume $2\,\text{m}^3$ at $27\,^\circ\text{C}$ is (a) heated to $327\,^\circ\text{C}$, (b) cooled to $-123\,^\circ\text{C}$, at constant pressure. What are its new volumes?
2. A container holds gas at $0\,^\circ\text{C}$. To what temperature must it be heated for its pressure to double? Assume the container does not expand. (E.A.)
3. A mass of gas occupies a volume of $200\,\text{cm}^3$ at a temperature of $27\,^\circ\text{C}$ and a pressure of 1 atmosphere. Calculate the volume when
   (i) the pressure is doubled at constant temperature,
   (ii) the absolute temperature is doubled at constant pressure,
   (iii) the pressure is $1\frac{1}{2}$ atmospheres and the Celsius temperature is $127\,^\circ\text{C}$. (E.A.)
4. A gas is heated in a closed container so that its volume cannot change. Which of the following will NOT happen?
   A The average speed of the molecules will increase.
   B The molecules will move in all directions.
   C The number of molecules will increase.
   D The molecules will hit the walls of the container more often.
   E The pressure of the gas will increase. (W.Y.)

46 Specific heat capacity

If 1 kg of water and 1 kg of paraffin are heated in turn for the same time by the same heater, the temperature rise of the paraffin is about *twice* that of the water. Since the heater gives equal amounts of heat energy to each liquid, it seems that different substances require different amounts of heat to cause the same temperature rise in the same mass, say 1 °C in 1 kg.

The 'thirst' of a substance for heat is measured by its *specific heat capacity* (symbol *c*).

The specific heat capacity of a substance is the heat required to produce unit temperature rise in unit mass.

Heat, like other forms of energy, is measured in joules (J) and the unit of specific heat capacity is the joule per kilogram °C (J/kg °C).

In physics the word 'specific' means 'unit mass' is being considered.

The heat equation

If a substance has a specific heat capacity of 1000 J/kg °C then

$$1000 \text{ J raise the temp. of 1 kg by 1 °C}$$
$$\therefore \quad 2 \times 1000 \text{ J} \quad ,, \quad ,, \quad ,, \quad ,, \text{ 2 kg by 1 °C}$$
$$\therefore \quad 3 \times 2 \times 1000 \text{ J} \quad ,, \quad ,, \quad ,, \quad ,, \text{ 2 kg by 3 °C}$$

That is, 6000 J will raise the temperature of 2 kg of this substance by 3 °C. We have obtained this answer by multiplying together:

(*i*) the *mass* in kg,
(*ii*) the *temperature rise* in °C, and
(*iii*) the *specific heat capacity* in J/kg °C.

If the temperature of the substance fell by 3 °C, the heat given out would also be 6000 J. In general, we can write the 'heat equation' as

HEAT RECEIVED OR GIVEN OUT
= MASS × TEMP. CHANGE × SPEC. HEAT CAPACITY

For example, if the temperature of a 5 kg mass of copper of specific heat capacity 400 J/kg °C rises from 15 °C to 25 °C, the heat received

$$= 5 \text{ kg} \times (25 - 15) \text{ °C} \times 400 \text{ J/kg °C}$$
$$= 5 \times 10 \times 400 = 20\,000 \text{ J}$$

Experiment: finding specific heat capacities

You need to know the power of the 12-volt electric immersion heater to be used. A 40-watt heater converts 40 joules of electrical energy into heat energy per second. If the power is not marked on the heater ask about it.[1]

(*a*) *Water.* Weigh out 1 kg of water into a container, e.g. an aluminium saucepan. Note the temperature of the water, insert the heater, Fig. 46.1, and switch on the 12 V supply. Stir the water and after 5 minutes switch off, but continue stirring and note the *highest* temperature reached.

thermometer   electric immersion heater

12 V supply

water

aluminium saucepan

Fig. 46.1

Assuming that the heat supplied by the heater equals the heat received by the water, work out the specific heat capacity of water in J/kg °C, as shown below.

Heat received by water (J)
= power of heater (J/s) × time heater on (s)

Rearranging the 'heat equation' we get

$$\frac{\text{sp. heat cap.}}{\text{of water}} = \frac{\text{heat received by water (J)}}{\text{mass (kg)} \times \text{temp. rise (°C)}}$$

Suggest causes of error in this experiment.

---

[1] The power is found by immersing the heater in water, connecting it to a 12-volt d.c. supply and measuring the current taken (usually 3–4 amperes). Then power in watts = volts × amperes.

(b) *Aluminium.* A cylinder weighing 1 kg and having two holes drilled in it is used. Place the immersion heater in the central hole and a thermometer in the other hole, Fig. 46.2.

electric immersion heater

thermometer

12 V supply

aluminium block

Fig. 46.2

Note the temperature, connect the heater to a 12 V supply and switch it on for 5 minutes. When the temperature stops rising record its highest value.

Calculate the specific heat capacity as before.

Importance of high specific heat capacity of water

The specific heat capacity of water is 4200 J/kg °C and of soil it is about 800 J/kg °C. As a result, the temperature of the sea rises and falls more slowly than that of the land. A certain mass of water needs five times more heat for its temperature to rise by 1 °C than does the same mass of soil. Water also has to give out more heat to fall 1 °C. Since islands are surrounded by water they therefore experience much smaller changes of temperature from summer to winter than do large land masses such as Central Asia.

The high specific heat capacity of water (as well as its cheapness and availability) accounts for its use to cool car engines and in the radiators of central heating systems.

Worked examples

1. A tank holding 60 kg of water is heated by a 3 kW electric immersion heater. If the specific heat capacity of water is 4200 J/kg °C, estimate the time for the temperature to rise from 10 °C to 60 °C.

A 3 kW (3000 W) heater supplies 3000 J of heat energy per second.

Let t = time taken in seconds to raise the temperature of the water by $(60 - 10) = 50$ °C,

$\therefore$ heat supplied to water in time $t = 3000 \times t$ J

132

From the 'heat equation', we can say

heat received by water $= 60 \times 4200 \times 50$ J

Assuming heat supplied = heat received

$$3000 \times t = 60 \times 4200 \times 50$$

$$\therefore \quad t = \frac{60 \times 4200 \times 50}{3000} = 4200 \text{ s (70 mins)}$$

2. A piece of aluminium of mass 0.5 kg is heated to 100 °C and then placed in 0.4 kg of water at 10 °C. If the resulting temperature of the mixture is 30 °C, what is the specific heat capacity of aluminium if that of water is 4200 J/kg °C?

When two substances at different temperatures are mixed, heat flows from the one at the higher temperature to the one at the lower temperature until both are at the same temperature—the temperature of the mixture. If there is no loss of heat, then in this case

heat given out by aluminium
$\qquad$ = heat taken in by water

Using the 'heat equation' and letting c be the sp. heat cap. of aluminium in J/kg °C, we have

heat given out $= 0.5 \times c \times (100 - 30)$ J
heat taken in $= 0.4 \times 4200 \times (30 - 10)$ J
$0.5 \times c \times 70 = 0.4 \times 4200 \times 20$

$$\therefore \quad c = \frac{4200 \times 8}{35} = 960 \text{ J/kg °C}$$

Conversion of mechanical energy to heat

(a) *p.e.* The p.e. of water at the top of a waterfall becomes k.e. as the water falls and when it strikes the ground, heat (and sound) are produced. The temperature of the water at the bottom is higher than that at the top. If we assume all the p.e. becomes heat the temperature rise can be calculated.

Consider 1 kg of water falling a vertical distance of 105 m. We have, taking $g = 10$ m/s²,

p.e. of water $= mgh = 1 \times 10 \times 105$ J

Using the 'heat equation' and taking the sp. heat cap. of water as 4200 J/kg °C,

heat produced $= 1 \times 4200 \times \theta$ J

where θ is the temperature rise of the water in °C.

$$\therefore \quad 4200\,\theta = 1050$$
$$\therefore \qquad \theta = 1050/4200 = 0.25 \text{ °C}$$

(b) k.e. When a car is brought to rest by the brakes, k.e. becomes heat and the temperature of the brake linings (or disc pads) rises.

Energy of food

When food is eaten it reacts with the oxygen we breathe into our lungs and is slowly 'burnt'. As a result chemical energy stored in food becomes *heat* to warm the body and *mechanical energy* for muscular movement.

The calorific value of a substance is the amount of energy released when unit mass is completely oxidized.

It is measured in J/kg. Dieticians sometimes use kilocalories instead of joules. The calorie was the previous unit of heat and equals 4.2 J. Some calorific values are given below in megajoules per kilogram (MJ/kg: 1 MJ = 1 000 000 J).

Fat	38	Sugar	16	Ice cream	9	Milk	2.9
Butter	31	Flour	15	Eggs	7	Apples	2.6
Cheese	21	Beef	10	Potatoes	4	Carrots	1.7

Foods with high values are 'fattening' and if more are eaten than the body really needs they are stored as fat. The average person requires about 12 MJ per day.

Our muscles change chemical energy into mechanical energy when we exert a force, to lift a weight for example. Unfortunately they are, at best, only about 25% efficient at doing this. Every 100 J of mechanical energy supplied by our muscles therefore uses 400 J of chemical energy. The other 300 J becomes heat, most of which the body has to get rid of (p. 139).

The energy crisis

Energy changes from one form to another, it cannot be destroyed. However it usually ends up as heat (as a result of overcoming friction) and raises the temperature of its surroundings. It is then not easy to use.

Fossil fuels such as coal and oil are the stores of chemical energy from which most other useful forms of energy come at present. Stocks of these are running down and there is now world-wide concern to make the best of what we still have and to develop other sources, especially nuclear and solar energy.

Although there are safety and environmental problems connected with nuclear energy, it seems likely to be the main solution to our fuel problems in the foreseeable future (p. 228). Solar energy is difficult to capture directly in the amount required. The average family in Britain needs about 15 000 J/s for all purposes, i.e. 15 kW. The average solar power over the whole of the earth's surface is roughly 1.5 kW/m^2. Each family would therefore require a collecting area of 10 m^2 but, since the efficiency of solar panels is very low, the actual area would be much greater.

Questions

1. How much heat is needed to raise the temperature by 10 °C of 5 kg of a substance of specific heat capacity 300 J/kg °C?

2. 2000 J of energy is needed to heat 1 kg of paraffin through 1 °C. How much heat is needed to heat 2 kg of paraffin through 10 °C?

    A 4010 J   B 4020 J   C 10 000 J   D 24 000 J   E 40 000 J
                                      (J.M.B./A.L./N.W.16+)

3. The same quantity of heat was given to different masses of three substances A, B and C. The temperature rise in each case is shown in the table. Calculate the specific heat capacities of A, B and C.

Material	Mass (kg)	Heat given (J)	Temp. rise (°C)
A	1.0	2000	1.0
B	2.0	2000	5.0
C	0.5	2000	4.0

4. How much heat is given out when an iron ball of mass 2 kg and specific heat capacity 440 J/kg °C cools from 300 °C to 200 °C?

5. How many joules of heat energy are supplied by a 2 kW heater in (a) 10 s, (b) 1 minute?

6. 1 kg of water is contained in a vessel with a 50 W immersion heater. When the immersion heater is switched on the temperature of the water soon begins to rise at a rate of 1 °C every 2 minutes.

    (a) How much heat is supplied by the immersion heater every 2 minutes?

    (b) From these results what is the approximate specific heat capacity of water?   (O./S.R.16+)

7. An electric water heater raises the temperature of 0.5 kg of water by 30 °C every minute. The specific heat capacity of water is 4200 J/kg °C. Assuming that no heat is lost, what is the power of the heater?

8. The jam in a hot 'roly-poly' pudding always seems hotter than the pastry. Why?

9. What mass of cold water at 10 °C must be added to 60 kg of hot water at 80 °C by someone who wants to have a bath at 50 °C? Neglect heat losses and take the specific heat capacity of water as 4200 J/kg °C.

47 Latent heat

When a solid is heated, it may melt and change its state from solid to liquid. If ice is heated it becomes water. The opposite process of freezing occurs when a liquid solidifies.

A pure substance melts at a definite temperature, called the *melting point*; it solidifies at the same temperature—*the freezing point*.

Experiment: cooling curve of naphthalene

Half-fill a test-tube with naphthalene (moth balls) and place it in a beaker of water, Fig. 47.1*a*. Heat the water until all the naphthalene has melted.

Fig. 47.1

Remove the test-tube and arrange it as in Fig. 47.1*b* with a thermometer in the liquid naphthalene. Record the temperature every minute until it has fallen to 70 °C.

Plot a cooling curve of temperature against time. What is the freezing (melting) point of naphthalene?

Latent heat of fusion

The previous experiment shows that the temperature of liquid naphthalene falls until it starts to solidify (at 80 °C) and remains constant till it has all solidified. The cooling curve in Fig. 47.2 is for a pure substance; the flat part AB occurs at the melting point when the substance is solidifying.

During solidification a substance loses heat to its surroundings but its temperature does not fall.

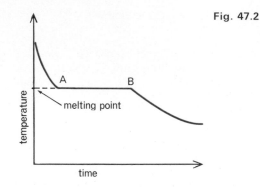

Fig. 47.2

Conversely when a solid is melting, the heat supplied does not cause a temperature rise. For example, the temperature of a well-stirred ice-water mixture remains at 0 °C until all the ice is melted.

Heat which is *absorbed* by a solid during melting or *given out* by a liquid during solidification is called *latent heat of fusion*. Latent means hidden and fusion means melting. Latent heat does not cause a temperature change; it seems to disappear.

The specific latent heat of fusion of a substance is the quantity of heat needed to change unit mass from solid to liquid without temperature change.

It is measured in J/kg or J/g.

Experiment: specific latent heat of fusion of ice

Fig. 47.3

Place a 12 V electric immersion heater of known power in a filter funnel and pack small pieces of ice round it, Fig. 47.3. Switch on the heater for 3 minutes and find the mass of water which collects in a beaker. Arrange the results as shown.

Power of immersion heater = W(J/s)
Time heat supplied = s
∴ Heat supplied to ice = J
Mass of beaker empty = g
Mass of beaker + melted ice = g
∴ Mass of melted ice = g

Calculate the heat needed to melt 1 g of ice. What are causes of error in this experiment?

Latent heat of vaporization

Latent heat is also needed to change a liquid into a vapour. The reading of a thermometer in boiling water remains constant at 100 °C even though heat, called *latent heat of vaporization*, is still being absorbed by the water from whatever is heating it.

When steam condenses to form water, latent heat is given out. This is why a scald from steam may be more serious than one from boiling water.

The specific latent heat of vaporization of a substance is the quantity of heat needed to change unit mass from liquid to vapour without change of temperature.

240 V a.c.

electric immersion heater (500 W)

water

can

balance

Fig. 47.4

An estimate of its value for water can be made using the apparatus of Fig. 47.4. The mains-operated immersion heater is clamped so that it is well covered by the water in the can. When the water is *boiling briskly* the reading on the balance is noted and a stop clock started. The time for 50 g of water to be boiled off is found.

Suppose a 500 W heater is used and that the time required is 4 minutes (240 s), then

$$\text{heat supplied in } 240\,\text{s} = 500\,\text{J/s} \times 240\,\text{s}$$
$$= 120\,000\,\text{J}$$
∴ latent heat of vaporization $= 120\,000\,\text{J}/50\,\text{g}$
$$= 2400\,\text{J/g}$$

The accepted value is $2300\,\text{J/g} = 2\,300\,000\,\text{J/kg} = 2.3 \times 10^6\,\text{J/kg} = 2.3\,\text{MJ/kg}$. Errors arise because the can and water lose heat to the surroundings.

Latent heat and the kinetic theory

(*a*) *Fusion.* The kinetic theory explains latent heat of fusion as being the energy which enables the molecules of a solid to change their vibratory motion about a fixed position to the greater range of movement they have as liquid molecules. Their p.e. increases but not their average k.e. as happens when the heat causes a temperature rise.

(*b*) *Vaporization.* If liquid molecules are to overcome the forces holding them together and gain the freedom to move around independently as gas molecules, they need a large amount of energy. They receive this as latent heat of vaporization which, like latent heat of fusion, increases the p.e. of the molecules but not their k.e. It also gives the molecules the energy required to push back the surrounding atmosphere in the large expansion that occurs when a liquid vaporizes.

Worked examples

The following values are required.

	Water	Ice	Aluminium
Sp. ht. cap. (J/g °C)	4.2	2.0.	0.90
Sp. lat. ht. (J/g)	2300	340	

1. How much heat is needed to change 20 g of ice at 0 °C to steam at 100 °C?

There are three stages in the change.

Heat to change 20 g *ice at 0 °C to water at 0 °C*
= mass of ice × sp. lat. ht. of ice
= 20 g × 340 J/g = 6800 J

Heat to change 20 g *water at 0 °C to water at 100 °C*
= mass of water × sp. ht. cap. of water × temp. rise
= 20 g × 4.2 J/g °C × 100 °C = 8400 J

135

Heat to change 20 g *water at 100 °C* to *steam at 100 °C*

    = mass of water × sp. lat. ht. of steam
    = 20 g × 2300 J/g = 46 000 J

∴ Total heat supplied
    = 6800 + 8400 + 46 000 = 61 200 J

2. An aluminium can of mass 100 g contains 200 g of water. Both, initially at 15 °C, are placed in a refrigerator at −5.0 °C. Calculate the quantity of heat that has to be removed from the water and the can for their temperatures to fall to −5.0 °C.

Heat lost by *can* in falling from 15 °C to −5.0 °C
    = mass of can × sp. ht. cap. aluminium × temp. fall
    = 100 × 0.90 × [15 − (−5)] = 100 × 0.90 × 20
    = 1800 J

Heat lost by *water* in falling from 15 °C to 0 °C
    = mass of water × sp. ht. cap. water × temp. fall
    = 200 × 4.2 × 15 = 12 600 J

Heat lost by *water* at 0 °C freezing to ice at 0 °C
    = mass of water × sp. lat. ht. of ice
    = 200 × 340 = 68 000 J

Heat lost by *ice* in falling from 0 °C to −5.0 °C
    = mass of ice × sp. ht. cap. of ice × temp. fall
    = 200 × 2.0 × 5.0 = 2000 J

∴ Total heat removed
    = 1800 + 12 600 + 68 000 + 2000 = 84 400 J

Questions

Use values given in *Worked examples.*

1. (*a*) How much heat will change 10 g of ice at 0 °C to water at 0 °C?

(*b*) What quantity of heat must be removed from 20 g of water at 0 °C to change it to ice at 0 °C?

2. (*a*) How much heat is needed to change 5 g of ice at 0 °C to water at 50 °C?

(*b*) If a refrigerator cools 200 g of water from 20 °C to its freezing point in 10 minutes, how much heat is removed per minute from the water?

3. How long will it take a 50 W heater to melt 100 g of ice at 0 °C?

4. Some small aluminium rivets of total mass 170 g and at 100 °C are emptied into a hole in a large block of ice at 0 °C.

(*a*) What will be the final temperature of the rivets?

(*b*) How much ice will melt?

5. (*a*) How much heat is needed to change 4 g of water at 100 °C to steam at 100 °C?

(*b*) Find the heat given out when 10 g of steam at 100 °C condenses and cools to water at 50 °C.

6. A 3 kW electric kettle is left on for 2 minutes after the water starts to boil. What mass of water is boiled off in this time?

7. 200 g of metal are heated in a flame to a temperature of 600 °C and dropped into a boiling liquid. It is found that 20 g of liquid vaporizes. If the specific heat capacity of the metal is 0.50 J/g °C and the boiling point of the liquid is 100 °C, find the specific latent heat of the liquid. (*N.W.*)

48 Melting and boiling

Effect of pressure on melting point

Fig. 48.1

Increasing the pressure on ice lowers its melting point. This may be shown by the demonstration in Fig. 48.1 in which a weighted copper wire passes through a block of ice without cutting it in two.

A large pressure is exerted on the ice below the wire. The *melting point* is lowered and the ice, being at 0 °C, melts since its temperature is now above its new melting point. The wire sinks through the water which is no longer under pressure and refreezes above the wire because the melting point returns to 0 °C. In refreezing the water gives out latent heat of fusion and this is *conducted* down through the wire to enable the ice below it to melt.

The effect is called *regelation* (refreezing).

If an iron wire is used in the demonstration it passes through the ice more slowly. No effect is obtained if string is used. Why?

Regelation causes the snow to 'bind' together when a snowball is made. It may also account for the motion of glaciers like that in Fig. 48.2.

The actual depression of the melting point is only 0.0075 °C for ice if normal atmospheric pressure is doubled. Larger pressures cause proportionate decreases.

Fig. 48.2

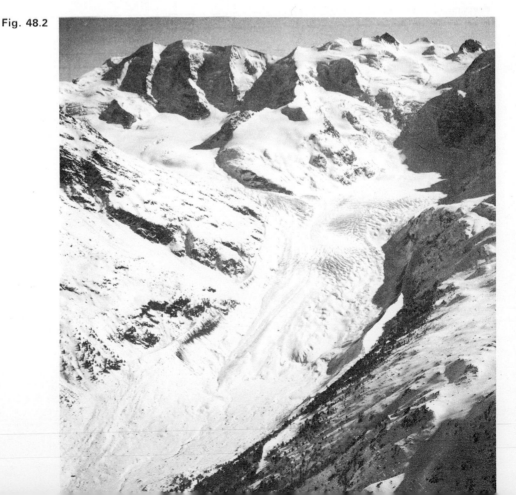

Effect of impurities on melting point

The temperature of a well-stirred ice-water mixture is normally 0 °C but when an 'impurity' such as salt is added, it may fall to −20 °C. The freezing mixture so formed can be used for cooling purposes.

The fall in temperature is due to the salt lowering the *melting point* of the ice. The ice, however, is still at 0 °C, i.e. abôve its new melting point. It therefore melts, absorbing latent heat from the mixture whose temperature falls till it freezes at the new melting point.

This effect explains the use of anti-freeze in car radiators and also why brine (and sea sand) is spread on icy roads. The 'impurity' lowers the freezing point of the mixture and may prevent it freezing. When water does freeze it expands and exerts tremendous forces if resisted.

Effect of pressure on boiling point

The boiling point of water rises when the pressure above it is raised. Using the apparatus in Fig. 48.3a the pressure can be increased by pinching the rubber tube for *just long enough* to see that the thermometer reading rises.

Fig. 48.3

To show that decreasing the pressure lowers the boiling point, the water should be boiled for a few minutes so that the steam sweeps out most of the air. The heating is then stopped and the clip closed. Cold water is run over the inverted flask, Fig. 48.3b, so condensing the water vapour inside it and reducing the pressure above the water. The water starts to boil and if the cooling in this way is continued, it may go on boiling until about 40 °C.

Fig. 48.4

In a pressure cooker, Fig. 48.4, food cooks more quickly because the pressure of the steam above the water in the cooker can rise to twice the normal atmospheric value. The water then boils at about 120 °C.

Effect of impurities on boiling point

An 'impurity' such as salt when added to water raises the boiling point.

Evaporation

In evaporation a liquid changes to a vapour without ever reaching its boiling point. A pool of water in the road evaporates and does so most rapidly when there is (i) a wind, (ii) sun and (iii) only a little water vapour present in the air.

Evaporation and boiling are compared below.

Evaporation	Boiling
1. Occurs at any temperature.	Occurs at a definite temperature—the boiling point.
2. Occurs at surface of liquid; no bubbles.	Occurs within liquid: bubbles appear.

Both processes need latent heat of vaporization. In evaporation this is obtained by the liquid from its surroundings, as may be shown by the demonstration in Fig. 48.5.

Ether is a *volatile* liquid, that is, it has a low boiling point (35 °C) and evaporates readily at room temperature, especially when air is blown through it. Latent heat is taken first from the ether itself and then from the water below the can. The water soon freezes causing the block and can to stick together.

Volatile liquids feel cold when spilt on the hand. They are used in perfumes.

Fig. 48.5

Fig. 48.6

Water evaporates from the skin when we sweat. This is the body's way of using unwanted heat (see p. 133) and keeping a constant temperature. After vigorous exercise there is a risk of the body being overcooled, especially in a draught; it is then less able to resist infection.

Cooling by evaporation and the kinetic theory

The molecules of a liquid have an average speed at a particular temperature but some are moving faster than others. Evaporation occurs when faster molecules escape from the surface of the liquid. The average speed, and therefore the average k.e. of the molecules left behind, decreases, i.e. the temperature of the liquid falls.

Refrigerator

In a refrigerator heat is taken in at one place and given out at another by the refrigerating substance as it is pumped round a circuit, Fig. 48.6.

The coiled pipe round the *freezer* at the top of the refrigerator contains a volatile liquid. This evaporates and takes latent heat from its surroundings, so causing cooling. The electrically-driven pump removes the vapour (so reducing the pressure, lowering the boiling point and encouraging evaporation or even boiling) and forces it into the *heat exchanger* (pipes with cooling fins outside the rear of the refrigerator). Here the vapour is compressed

and liquefies, giving out latent heat of vaporization to the surrounding air. The liquid returns to the coils round the freezer and the cycle is repeated.

An adjustable thermostat switches the pump on and off, controlling the rate of evaporation and so the temperature in the refrigerator.

Questions

1. Explain the following.
   (*a*) On a very cold day good snowballs cannot be made.
   (*b*) When walking on snow it 'cakes' and sticks to the sole of the shoe.
   (*c*) A good cup of tea cannot be brewed on a high mountain.

2. (*a*) Give two reasons why the boiling point of water is sometimes greater than 100 °C.
   (*b*) What would you expect the freezing point of the water to be if its boiling point were greater than 100 °C?
   (*c*) Name and explain the use of a practical device which makes use of one of the effects mentioned in (*a*).   (*W.M.*)

3. Some water is stored in a bag of a porous material, e.g. canvas, which is hung where it is exposed to a draught of air. Explain why the temperature of the water is lower than that of the air.

4. Explain why a bottle of milk keeps better when it stands in water in a porous pot in a draught.

49 Conduction and convection

To keep a building or a house at a comfortable temperature, in winter and summer, requires a knowledge of how heat travels, if it is to be done economically and efficiently.

Conduction

The handle of a metal spoon held in a hot drink soon gets warm. Heat passes along the spoon by *conduction*.

Conduction is the flow of heat through matter from places of higher to places of lower temperature without movement of the matter as a whole.

A simple demonstration of the different conducting powers of various metals is shown in Fig. 49.1.

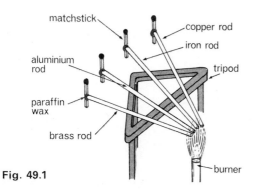

Fig. 49.1

A matchstick is fixed to one end of each rod using a little melted wax. The other ends of the rods are heated by a burner. When the temperatures of the far ends reach the melting point of wax, the matches drop off. The match on copper falls first showing it is the best conductor, followed by aluminium, brass and perhaps iron.

Most metals are good conductors of heat; materials such as wood, glass, cork, plastics and fabrics are bad conductors. The apparatus in Fig. 49.2 can be used to show the difference between brass and wood. If the rod is passed through a flame several times, the paper over the wood scorches but not over the brass. The brass conducts the heat away from the paper quickly and prevents it reaching the temperature at which it burns. The wood only conducts it away slowly.

Fig. 49.2

Metal objects below body temperature *feel* colder than those made of bad conductors because they carry heat away faster from the hand—even though all the objects are at the same temperature.

Fig. 49.3

Liquids and gases also conduct heat but only very slowly. Water is a very poor conductor as may be shown in Fig. 49.3. The water at the top of the tube can be boiled before the ice at the bottom melts.

Uses of conductors

(a) *Good conductors*. These are used whenever heat is required to travel quickly through something. Kettles, saucepans, boilers and radiators are made of metals such as aluminium, iron and copper.

(b) *Bad conductors* (insulators). The handles of teapots, kettles and saucepans are made of wood or plastic. Cork is used for table mats.

Air is one of the worst conductors, i.e. best insulators. This is why houses with cavity walls (i.e. two walls separated by an air space), Fig. 49.4a, and double-glazed windows, keep warmer in winter and cooler in summer.

Materials which trap air, e.g. wool, felt, fur, feathers, polystyrene, fibre glass, are also very bad conductors. Some are used as 'lagging' to insulate

140

(a)

(b)

Fig. 49.4

water pipes, hot water cylinders, ovens, refrigerators and the roofs (and walls) of houses, Fig. 49.4b. Others make warm winter clothes.

Conduction and the kinetic theory

Two processes occur in metals. These have a large number of 'free' electrons (p. 170) which wander about inside them. When one part of a metal is heated, the electrons there move faster (i.e. their k.e. increases) and farther. As a result they 'jostle' atoms in cooler parts, so passing on their energy and raising the temperature of these parts. This process occurs quickly.

The second process is much slower. It is less important in metals but is the only way conduction occurs in non-metals since these do not have 'free' electrons. In it the atoms themselves at the hot part make 'colder' neighbouring atoms vibrate more vigorously.

Convection in liquids

Convection is the usual method by which heat travels through fluids, i.e. liquids and gases. It can be shown in water by dropping a few crystals of potassium permanganate down a tube to the bottom of a flask of water. When the tube is removed and the flask heated just below the crystals by a *small* flame, Fig. 49.5, purple streaks of water rise upwards and fan outwards.

Fig. 49.5

Streams of warm moving fluids are called *convection currents*. They arise when a fluid is heated because it expands, becomes less dense and is forced upwards by surrounding cooler, denser fluid which moves under it. We say 'hot water (or hot air) rises'. Warm fluid behaves like a cork released under water: being less dense it bobs up. In convection, however, a fluid floats in a fluid, not a solid in a fluid.

Convection is the flow of heat through a fluid from places of higher to places of lower temperature by movement of the fluid itself.

141

Fig. 49.6

Fig. 49.7

House hot water and central heating systems

(*a*) *Hot water system.* One is shown in Fig. 49.6. A convection current of hot water from the *top* of the boiler rises up pipe A to the *top* of the hot water cylinder and cold water flows down pipe B from the *bottom* of the cylinder to the *bottom* of the boiler. Hot water is drawn off from the *top* of the cylinder and is replaced by cold water from the cold water tank which enters the *bottom* of the cylinder by pipe C.

Water is supplied from the mains to the cold tank through a ballcock. The expansion pipe D allows the escape of (*i*) dissolved air which comes out of the water when it is heated and (*ii*) steam if the water boils. The first might otherwise cause air-locks in the pipes and the second an explosion.

(*b*) *Combined hot water and central heating system,* Fig. 49.7. The water in the central heating part is quite separate from the water in the hot water part. The latter is similar to Fig. 49.6 except that the hot water cylinder is heated indirectly by a heat exchange coil in the cylinder. When hot water is drawn off, the temperature of the central heating water in the boiler and radiators is therefore hardly affected. A second small cold water tank keeps the boiler and radiators topped up.

Modern systems use narrow pipes and the water is pumped round them.

Convection in air

Black marks often appear on the wall or ceiling above a lamp or a radiator. They are caused by dust being carried upwards in air convection currents produced by the hot lamp or radiator.

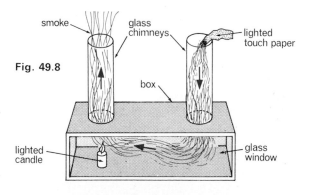

Fig. 49.8

A laboratory demonstration of convection currents in air can be given using the apparatus of Fig. 49.8. The direction of the convection current created by the candle is made visible by the smoke from the touch paper (made by soaking brown paper in strong potassium nitrate solution and drying it).

Convection currents set up by electric, gas and oil heaters help to warm our homes. Many so-called 'radiators' are really convector heaters.

Fig. 49.9

Natural convection currents

(*a*) *Coastal breezes*. During the day the temperature of the land increases more quickly than that of the sea (because the specific heat capacity of the land is much smaller). The hot air above the land rises and is replaced by colder air from the sea. A breeze from the sea results, Fig. 49.9*a*.

At night the opposite happens. The sea has more heat to lose and cools more slowly. The air above the sea is warmer than that over the land and a breeze blows from the land, Fig. 49.9*b*.

(*b*) *Gliding*. Gliders, including 'hang-gliders', Fig. 49.10, depend on hot air currents, called *thermals*. By flying from one thermal to another gliders can stay airborne for several hours.

Questions

1. Explain why (*a*) newspaper wrapping keeps hot things hot, e.g. fish and chips, and cold things cold, e.g. ice-cream, (*b*) fur

Fig. 49.10

coats would keep their owners warmer if they were worn inside out, (*c*) a string vest keeps a person warm even though it is a collection of holes bounded by string.

2. Why is a glass milk bottle likely to crack if boiling water is poured into it?

3. As fuels become more expensive, more people are finding it worthwhile to reduce heat losses from their homes. Fig. 49.11 illustrates three ways of doing this.

Fig. 49.11

(*a*) As far as you can, explain how each of the three methods reduces heat losses. Draw diagrams where they will help your explanations.

(*b*) Why are fibreglass and plastic foam good substances to use?

(*c*) Air is one of the worst conductors of heat. What is the point of replacing it by the plastic foam in (*ii*)?

(*d*) A vacuum is an even better heat insulator than air. Suggest one scientific reason why the double glazing should not have a vacuum between the sheets of glass.

(*e*) The manufacturers suggest that two layers of fibreglass are more effective than one. Suggest how you might set up an experiment in the laboratory to test whether this is true.   (*W.Y.*)

4. Convection takes place

    A only in solids   **B** only in liquids   **C** only in gases
    D in solids and liquids   **E** in liquids and gases   (*N.II.*)

5. What is the advantage of placing an electric immersion heater (*a*) near the top, (*b*) near the bottom, of a tank of water?

50 Radiation

Radiation is a third way in which heat can travel but whereas conduction and convection both need matter to be present, radiation can occur in a vacuum. It is the way heat reaches us from the sun.

Radiation has all the properties of electromagnetic waves (p. 43), e.g. it travels at the speed of radio waves and gives interference effects. When it falls on an object, it is partly reflected, partly transmitted and partly absorbed; the absorbed part raises the temperature of the object.

Radiation is the flow of heat from one place to another by means of electromagnetic waves.

Radiation is emitted by all bodies above absolute zero and consists mostly of infrared radiation (p. 43) but light and ultraviolet are also present if the body is very hot (e.g. the sun).

Good and bad absorbers

Some surfaces absorb radiation better than others as may be shown using the apparatus in Fig. 50.1. The inside surface of one lid is shiny and of the other dull black. The coins are stuck on the outside of each lid with candle wax. If the heater is mid-way between the lids they each receive the same amount of radiation. After a few minutes the wax on the black lid melts and the coin falls off. The shiny lid stays cool and the wax unmelted.

Fig. 50.1

shiny surface — electric heater — dull black surface

coin

candle wax — tin lid

Dull black surfaces are better absorbers of radiation than white shiny surfaces—the latter are good reflectors of radiation. This is why buildings in hot countries are often painted white and why light-coloured clothes are cooler in summer. Also, reflectors on electric fires are made of polished metal because of their good reflecting properties.

Good and bad emitters

Some surfaces also emit radiation better than others when they are hot. If you hold the backs of your hands on either side of a hot copper sheet which has one side polished and the other blackened, Fig. 50.2, it will be found that the *dull black surface is a better emitter of radiation than the shiny one.*

Fig. 50.2

hot copper sheet

back of hand towards sheet

The cooling fins on the heat exchanger of a refrigerator (p. 139, Fig. 48.6) are painted black so that they lose heat more quickly. By contrast teapots and kettles which are polished are poor emitters and keep their heat longer.

In general surfaces that are good absorbers of radiation are good emitters when hot.

Vacuum flask

A vacuum or Thermos flask keeps hot liquids hot or cold liquids cold. It is very difficult for heat to travel into or out of the flask.

Transfer by conduction and convection is minimized by making the flask a double-walled glass vessel with a vacuum between the walls, Fig. 50.3. Radiation is reduced by silvering both walls on the

Fig. 50.3

- stopper
- double-walled glass vessel
- silvered surfaces
- case
- vacuum
- felt pad

Fig. 50.4

vacuum side. Then, if for example, a hot liquid is stored, the small amount of radiation from the hot inside wall is reflected back across the vacuum by the silvering on the outer wall. The slight heat loss which does occur is by conduction up the walls and through the stopper.

The greenhouse

The warmth from the sun is not cut off by a sheet of glass but the warmth from a red-hot fire is. The radiation from very hot bodies like the sun is mostly in the form of light and short wavelength infrared. The radiation from less hot objects, e.g. a fire, is largely long wavelength infrared which, unlike light and short wavelength infrared, cannot pass through glass.

Light and short wavelength infrared from the sun penetrate the glass of a greenhouse and are absorbed by the soil, plants, etc., raising their temperature. These in turn emit infrared but, because of their relatively low temperature, this has a long wavelength and is not transmitted by the glass. The greenhouse thus acts as a 'heat-trap' and its temperature rises.

Questions

1. We feel the heat from a coal fire by

    A convection   **B** conduction   **C** regelation
    D diffusion   **E** radiation

2. (*a*) Three beakers are of identical size and shape; one beaker is painted matt black, one is dull white and one is gloss white. The beakers are filled with boiling water. In which beaker will the water cool most quickly? Give a reason.

(*b*) State a process, in addition to conduction, convection and radiation, by which heat energy will be lost from the beakers. *(E.A.)*

3. The door canopy in Fig. 50.4 shows in a striking way the difference between white and black surfaces when radiation falls on them. Explain why.

Fig. 50.5

4. Fig. 50.5 shows an electric heater H placed mid-way between two flasks A and B. Flask A is shiny on the outside and flask B is blackened on the outside.

(*a*) Name the process by which heat travels from the heater to the flasks.

(*b*) What happens to the liquid in the tube XY?

(*c*) Give a reason for your answer to (*b*). *(E.M.)*

5. (*a*) The earth has been warmed by the radiation from the sun for millions of years yet we think its average temperature has remained fairly steady. Why is this?

(*b*) Why is frost less likely on a cloudy night than a clear one?

6. A Thermos flask has a silver layer on its thin glass walls to reduce loss of heat by

    A convection   **B** evaporation
    C conduction   **D** radiation   *(W.M.)*

51 Heat engines

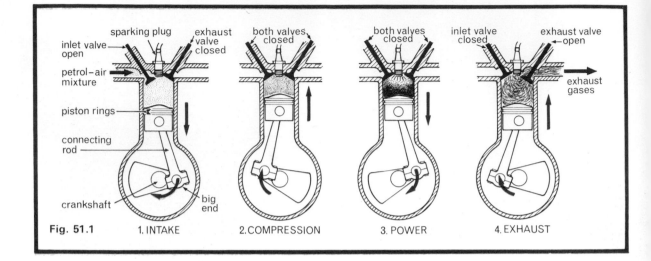

Fig. 51.1

1. INTAKE   2. COMPRESSION   3. POWER   4. EXHAUST

A heat engine is a machine which changes heat energy, obtained by burning a fuel, to kinetic energy. In an *internal combustion* engine, e.g. petrol, Diesel, jet engine, the fuel is burnt in the cylinder or chamber where the energy change occurs. This is not so in other engines, e.g. steam turbine.

Petrol engine

(*a*) *Four-stroke engine*, Fig. 51.1 shows the action. On the *intake stroke*, the piston moves down (due to the starter motor in a car or the kickstart in a motor cycle turning the crankshaft) so reducing the pressure inside the cylinder. The inlet valve opens and the petrol-air mixture from the carburettor is forced into the cylinder by atmospheric pressure.

On the *compression stroke*, both valves are closed and the piston moves up, compressing the mixture.

On the *power stroke*, a spark jumps across the points of the sparking plug and explodes the mixture, forcing the piston down.

On the *exhaust stroke*, the outlet valve opens and the piston rises, pushing the exhaust gases out of the cylinder.

The crankshaft turns a flywheel (a heavy wheel) whose momentum keeps the piston moving between power strokes.

Most cars have at least four cylinders on the same crankshaft, Fig. 51.2. Each cylinder 'fires' in turn,

Fig. 51.2

in the order 1–3–4–2, giving a power · stroke every half revolution of the crankshaft. Smoother running results.

(*b*) *Two-stroke engine*. This is used in mopeds, lawn-mowers and small boats. Valves are replaced by ports on the side of the cylinder which are opened and closed by the piston as it moves.

In Fig. 51.3*a*, the piston is at the top of the cylinder and the mixture above it is compressed. The exhaust and transfer ports are closed but fresh mixture enters the crankcase by the inlet port. When the spark ignites the compressed mixture, the piston is driven down on its power stroke, closing the inlet port and compressing the mixture in the crankcase.

Fig. 51.3

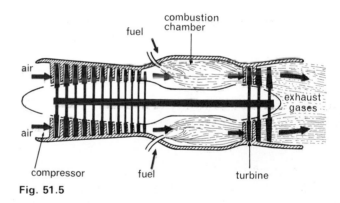

Fig. 51.4

In Fig. 51.3*b*, the piston is near the bottom of the power stroke and the mixture below it passes through the transfer port into the cylinder above the piston. The exhaust port is now open and the burnt gases are pushed out as the piston moves up again. The shape of the piston helps to stop fresh fuel and burnt gases mixing. The cycle of operations is completed in two strokes.

The efficiency of petrol engines is about 30%, which means that only 30% of the heat energy supplied becomes kinetic energy; much of the rest is lost with the exhaust gases.

Diesel engine

The operation of two- and four-stroke Diesel engines is similar to that of the petrol varieties. However, fuel oil is used instead of petrol, there is no sparking plug and the carburettor is replaced by a fuel injector.

Air is drawn into the cylinder on the downstroke of the piston, Fig. 51.4, and on the upstroke it is compressed to about one-sixteenth of its original volume (which is twice the compression in a petrol engine). This very high compression increases the temperature of the air considerably and when, at the end of the compression stroke, fuel is pumped into the cylinder by the fuel injector, it ignites automatically. The resulting explosion drives the piston down on its power stroke. (You may have noticed that the air in a bicycle pump gets hot when it is squeezed.)

Diesel engines, sometimes called *compression ignition* (C.I.) engines, though heavier than petrol engines, are reliable and economical. Their efficiency of about 40% is higher than that of any other heat engine.

Jet engines (gas turbines)

There are several kinds of jet engine; Fig. 51.5 is a simplified diagram of a turbo-jet.

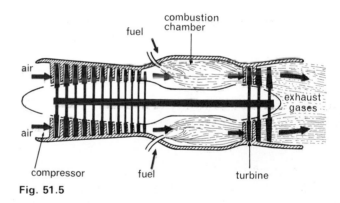

Fig. 51.5

To start the engine, an electric motor sets the compressor rotating. The compressor is like a fan, its blades draw in and compress air at the front of the engine. Compression raises the temperature of the air before it reaches the combustion chamber. Here, fuel (kerosene, i.e. paraffin) is injected and burns to produce a high-speed stream of hot gas which escapes from the rear of the engine, so thrusting it forward (as explained on p. 113 when we considered momentum). The exhaust gas also drives a turbine (another fan) which, once the engine is started, turns the compressor, since both are on the same shaft.

Turbo-jet engines have a high power-to-weight ratio (i.e. produce large power for their weight) and are ideal for use in aircraft. They are also being tried in ships, trains and cars.

Rockets

Rockets, like jet engines, obtain their thrust from the hot gases they eject by burning a fuel. They can, however, travel where there is no air since they carry the oxygen needed for burning, instead of taking it from the atmosphere as does a jet engine.

Space rockets use liquid oxygen (at $-183\,°C$). Common fuels are kerosene and liquid hydrogen (at $-253\,°C$), but solid fuels are also used. Fig. 51.6 is a simplified drawing of a rocket.

Steam turbine

Steam turbines are used in power stations and ocean liners such as Queen Elizabeth 2, Fig. 51.7. They have efficiencies of about 30%.

The action of a steam turbine resembles that of a water wheel but moving steam not moving water causes the motion. Steam produced in a separate boiler enters the turbine and is directed by the *stator* (sets of fixed blades) on to the *rotor* (sets of blades on a shaft that can rotate). The rotor revolves and drives whatever is coupled to it, e.g. an electrical generator or a ship's propeller. The steam expands as it passes through the turbine and the size of the blades increases along the turbine to allow for this. Fig. 51.8 shows the rotor of a steam turbine.

Rotary engines like the steam turbine are smoother than piston (reciprocating) engines.

Fig. 51.6

liquid oxygen
fuel
pump
pump
hot exhaust gases

Fig. 51.7

Fig. 51.8

Questions

1. Most car engines are four-stroke petrol engines.

(*a*) Name the four strokes, in the correct sequence.

(*b*) How many times does the crankshaft revolve during the four strokes? (*E.A.*)

2. (*a*) Fig. 51.9 shows the cylinder of a four-stroke petrol engine. If the spark plug has just fired, what is wrong with the diagram? Explain why the engine would not work very well with this fault.

(*b*) What are the basic differences between four-stroke and two-stroke engines? (*E.A.*)

Fig. 51.9

3. In a motor-car engine chemical energy is converted into mechanical energy. What other forms of energy are produced? Some of the mechanical energy is not usefully employed. What happens to it? Describe the energy changes involved when the brakes are applied.

4. (*a*) Explain the actions of (*i*) a compressor, (*ii*) a turbine, in a jet engine.

(*b*) Draw a labelled diagram of a jet engine, showing the positions of the compressor and the turbine.

(*c*) The graphs in Fig. 51.10 compare the performances of a propeller-driven aircraft with that of a turbo-jet. Explain what the graphs show. (*W.Y.*)

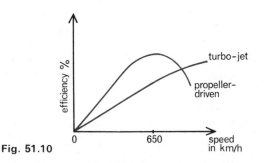

Fig. 51.10

5. (*a*) Explain how a rocket engine obtains its forward thrust.

(*b*) Draw a labelled diagram of a typical rocket engine.

(*c*) What fuels are used in modern rockets?

(*d*) Why does a rocket work better outside the atmosphere? (*W.Y.*)

52 Further questions

Thermometers

1. Fig. 52.1 shows three thermometers, *A*, *B* and *C*. The lowest reading on each thermometer is 0 °C. One thermometer reads up to 50 °C, another to 100 °C and the third to 200 °C. Which thermometer is which? Give the reasoning by which you obtain your answer. (*E.A.*)

Fig. 52.1

2. (*a*) Explain the terms *scale of temperature* and *fixed points*.

State *three* reasons why mercury is suitable for use as a thermometric liquid.

(*b*) What features of a clinical thermometer make it (*i*) sensitive, (*ii*) quick acting and (*iii*) short in length?

Why is it inadvisable to sterilize a clinical thermometer in boiling water? (*A.E.B.*)

3. A mercury-in-glass thermometer is graduated from −5 °C to 105 °C. Describe how you would test experimentally that the 0 and 100 marks are correct. Illustrate with diagrams where necessary.

Explain why, if water is used to check the 0 °C reading, the water must be pure, but for checking the 100 °C temperature the water need not be pure. Indicate the effect on the water at both these temperatures of the impurities normally considered.

State, giving a reason, a circumstance in which an alcohol thermometer could be used but a mercury one could not. (*L.*)

Expansion of solids and liquids

4. Fig. 52.2 shows a metal rod which is 0.5 m long at 15 °C. It is fixed at one end and the other end touches a lever arm pivoted at the fixed point P; the tip B of the free end moves over a circular scale graduated in mm. The rod can be heated or cooled

Fig. 52.2

by suitable means which are not shown. The linear expansivity of the metal is 4×10^{-5} per °C.

(*a*) What is the expansion of the rod when it is heated from 15 °C to 85 °C?

(*b*) The end of the pointer B reads zero on the scale at 15 °C. What is its reading when the rod is at 85 °C?

(*c*) If the end of the pointer reads 25 mm on the scale, what is the temperature of the rod, supposing this is uniform? (*O.*)

5. Calculate the increase in length of a rod 100 mm long if its temperature is raised by 200 °C. The linear expansivity of the rod = 0.000 015 per °C.

A sheet of the same material is drilled with a hole of diameter 100 mm. How would this diameter change when the sheet is heated through 200 °C? (*S.*)

6. A bimetallic strip, Fig. 52.3, is used as the basis of a temperature measuring instrument. What factors will determine the sensitivity of the instrument and the range over which it can be used? (*O./S.R.16+*)

Fig. 52.3

7. Which one of the graphs in Fig. 52.4 most nearly shows how the volume of water changes with temperature between −5 °C and +10 °C? (*J.M.B./A.L./N.W.16+*)

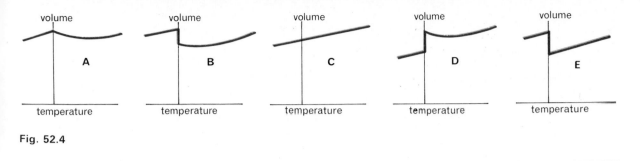

Fig. 52.4

The gas laws

8. Describe fully the apparatus to be used, the precautions which should be taken, and the observations to be made to establish the relationship at constant pressure between the volume of a fixed mass of gas and its temperature over the range approximately 0 °C to 100 °C.

Sketch the graph you would expect to obtain and indicate the expected relationship.

A thick-walled steel cylinder used for storing compressed air is fitted with a safety valve which lifts at a pressure of 1.0 Pa. It contains air at 17 °C and 0.8 Pa. At what temperature will the valve lift? *(L.)*

9. A long capillary tube of uniform bore, and sealed at one end, has dry air trapped in it by a small pellet of mercury. The length of the air column is 145 mm at 17 °C. Find (*i*) the length of the air column at 91 °C, (*ii*) the temperature at which the air column is 132 mm long. *(W.)*

10. The pressure of the air inside a car tyre increases if the car stands for some time in full sunlight. According to kinetic theory this is due to an increase inside the tyre of

A the size of the molecules
B the number of air molecules
C the speed of the air molecules
D the average distance between the air molecules
E the total mass of the air molecules.
(O./S.R.16+)

Specific heat capacity

11. A certain liquid has a specific heat capacity of 3.0 J/g °C. What mass of the liquid may be heated from 20 °C to 50 °C by 630 J of heat?

A 4.2 g   **B** 7.0 g   **C** 10.5 g   **D** 11.4 g
E 12.0 g   *(J.M.B./A.L./N.W.16+)*

12. An immersion heater rated at 100 W supplies heat for 440 s to 2 kg of paraffin oil. Assuming that the specific heat capacity of paraffin oil is 2.2×10^3 J/kg °C and that all the heat from the heater is used to heat the paraffin, the rise in temperature of the paraffin in °C, is

A 1   **B** 10   **C** 20   **D** 40   **E** 100
(N.I.)

13. 100 g of metal at 100 °C is dropped into 50 g of liquid at 20 °C and the final temperature of the mixture is 40 °C. If the specific heat capacity of the liquid is 3.0 J/g °C, calculate the specific heat capacity of the metal. *(N.W.)*

14. If 5 kg of water at 290 K falls through a vertical height of 315 m what would be its temperature in K after the fall if there is no heat exchange with the air or the ground? (Specific heat capacity of water = 4200 J/kg K; g = 10 m/s².)

A 289.250   **B** 290.000   **C** 290.075
D 290.750   **E** 293.750   *(N.I.)*

15. Explain the meaning of the term *specific heat capacity*.

Mention one consequence of the high specific heat capacity of water.

In order to reduce its diameter a wire is pulled through a small hole in a metal plate. The wire is made of metal whose specific heat capacity is 400 J/kg °C and, on emerging from the hole, has a mass of 5.0 g per m. A steady force of 600 N is required. If all the heat generated were retained in the wire, what would be the rise in temperature of the wire?

If, however, the temperature of the wire were kept constant by spraying it with cold water as it emerged at a speed of 8.4 m/s, what mass of water would be needed per second if the temperature rise of this water were to be 12 °C?

Take the specific heat capacity of water as 4200 J/kg °C. *(O. and C.)*

Latent heat

16. Fig. 52.5 shows a graph of temperature against time for a substance which is heated at a constant rate from a low to high temperature. Use the letters to answer the following questions.

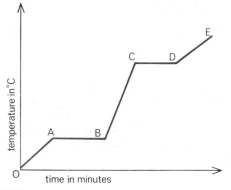

Fig. 52.5

(*a*) Which part, or parts, of the graph correspond to the substance existing in two states at the same time?

(*b*) Over which part is the substance increasing in temperature at the fastest rate?

(*c*) Which point of the graph corresponds to the molecules of the substance having the greatest average kinetic energy? (*W.*)

17. 3 kg of ice at 0 °C are supplied with 1 509 000 J of heat. The specific latent heat of ice is 335 000 J/kg and the specific heat capacity of water is 4200 J/kg °C.

(*a*) How much heat is used in melting the ice?

(*b*) How much heat is used to warm the water?

(*c*) What will be the final temperature of the water?

(*J.M.B./A.L./N.W.16+*)

18. A mass of water was heated in a vessel with an immersion heater of power 40 W. The heater was used to boil the water for 100 s during which time the mass of water decreased by 0.002 kg. Assuming all the heat energy was given to the water, the specific latent heat of vaporization of water is

A $40 \times 100 \times 0.002$ J/kg   **B** $40/(100 \times 0.002)$ J/kg
C $100/(40 \times 0.002)$ J/kg   **D** $40 \times 100/0.002$ J/kg
E 40×0.002 J/kg   (*J.M.B.*)

19. Describe an experiment to determine a value for the specific latent heat of fusion of ice. Your account should include the precautions taken to obtain as accurate a result as possible and show how the result is calculated from the readings taken.

An aluminium tray of mass 400 g containing 300 g of water is placed in a refrigerator. After 80 minutes the tray is removed and it is found that 60 g of water remain unfrozen at 0 °C. If the initial temperature of the tray and its contents was 20 °C, determine the average amount of heat removed per minute by the refrigerator. (Assume specific heat capacity of aluminium = 1 J/g °C; specific heat capacity of water = 4 J/g °C; specific latent heat of fusion of ice = 340 J/g.) (*L.*)

20. Explain the terms *specific heat capacity of water*, *specific latent heat of steam*.

Describe an experiment to determine the specific heat capacity of water, explaining carefully how the result is calculated.

When heat is supplied at the rate of 450 W to an electric kettle containing boiling water, steam escapes at such a rate that the loss of water is 0.15 g/s. When heat is supplied at the rate of 680 W the rate of water loss becomes 0.25 g/s. Calculate (*a*) the specific latent heat of steam, and (*b*) the rate of loss of heat from the kettle due to factors other than evaporation. (*O. and C.*)

Melting and boiling

21. (*a*) State *two* similarities and *two* differences between the processes of evaporation and boiling.

State two ways in which the rate of evaporation of a liquid could be increased.

(*b*) Describe experiments, one in each case, to show the effect on the boiling point of water of (*i*) dissolving common salt in the water, (*ii*) reducing the air pressure over the pure water. State the result you would expect in each case. (*J.M.B.*)

22. (*a*) How would you show experimentally that evaporation produces cooling? Explain the effect by considering the kinetic energy of the molecules.

(*b*) Draw a labelled diagram of a refrigerator and describe the action of the refrigerator. (*J.M.B.*)

Conduction and convection: radiation

23. On a frosty day the metal handlebars of a bicycle feel colder than the rubber grips because

   A the rubber is a better absorber of radiation than the metal
   B the metal is colder than the rubber
   C the rubber has a higher heat capacity than the metal
   D the metal is a better conductor of heat than the rubber
   E the metal is a better radiator of heat than the rubber. (*O./S.R.16+*)

24. (*a*) Two rods, of identical dimensions but of *different* metals, are placed on a sheet of heat-sensitive paper with the same fraction of their lengths projecting from one of its edges, as in Fig. 52.6. The

Fig. 52.6

boiling water

A

B

heat

projecting ends are surrounded by water which is kept boiling. As the rods become hot the paper beneath them changes colour at a certain temperature. When the steady state has been reached it is found that the discoloration of the paper around rod A extends farther from the edge than does that around rod B.

(*i*) Explain the process by which heat is transmitted along the rods.

(*ii*) Why does the final temperature vary with position along each of the rods?

(*iii*) What do you deduce from the fact that the point on A at a certain final temperature is seen to be farther from the edge of the paper than the point on B at this temperature?

(*iv*) It is observed that initially the discoloration spreads faster along the paper around B than around A. What can you deduce from this?

(*b*) What is meant by convection? Describe a simple experiment which illustrates the circulation of convection currents in a fluid. (*O.*)

25. (*a*) Describe the differences in the manner in which heat is transmitted by *conduction* and *radiation*.

Describe an experiment which shows that a shiny or white surface is a poorer *absorber* of heat radiation than a dull or black surface. Give a brief explanation of one use made of this fact in everyday life.

(*b*) Describe a method of showing that heat radiation is to be found spread over an infrared region in the spectrum of electromagnetic radiation from the sun.

How does the action of a greenhouse depend on the difference in behaviour between longer and shorter wavelengths of infrared radiation? (*L.*)

26. Explain in terms of heat transfer the function of the following features of a Thermos flask.

(*a*) A tight fitting cork or plastic stopper.

(*b*) The silver coating on the inside of the outer glass wall and the outside of the inner glass wall.

(*c*) The evacuated enclosure between the walls. (*N.I.*)

53 Permanent magnets

Permanent magnets do not readily lose their magnetism with normal treatment. The first permanent magnets were made of steel (an alloy of iron); modern magnets are much stronger and are of two types.

1. Alloy magnets contain metals, e.g. iron, nickel, copper, cobalt, aluminium. They have trade names such as Alnico and Alcomax.

2. Ceramic magnets are made from powders called ferrites which consist of iron oxide and barium oxide. They are brittle. One has the trade name Magnadur.

Magnets are used in cycle dynamos, electric motors, loudspeakers and telephones. Ferrite powder can be bonded with plastic and rubber to give a flexible magnet or one of any shape. Very fine powder, each particle of which can be magnetized, is used to coat tapes for tape recorders. In large computers many tiny ceramic ring magnets, each about 1 mm in diameter, are threaded together to act as memory stores. A close-up of a memory is shown in Fig. 53.1.

Fig. 53.1

Properties of magnets

1. Magnetic materials. Magnets only attract strongly certain materials such as iron, steel, nickel, cobalt, which are called ferromagnetics.

2. Magnetic poles. These are the places in a magnet to which magnetic materials are attracted, e.g. iron filings. They are near the ends of a bar magnet and occur in pairs of equal strength.

3. North and south poles. If a magnet is supported so that it can swing in a horizontal plane it comes to rest with one pole, the North-seeking or N pole, always pointing roughly towards the earth's north pole. A magnet can therefore be used as a compass.

4. Law of magnetic poles. If the N pole of a magnet is brought near the N pole of a suspended magnet repulsion occurs, Fig. 53.2a. Two S poles also repel.

Fig. 53.2

By contrast, N and S poles always attract, Fig. 53.2b. The law of magnetic poles summarizes these facts and states:

like poles repel, unlike poles attract.

Test for a magnet

A permanent magnet causes repulsion with one pole when both poles are, in turn, brought near to a suspended magnet. An unmagnetized magnetic material would give attraction with both poles of the suspended magnet.

Repulsion is the only sure test for a magnet.

Making a magnet

(a) By stroking. The methods of single and double touch are shown in Fig. 53.3a, b; steel knitting needles, hair grips or pieces of clockspring can be

magnetized. In single touch, the steel is stroked from end to end about 20 times in the same direction by the same pole of a permanent magnet. In the better method of double touch, stroking is done the solenoid in the direction of the current (i.e. from the positive of the supply), the thumb points to the N pole, Fig. 53.4b.

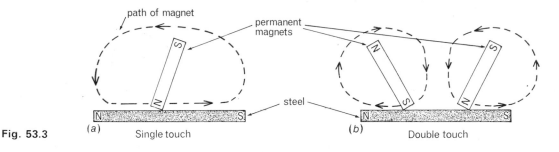

Fig. 53.3 (a) Single touch   (b) Double touch

the better method of double touch, stroking is done from the centre outwards with unlike poles of two magnets at the same time. The magnets must be lifted high above the steel at the end of each stroke in both methods.

The pole produced at the end of the steel where the stroke ends is of the opposite kind to that of the stroking pole.

(b) *Electrically.* The magnetic material is placed inside a cylindrical coil called a solenoid, having several hundred turns of insulated copper wire, which is connected to a 6–12 V *direct current* (d.c.) supply, Fig. 53.4a. If the current is switched on for a second and then off, the material is found to be a magnet when removed from the solenoid.

The polarity of the magnet depends on the direction of the current and is given by the *Right-hand grip rule*. It states that if the fingers of the right hand grip

In practice magnets are made electrically using a very large current for a fraction of a second. Fig. 53.5 shows loudspeakers being magnetized.

Fig. 53.5

Fig. 53.4

Demagnetizing a magnet

The magnet is placed inside a solenoid through which *alternating current* (a.c.) is flowing, Fig. 53.6. With the current still passing, the magnet is slowly removed to a distance from the solenoid.

Fig. 53.6

Induced magnetism

When a piece of unmagnetized magnetic material touches or is brought near to the pole of a permanent magnet, it becomes a magnet itself. The material is said to have magnetism *induced* in it. Fig. 53.7 shows that a N pole induces a N pole in the far end.

Fig. 53.7

This can be checked by hanging two iron nails from the N pole of a magnet. Their lower ends repel each other, Fig. 53.8*a*, and both are repelled by the N pole of another magnet, Fig. 53.8*b*.

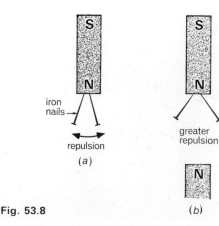

Fig. 53.8

156

Magnetic properties of iron and steel

Chains of small iron paper clips and steel pen nibs can be hung from a magnet, Fig. 53.9. Each clip or nib magnetizes the one below it by induction and the unlike poles so formed attract.

Fig. 53.9

If the iron chain is removed by pulling the top clip away from the magnet, the chain collapses, showing that *magnetism induced in iron is temporary*. When the same is done with the steel chain, it does not collapse; *magnetism induced in steel is permanent*.

Magnetic materials like iron which magnetize easily but do not keep their magnetism, are said to be 'soft'. Those like steel which are harder to magnetize than iron but stay magnetized, are 'hard'. Both types have their uses; very hard ones are used to make permanent magnets.

Theory of magnetism

If a magnetized piece of steel clockspring or thin rod is cut into smaller pieces, each piece is a magnet with a N and a S pole, Fig. 53.10. It is therefore reasonable

Fig. 53.10

to suppose that a magnet is made up of lots of 'tiny' magnets all lined up with their N poles pointing in the same direction, Fig. 53.11*a*. At the ends, the 'free' poles of the 'tiny' magnets repel each other and

Fig. 53.11

(*a*) Magnetized bar   (*b*) Unmagnetized bar

fan out so that the poles of the magnet are *round* the ends.

In an unmagnetized bar we can imagine the 'tiny' magnets pointing in all directions, the N pole of one being neutralized by the S pole of another. Their magnetic effects cancel out and there are no 'free' poles near the ends, Fig. 53.11*b*.

As well as explaining the breaking of a magnet, this theory accounts for the following.

(*i*) *Magnetic saturation.* There is a limit to the strength of a magnet. It occurs when all the 'tiny' magnets are lined up.

(*ii*) *Demagnetization by heating or hammering.* Both processes cause the atoms of the magnet to vibrate more vigorously and disturb the alignment of the 'tiny' magnets.

There is evidence to show that the 'tiny' magnets are groups of millions of atoms, called *domains*. In a ferromagnetic material each atom is a magnet and the magnetic effect of every atom in a particular domain acts in the same direction.

Storing magnets

A magnet tends to become weaker with time due to the 'free' poles near the ends repelling each other and upsetting the alignment of the domains. To prevent this bar magnets are stored in pairs with unlike poles opposite and pieces of soft iron, called *keepers*, across the ends, Fig. 53.12.

Fig. 53.12

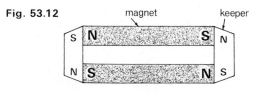

The keepers become induced magnets and their poles neutralize the poles of the bar magnets. The domains in both magnets and keepers form closed chains with no 'free' poles.

Questions

1. A magnet attracts

    A plastics   **B** any metal   **C** iron and steel
    D aluminium   **E** carbon

2. To test a piece of metal to determine whether it was a magnet or not, one would see if it

    A attracted steel filings   **B** repelled a metal bar
    C attracted a magnet   **D** repelled a known magnet.

                                      (*W.M.*)

3. The north pole N of a magnet is stroked along a metal bar in the direction shown in Fig. 53.13.

(*a*) Name a metal which would become permanently magnetized by stroking in this way.

(*b*) If such a metal were used, what pole would be produced at A?   (*E.A.*)

Fig. 53.13   **Fig. 53.14**

4. Fig. 53.14 shows an iron rod AB inside a coil of wire. When a current flows through the coil in the direction shown, which end of AB will become a N pole?   (*A.L.*)

5. Explain why needles hung from either end of a bar magnet held horizontally incline towards one another as shown in Fig. 53.15.

Fig. 53.15

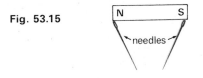

6. Two soft iron rods are placed inside a coil of wire connected to a battery as shown in Fig. 53.16. State the effect on the rods when the switch is closed.   (*E.A.*)

Fig. 53.16

7. The graphs in Fig. 53.17 are for two magnetic materials.

(*a*) Does material A or B become the stronger magnet?

(*b*) Which material is easier to magnetize?

Fig. 53.17

8. (*a*) Describe how electricity may be used to: (*i*) make a temporary magnet, (*ii*) make a permanent magnet, (*iii*) demagnetize a magnet.

(*b*) (*i*) Why is there a limit to the strength of the magnet that may be produced? (*ii*) Why does heating reduce the strength of a magnet?   (*E.M.*)

54 Magnetic fields

The space surrounding a magnet where it produces a magnetic force is called a *magnetic field*. The force around a bar magnet can be detected and shown to vary in direction using the apparatus in Fig. 54.1. If the floating magnet is released near the N pole of the bar magnet, it is repelled to the S pole and moves along a curved path known as a *line of force* or a *field line*. It moves in the opposite direction if its south pole is uppermost.

Fig. 54.1

It is useful to consider that a magnetic field has a direction and to represent the field by lines of force. It has been decided that *the direction of the field at any point should be the direction of the force on a N pole*. To show the direction, arrows are put on the lines of force and point away from a N pole towards a S pole.

Experiment: plotting lines of force

(*a*) *Plotting compass method.* A plotting compass is a small pivoted magnet in a glass case with brass walls, Fig. 54.2*a*.

Fig. 54.2

Lay a bar magnet NS on a sheet of paper, Fig. 54.2*b*. Place the plotting compass at a point such as A near one pole of the magnet. Mark the position of the poles *n*, *s* of the compass by pencil dots A, B. Move the compass so that pole *s* is exactly over B, mark the new position of *n* by dot C.

Continue this process until the S pole of the bar magnet is reached. Join the dots to give one line of force and show its direction by putting an arrow on it. Plot other lines by starting at different points round the magnet.

This method is slow but suitable for weak fields.

(*b*) *Iron filings method.* Place a sheet of paper *on top of* a bar magnet and sprinkle iron filings *thinly and evenly* on to the paper from a 'pepper pot'.

Tap the paper gently with a pencil and the filings should form patterns of the lines of force. Each filing is magnetized by induction and turns in the direction of the field when the paper is tapped.

The method is quick but no use for weak fields. Fig. 54.3*a, b* shows typical patterns with two magnets. Why are they different?

Fig. 54.3   (*a*)   (*b*)

Earth's magnetic field

If lines of force are plotted on a sheet of paper with no magnets near, a set of parallel straight lines are obtained. They run roughly from S to N geographically, Fig. 54.4, and represent a small part of the earth's magnetic field in a horizontal plane.

Fig. 54.4

The *combined* field due to the earth and a bar magnet with its N pole pointing N is shown in Fig. 54.5*a*: it is obtained by the plotting compass method. At the points marked X, the fields of the earth and the magnet are equal and opposite and the resultant field is zero. They are called *neutral points* and no lines of force pass through them. At

Fig. 54.5

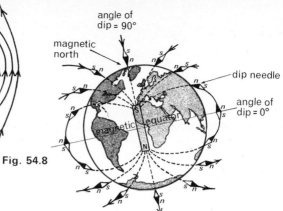

Fig. 54.8

A the magnet's field is stronger than the earth's field; at B it is weaker.

When the N pole of the magnet points S, the neutral points Y are along the axis of the magnet, Fig. 54.5*b*.

Declination and dip

(*a*) *Declination.* At most places on the earth's surface a magnetic compass points east or west of true north, i.e. the earth's geographical and magnetic north poles do not coincide. The angle between magnetic north and true north is called the *declination*, Fig. 54.6. In London at present (1977) it is 7° W of N and is decreasing. By about the year 2140 it should be 0°.

Fig. 54.6   Fig. 54.7

(*b*) *Dip.* A magnet pivoted at its centre of gravity so that it can rotate in a vertical plane is called a *dip needle*, Fig. 54.7. When placed in the magnetic meridian, i.e. in the vertical plane containing magnetic N and S, it comes to rest with its N pole pointing downwards at an angle, in London, of about 67°. The angle a dip needle makes with the horizontal in the magnetic meridian is called the *angle of dip* or *inclination*.

The angle of dip varies over the earth's surface from 0° at the earth's magnetic equator to 90° at its magnetic poles. This can be explained if we consider the earth behaves as though it had, at its centre, a strong bar magnet whose S pole points to magnetic N, Fig. 54.8.

The cause of the earth's magnetism may be electric currents in the liquid core at its centre but there is no generally accepted theory.

Questions

1. Copy Fig. 54.9 which shows a plotting compass and a magnet. Label the N pole of the magnet and draw the field line on which the compass lies. (*L.*)

Fig. 54.9

2. The three diagrams in Fig. 54.10 show the lines of force (field lines) between the poles of two magnets. Identify the poles A, B, C, D, E, F. (*E.M.*)

Fig. 54.10

3. The magnetic field between the poles of two bar magnets is shown in Fig. 54.11. The neutral point X is marked.
   (*a*) Explain what is meant by a neutral point.
   (*b*) C is a S pole. What is (*i*) A, (*ii*) B, (*iii*) D?
   (*c*) Which is the stronger pole, A or B? Give a reason for your answer. (*Met.*)

Fig. 54.11

4. Fig. 54.12 shows three similar magnets and the lines of force in part of the resulting magnetic field.
   (*a*) Copy and complete the diagram to show the lines of force in the remainder of the field due to the three magnets.
   (*b*) Mark the polarity of the magnets.
   (*c*) Mark any neutral points with an X. (*E.A.*)

Fig. 54.12

159

55 Static electricity

A nylon garment often crackles when it is taken off. We say it has become 'charged with static electricity'; the crackles are caused by tiny electric sparks which can be seen in the dark. Pens and combs made of certain plastics become charged when rubbed on the sleeve and can then attract scraps of paper.

Static electricity is used (*i*) in coal-burning power stations to stop flue-ash and dust escaping into the atmosphere, (*ii*) in paint-spraying and (*iii*) in office-copying machines.

Sparks from static electricity can be dangerous when flammable vapour is present. For example, an aircraft in flight may become charged by 'rubbing' the air. Its tyres are of conducting rubber which lets the charge pass harmlessly to earth on landing. Otherwise an explosion could be 'sparked-off' when it refuels.

A flash of lightning is nature's most spectacular static electricity effect, Fig. 55.1.

Positive and negative charges

When a strip of polythene (white) is rubbed with a cloth it becomes charged. If it is hung up and another rubbed polythene strip is brought near, repulsion occurs, Fig. 55.2. Attraction occurs when a rubbed cellulose acetate (clear) strip approaches.

This shows there are two kinds of electric charge. That on cellulose acetate is taken as *positive* (+) and that on polythene is *negative* (−). It also shows that

like charges (+ and + or − and −) *repel,*
unlike charges (+ and −) *attract.*

Fig. 55.1

Fig. 55.2

Charges, atoms and electrons

There is evidence (Topic 75) that we can picture an atom as made up of a small central nucleus containing positively charged particles called *protons*, surrounded by an equal number of negatively charged *electrons*. The charges on a proton and an electron are equal and so an atom as a whole is normally electrically neutral, i.e. has no net charge.

Fig. 55.3

Hydrogen is the simplest atom with one proton and one electron, Fig. 55.3. A copper atom has 29 protons in the nucleus and 29 surrounding electrons. All nuclei (plural of nucleus) also contain uncharged particles called *neutrons*.

The production of charges by rubbing can be explained by supposing that electrons are transferred from one material to the other. For example, when cellulose acetate is rubbed, electrons go from the acetate to the cloth, leaving the acetate short of electrons, i.e. positively charged. The cloth now has more electrons than protons and becomes negatively charged. Note that it is electrons which move, the protons remain in the nucleus.

How does polythene become charged when rubbed?

Experiment: gold-leaf electroscope

A gold-leaf electroscope consists of a metal cap on a metal rod at the foot of which is a metal plate having a leaf of gold foil attached, Fig. 55.4. The rod is held by an insulating plastic plug in a case with glass sides to protect the leaf from draughts.

Fig. 55.4

- metal cap
- metal rod
- insulating plug
- metal plate
- gold leaf
- glass window

wooden or metal case earthed by resting on bench

(a) *Detecting a charge.* Bring a charged polythene strip towards the cap: the leaf rises away from the plate. On removing the charged strip the leaf falls again. Repeat with a charged acetate strip.

(b) *Charging by contact.* Draw a charged polythene strip *firmly across the edge* of the cap. The leaf should rise and stay up when the strip is removed. If it does not, repeat the process but press harder. The electroscope has now become negatively charged by contact with the polythene strip.

(c) *Finding the sign of a charge.* Recharge the polythene strip and bring it near the cap of the negatively charged electroscope. The leaf should rise farther.

Remove the polythene strip and bring up a charged acetate strip. The leaf should fall a bit.

Discharge the electroscope by touching the cap with your hand. Its charge then passes through your body to the earth and the leaf collapses completely.

Charge the electroscope positively by contact with a charged acetate strip. Show that the leaf rises farther when a charged acetate strip approaches the cap but falls when a charged polythene strip approaches.

We can conclude that *if the leaf rises more, the sign of the charge being investigated is the same as the charge on the electroscope.*

If the leaf falls it does not always follow that a charge of the opposite sign has approached the cap. An uncharged body has the same effect, as you can show by holding your hand near the cap. The sure test is when the leaf rises farther, i.e. diverges.

(d) *Insulators and conductors.* Touch the cap of the charged electroscope with different things, e.g. a piece of paper, a wire, your finger, a comb, a cotton handkerchief, a piece of wood, a glass rod, a plastic pen, rubber tubing.

When the leaf falls, charge is passing to or from the earth through you and the material touching the cap. If the fall is rapid the material is a *good*

conductor, if slow, it is a poor conductor and if the leaf does not alter, the material is a *good insulator*. Record your results.

Electrons, insulators and conductors

In an insulator all electrons are bound firmly to their atoms; in a conductor some electrons can move freely from atom to atom. An insulator can be charged by rubbing because the charge produced cannot move from where the rubbing occurs, i.e. the electric charge is static. A conductor will become charged by rubbing only if it is held in an insulating handle; otherwise the charge passes to earth via our body.

Good insulators are plastics such as polythene, cellulose acetate, Perspex, nylon. All metals and carbon are good conductors. In between are materials that are both poor conductors and (because they conduct to some extent) poor insulators. Examples are wood, paper, cotton, the human body, the earth. Water conducts and if it were not present in materials like wood and on the surface of, for example, glass, these would be good insulators. Dry air insulates well.

Questions

Fig. 55.5

1. Two light conducting balls, suspended on nylon threads, come to rest with the threads making equal angles with the vertical, Fig. 55.5. This shows that:

   A the balls are equally and oppositely charged.
   B the balls are oppositely charged but not necessarily equally charged.
   C one ball is charged and the other is uncharged.
   D the balls are equally charged and both carry the same charge.
   E one is charged and the other may or may not be charged.
                        (W.)

2. Explain in terms of electron movement, what happens when a polythene rod becomes charged negatively by being rubbed with a cloth.

3. A metal body, insulated from everything else, is given an electrostatic charge. This body is then touched with a rod of material, one end of which is held in the hand. Which of the following statements is/are true?

   (a) If the body retains its charge, the rod is made from a material which is a good insulator.
   (b) If the body loses its charge slowly, the rod is made from a material which is a poor insulator.
   (c) If the body loses its charge rapidly, the rod is made from a material which is a good conductor.

                 (J.M.B./A.L./N.W.16+)

56 More electrostatics

Electrostatics is the study of electric charges at rest.

Electrostatic induction

This is similar to magnetic induction (p. 156) and may be shown by bringing a negatively charged polythene strip near to an insulated metal sphere X which is touching a similar sphere Y, Fig. 56.1a. Electrons in the spheres are repelled to the far side of Y.

Fig. 56.1

If X and Y are separated, with the charged strip still in position, X is left with a positive charge (deficient of electrons) and Y with a negative charge (excess of electrons), Fig. 56.1b. The signs of the charges can be tested by removing the charged strip and taking X up to the cap of a positively charged electroscope and Y to a negatively charged one, Fig. 56.1c. In both cases the leaf should rise farther.

Electrostatic induction explains why a charged strip attracts scraps of paper and a slow stream of water, Fig. 56.2.

Fig. 56.2

Induction and the electroscope

Electrostatic induction occurs when a charged strip is brought near an electroscope. In Fig. 56.3a electrons in the cap of the *uncharged* electroscope are repelled down to the plate and leaf which both become negatively charged, causing the leaf to rise due to repulsion by the plate.

In Fig. 56.3b electrons are attracted from the plate and leaf of the positively *charged* electroscope up to the cap. The positive charge on the plate and leaf increases and the leaf rises more.

If a *large* charge is brought too near the cap of an oppositely charged electroscope, the leaf *rises* after first collapsing. A wrong conclusion may be drawn about the sign of the charge if it approaches too quickly and the initial fall is missed. The effect occurs because, in the case shown in Fig. 56.3c, the number of electrons repelled to the plate and leaf when the large charge is very close, exceeds the original positive charge they had.

Fig. 56.3

Fig. 56.4

1. Bring up charged strip
2. Touch cap
3. Remove finger
4. Remove charged strip

electrons flow to earth

Charging by induction

An electroscope can be charged more reliably by induction than by contact. The process is shown in Fig. 56.4. A strip is used with a charge of *opposite* sign to that required on the electroscope.

When the cap is 'earthed' by touching it with the finger, electrons flow from the electroscope to earth through the body. Removal of the negatively charged strip leaves the electroscope with a positive charge.

To charge the electroscope negatively by induction a positively charged acetate strip is used. In this case earthing the electroscope causes electrons to flow to the electroscope from earth.

Electrophorus

This is a device for producing by electrostatic induction any number of positive charges from one negative charge.

A polythene tile is charged negatively by rubbing and then a metal disc with a Perspex handle is placed on it. A positive charge is induced on the lower surface of the disc and a negative charge on the upper surface, Fig. 56.5a. (The disc does not become negatively charged by contact with the tile because so-called 'flat' surfaces only touch at a few points.)

If the disc is earthed by touching it briefly with the finger, the negative induced charge (electrons) is repelled to earth, Fig. 56.5b. The disc is left with a positive charge, Fig. 56.5c, which can be given to

another conductor (e.g. an electroscope), or a spark may be drawn from it by holding a finger close to its edge.

The disc can be repeatedly recharged, without further rubbing of the tile, by earthing the disc as before.

Distribution of charge on a conductor

The charge on a conductor is only on its *outside surface*. This may be shown by charging a hollow metal sphere with an electrophorus and touching its inside and outside with a proof plane (a small metal disc on an insulating handle), Fig. 56.6a. Any charge on the proof plane can be detected by an electroscope.

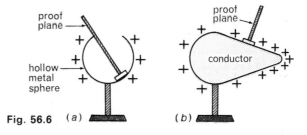

proof plane

hollow metal sphere

proof plane

conductor

Fig. 56.6 (a) (b)

In general the charge on the outside of a conductor is not evenly spread over it. The charge per unit area, called the *charge density*, is greatest where the surface is most curved. In the conductor of Fig. 56.6b this is at the pointed end, as a proof plane will show.

Fig. 56.5

Perspex handle

polythene tile

metal disc

(a)

(b)

(c)

163

Action of points

A lighted candle placed near the point of a pin which is connected to the dome of a van de Graaff generator (see below) is blown aside when the generator is working, Fig. 56.7a.

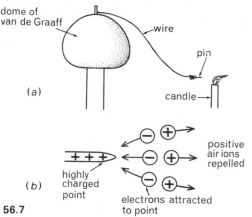

Fig. 56.7

Charge concentrates on the sharply curved point of the pin and the force it exerts on air molecules nearby may be large enough to remove some electrons from them. These air molecules will be left positively charged and are called positive *ions*. If the pin is positively charged it attracts the negative electrons and repels the positive ions which stream away from the point as an 'electric wind', Fig. 56.7b.

A lightning conductor uses the action of points to protect tall buildings from lightning. The conductor is a thick copper strip on the outside of the building connecting spikes that stick up at the top to a metal plate in the ground.

Thunderclouds carry charges and a negatively charged one passing overhead repels electrons from the spikes to earth, leaving the points positively charged. An 'electric wind' of positive air ions streams upwards to cancel some of the charge on the cloud. If a flash does occur it is less violent and the conductor gives it an easy path to earth.

van de Graaff generator

This produces a continuous supply of charge on a large metal dome when a rubber belt is driven over a Perspex roller, by hand or by an electric motor. Large versions are used in nuclear research.

Some demonstrations are shown in Fig. 56.8. In (a) sparks jump between the dome and the discharging sphere; in (b) the 'hair' stands on end (why?); in (c) the 'windmill' revolves (why?); in (d) the 'body' on the insulating stool first charges itself by touching the dome and a neon lamp is then lit from it.

The dome can be discharged painlessly by bringing your elbow (a 'point') close to it.

Electric fields

The space around an electric charge where it exerts a force on another charge is an electric field. As with a magnetic field, we represent it by *field lines* or *lines of force*.

The direction of the field at any point is taken as the direction of the force on a positive charge at the point. It is shown by arrows on the lines which we therefore imagine as starting on a positive charge and ending on a negative one.

Electric field patterns similar to the magnetic field patterns given by iron filings can be obtained with semolina powder or grass seed in castor oil. The field is created by charging metal plates or wires dipping in the oil using a van de Graaff generator. Fig. 56.9a shows the pattern given by parallel, positive and negative plates. Fig. 56.9b is the field of two like charges and Fig. 56.9c of two unlike charges.

Fig. 56.8

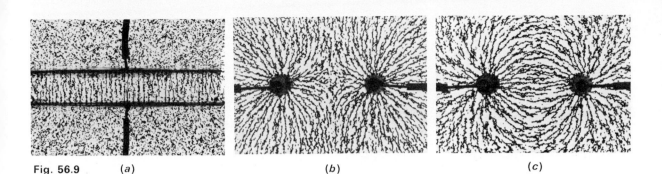

Fig. 56.9   (a)   (b)   (c)

Ice-pail experiment

Field lines can be used to explain an experiment on electrostatic induction first done by Faraday using, by chance, a pail he had for storing ice.

To repeat what he did, a small metal sphere (or disc) on a long insulating handle is charged from an electrophorus disc and then lowered slowly into a tall can resting on an electroscope, Fig. 56.10a, without touching it. The leaf rises and does not change if the sphere is moved about so long as it is well inside the can. Neither does it alter when the sphere touches the bottom of the can. On removing the sphere it is found to have lost *all* its charge. The charge given to the can is therefore on its *outside* surface, not the inside.

Fig. 56.10

insulating handle

tall can

metal sphere

electroscope

(a)   (b)

field line

We conclude that if all the field lines from the charge on the sphere end on the inside of the can, Fig. 56.10b, they induce an equal charge of opposite sign on the inside and an equal charge of the same sign as the inducing charge on the outside.

We also see that all the charge on a conductor can be transferred to a hollow can if it touches the can well down inside. Only part would be transferred if the outside were touched.

Questions

1. A negatively charged rod is brought close to an uncharged metal sphere which is held on an insulated stand.

A   B   C   D

Fig. 56.11

(*a*) Which of the diagrams in Fig. 56.11 best shows the distribution of charge on the sphere when the rod is near?

(*b*) What would happen if the sphere was earthed while the negatively charged rod was near?   (*E.A.*)

2. A leaf electroscope may be used as a simple charge detector.

Fig. 56.12

(*a*) Copy Fig. 56.12 and mark where insulation is required on the electroscope.

(*b*) Why does the leaf diverge when a negative charge is brought near the cap of an uncharged electroscope?

(*c*) What happens when the electroscope is weakly positively charged and a strong negative charge is brought near the cap?   (*O./S.R.16+*)

3. A balloon, if rubbed, will often 'stick' to the wall where it has been rubbed. Why?

57 Capacitors

Potential difference

If electric charge moves from one conductor to another when they are connected we say that it is due to a *potential difference* (p.d.) between the conductors.

Fig. 57.1

Fig. 57.2

In Fig. 57.1*a* electrons flow from earth to the positively charged conductor X, because X is at a higher potential than the earth and so there is a p.d. between them. In practice it is convenient to take the earth's potential as zero. The electron flow is in the opposite direction in Fig. 57.1*b* since Y has a negative charge and a negative potential, i.e. it is below earth potential.

Electrons flow from a *lower* to a *higher* potential. If positive charges could move they would do so from a high to a low potential. In what direction will electrons travel when the charged metal spheres in Fig. 57.1*c* are joined by a conductor?

More about p.d.

Just as heat flow is regarded as being due to a temperature difference, so the flow of charge is thought of as being the result of a potential difference.

The term potential arises as follows. When a charge is moved closer to a similarly charged body, say from A to B in Fig. 57.2, work has to be done against the force of repulsion. The energy supplied (e.g. from chemical energy in our muscles) is considered to become electrical potential energy associated with the charge. Because of its position in the electric field of the charged body, the charge

would move away if released. The situation is like that of a mass raised in the earth's gravitational field; the mass gains gravitational p.e. equal to the work done in raising it against gravity.

The potential of a conductor is affected if other charged bodies are near it. For example a positively charged body can have a negative potential if there is a large negative charge close to it.

The unit of p.d. is the *volt* (symbol V and defined on p. 173). Several hundred volts are needed to make the leaf rise in an electroscope. Very high p.d.s are involved in static electricity. For example, to produce a spark 10 cm long in dry air between the dome and discharging sphere of a van de Graaff generator requires a p.d. of about 500 000 V.

The electroscope and p.d.

Previously we used an electroscope to detect charge. It does this if the case is earthed (e.g. by standing on a wooden bench) and there are no other charged bodies near. But as we will now see it really measures the p.d. between the leaf and the case.

In Fig. 57.3*a* the positively charged strip raises the potential of the cap and leaf, and causes the leaf

Fig. 57.3

166

to rise because there is a p.d. between it and the case which is at zero (earth) potential.

In Fig. 57.3*b* the case is insulated on a polythene tile, the cap and leaf are at zero potential (by holding the cap) but the leaf rises when a negatively charged strip is brought near the case which then has a negative potential.

An electroscope can be used to show that the potential at all points on the surface of a charged *conductor* is the same. If this were not so electrons would flow from one place to another until it was.

Fig. 57.4

The leaf rises and stays at the same deflection when the end of a copper wire which is joined to the cap is moved over the surface, Fig. 57.4. (*Note.* Used in this way the electroscope becomes part of the conductor and indicates their common potential. When used to show that charge is unevenly spread on a pear-shaped conductor, p. 163, the potential it acquires depends on the size of the charge it receives from the proof plane.)

Capacitance

The potential of a conductor changes when it is given a charge and the *larger* the conductor the *smaller* is the change. This may be shown as in Fig. 57.5 by touching the bottom of the inside of each can with a charged sphere so that *equal* charges are

Fig. 57.5

given to each. The leaf deflection is smaller for the larger can, which, we say, has a larger *capacitance*. That is, it can store more charge before its potential reaches the value at which sparking occurs and it discharges.

If the potential of a conductor changes by an amount V when it is given a charge Q, its capacitance C is defined by

$$C = \frac{Q}{V}$$

Q is measured in *coulombs* (defined on p. 170) and if V is in *volts* then C is given in *farads*. A conductor has a capacitance of *1 farad* (F) *if a charge of 1 coulomb changes its potential by 1 volt.* In practice the farad is too large a unit—a sphere would need to have a radius of 9000 million metres to have a capacitance of 1 F! The microfarad (μF) is therefore used. This is one millionth of a farad.

Parallel plate capacitor

The potential of a charged conductor falls when another conductor, especially an earthed one, is brought up to it. For example, the leaf of a charged electroscope drops if you bring your hand near the cap.

Fig. 57.6

In Fig. 57.6 the positive charge on the cap first induces a negative charge on the lower side of the hand and a positive charge on the upper side. The former, being closer to the cap, lowers the potential of the electroscope more than the latter raises it. But the hand is connected to earth through the body and its induced positive charge is immediately neutralized by an electron flow from earth. There is therefore a further drop in the potential of the electroscope because only the induced negative charge is near it now.

The capacitance of the electroscope is thus increased by the presence of the hand since the charge Q on the electroscope remains the same but its

167

potential V decreases. Hence Q/V becomes larger, i.e. C increases.

A *capacitor* stores charge and in its simplest form it consists of a pair of parallel metal plates separated by an insulator. Its capacitance is still given by $C = Q/V$ and increases

(*i*) as the area of the plates increases,
(*ii*) as the separation of the plates decreases,
(*iii*) if the insulator is a solid and not air.

Fig. 57.7

These factors may be investigated using the apparatus of Fig. 57.7 in which X and Y are metal plates each fixed to an insulating stand or handle. X is given a charge and Y is earthed. Any change which reduces the deflection of the leaf of the electroscope indicates a fall of potential and hence an increase of capacitance.

Practical capacitors

Capacitors are used in radio, TV, computer and other electric circuits. Different types have different insulators (called *dielectrics*) between their plates.

A *waxed paper capacitor* consists of two long strips of tinfoil as plates, rolled up into a small cylinder, with waxed paper between them, Fig. 57.8*a, b*. A typical value is 0.1 μF.

Fig. 57.8

tinfoil

waxed paper

(*a*) connections to plates

(*b*)

In the *electrolytic type* a very thin dielectric of aluminium oxide is formed chemically between two strips of aluminium foil, giving a high-value (up to 100 000 μF = 0.1 F), compact capacitor, Fig. 57.9. One plate is marked + and should be charged positively.

Fig. 57.9

A *variable air capacitor* is used to tune a radio. It has two sets of parallel metal plates separated by air, each set consisting of several plates joined together to give, in effect, one large plate, Fig. 57.10. One set is fixed, the other can be rotated, thus varying the area of overlap of the plates. The maximum capacitance with the plates fully interleaved may be 0.0005 μF.

fixed plates

moving plates

Fig. 57.10

The p.d. that can be applied across a capacitor increases with the thickness of the dielectric; a 100 μF 25 V capacitor will withstand 25 V.

Charging by a battery

The easiest way to charge a capacitor is to connect a suitable battery across it. In Fig. 57.11 electrons flow from the negative of the battery on to plate Y of the capacitor and from plate X to the positive of the battery. Positive charge builds up on X and negative on Y until the p.d. between them is equal and opposite to that of the battery (1.5 V). Electron

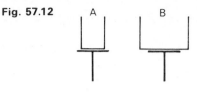

Fig. 57.11

Fig. 57.12

flow then stops. Equal flicks in the same direction occur on the meters but there are no permanent deflections.

We say the capacitor has charge Q, meaning that one plate has charge $+Q$ and the other $-Q$. If $V = 1.5\,V$ and $C = 500\,\mu F$ then

$$Q = VC$$
$$= 1.5\,V \times 500\,\mu F$$
$$= 1.5\,V \times 500 \times 10^{-6}\,F$$
$$= 750 \times 10^{-6}\,C$$
$$= 750\,\mu C \text{ (microcoulombs)}.$$

Questions

1. Two metal cans A and B of different sizes rest on two identical gold-leaf electroscopes as shown in Fig. 57.12. Each can is given exactly the same quantity of negative charge.

(*a*) Copy the diagram and show on it the divergence of the leaves on each electroscope.

(*b*) Which of the two arrangements has the greater capacitance, A or B?

(*c*) Which will have been charged to the greater potential?

(*d*) If the two cans are now carefully connected, without either being earthed, which way will electrons flow?

(*e*) Give a reason for your answer to part (*d*).   (*Mddx*)

2. Two metal spheres, one of radius 10 cm and the other of radius 0.5 cm, are supported on insulating stands a large distance apart. The larger sphere is then positively charged and the smaller sphere is brought up towards it until they are in contact. Explain what happens to the charge and potential of the two spheres during these processes.

Whilst the spheres are in contact, two proof planes of equal size are placed simultaneously in contact with them, one to each sphere. The proof planes are then tested separately with an uncharged leaf electroscope. State and explain the effects you would expect to observe.   (*J.M.B.*)

3. An insulated, charged metal plate is connected by a wire to a leaf electroscope. Describe and explain what happens to the electroscope when an earthed metal plate similar to and kept parallel to the first is brought up with its area gradually overlapping the charged plate, but with their distance apart kept constant. What, if anything, will be observed if now the distance of separation is increased with the plates kept directly opposite to each other. Give reasons for your answer.   (*L.*)

4. (*a*) What charge is stored in a 0.1 F capacitor when a 10 V supply is connected across it?

(*b*) A capacitor is marked 1000 μF. (*i*) What is its capacitance in farad? (*ii*) What is the charge on it at 20 V?

58 Electric current

An electric current consists of moving electric charges. In Fig. 58.1 when the van de Graaff is working, the table tennis ball dashes to and fro between the plates and the meter records a small current. As the ball touches each plate it becomes charged and is repelled to the other plate. In this way charge is carried across the gap. This also shows that 'static' charges cause a deflection on a meter just like that produced by a battery in current electricity.

Fig. 58.1

In a metal, each atom has one or more loosely held electrons that are free to move. When a p.d. (due to a van de Graaff or a battery) is connected across the ends of such a conductor, the free electrons drift slowly along it towards a higher potential, i.e. in the direction from the negative to the positive terminal of a battery. There is then a current of negative charge.

Effects of a current

An electric current has three effects that reveal its existence and which can be shown with the circuit of Fig. 58.2.

(*a*) *Heating and lighting.* The bulb lights due to a small wire in it (the filament) being made white hot by the current.

Fig. 58.2

(*b*) *Magnetic.* The plotting compass is deflected when it is placed in the magnetic field produced round any wire carrying a current.

(*c*) *Chemical.* Bubbles of gas are given off at the wires in the acid because of the chemical action of the current.

The ampere and the coulomb

The unit of current is the *ampere* (A) which, as we will see later (p. 202), is defined using the magnetic effect. One milliampere (mA) is one-thousandth of an ampere. Current is measured by an *ammeter* (p. 201).

The unit of charge, the *coulomb* (C), is defined in terms of the ampere.

One coulomb is the charge passing any point in a circuit when a steady current of 1 ampere flows for 1 second.

A charge of 3 C would pass each point in 1 s if the current was 3 A. In 2 s, $3 \times 2 = 6$ C would pass. In general, if a steady current I (amperes) flows for time t (seconds) the charge Q (coulombs) passing any point is given by

$$Q = I \times t$$

The charge on about 6 million million million (6×10^{18}) electrons equals 1 C.

Circuit diagrams

Current must have a complete path (a circuit) of conductors if it is to flow. Wires of copper are used to connect batteries, lamps, etc. in a circuit since copper is a good electrical conductor. If the wires are covered with insulation, e.g. plastic, the ends are bared for connecting up.

The signs or symbols used for various parts of an electrical circuit are shown in Fig. 58.3.

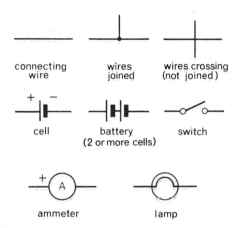

Fig. 58.3

Before the electron was discovered scientists *agreed* to think of current as positive charges moving round a circuit in the direction from positive to negative of a battery. This agreement still stands. Arrows on circuit diagrams show the direction of what we call the *conventional current*, i.e. the direction in which positive charges would flow.

Experiment: test of Q=It

Set up the circuit of Fig. 58.4. Connect A to B so charging the 500 μF capacitor to 2 V. Its charge $Q = VC = 2 \times 500 \times 10^{-6} = 10^{-3}$ C.

Fig. 58.4

Disconnect AB and connect A to C, starting a clock at the same time and also adjusting the 100 kΩ variable resistor to keep a constant current I (e.g. 20 μA = 20×10^{-6} A) through the meter. When this

is no longer possible stop the clock and note the time t.

Assume the charge lost by the capacitor is $I \times t$, both of which are known. Does $Q = It$ (roughly)?

Experiment: measuring current

Fig. 58.5

(a) Connect the circuit of Fig. 58.5a (on a circuit board if possible) ensuring that the + of the cell (the metal stud on an SP2) goes to the + of the ammeter (marked red). Note the current.
(b) Connect the circuit of Fig. 58.5b. The cells are *in series* (+ of one to − of other), as are the lamps. Record the current. Measure the current at B, C, and D by disconnecting the circuit at each point in turn and inserting the ammeter. What do you find?
(c) Connect the circuit of Fig. 58.5c. The lamps are *in parallel*. Read the ammeter. Also measure the currents at P, Q and R. What is your conclusion?

Series and parallel circuits

In a *series* circuit the current is the same at all points: it is not used up. In a *parallel* circuit the total current equals the sum of the currents in the separate branches. Kirchoff's first law states—*charge does not gather at any point in a circuit.*

Questions

1. If the current through a floodlamp is 5 A, what charge passes in (a) 1 s, (b) 10 s, (c) 5 minutes?
2. What is the current in a circuit if the charge passing each point is (a) 10 C in 2 s, (b) 20 C in 40 s, (c) 240 C in 2 minutes?

(a)

Fig. 58.6

(b)

3. (a) Fig. 58.6a shows a cell correctly connected to 2 lamps and a meter. Draw a circuit diagram for the same circuit.

(b) Fig. 58.6b shows 3 lamps and a cell. Draw a circuit diagram of the same circuit. (E.A.)

A

B

C

D

E

Fig. 58.7

4. Study the circuits in Fig. 58.7. The switch S is open (there is a break in the circuit at this point). The circuit in which lamp P would not light but lamps Q and R would is: (W.)

5. Using the circuit in Fig. 58.8, which of the following statements is correct?

Fig. 58.8

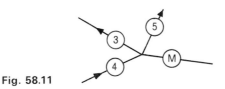

(a) When S_1 and S_2 are closed A and B are lit.
(b) With S_1 open and S_2' closed A and B are not lit.
(c) With S_2 open and S_1 closed A lights and B does not light. (A.L.)

6. In the circuit of Fig. 58.9, A, B, C, D are just positions and the switch is closed. Choose the correct statement.

Fig. 58.9

(a) The current at A will not be the same as the current at B.
(b) The two lamps are wired in parallel.
(c) The current reached B before it reached C.
(d) With an extra lamp (at D) the current would be less.
(e) With an extra lamp (at A) the batteries would run down faster. (S.R.)

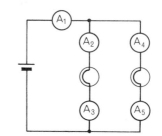

Fig. 58.10

7. If the lamps are all the same in Fig. 58.10 and if A_1 reads 0.5 A, what do A_2, A_3, A_4 and A_5 read?

Fig. 58.11

8. Fig. 58.11 represents a junction in an electrical circuit containing four ammeters, the numbers in the circles denoting the reading in amperes. The reading on M would be

A 0   B 2   C 4   D 6   E 12   (J.M.B.)

59 Potential difference

In electrostatics when there is a p.d. between two charged conductors which are connected, electrons pass from one to the other until their potentials are equal. A small current flows for a short time.

Constant currents are produced by batteries. They can maintain (by chemical action) a surplus of electrons at one terminal (the negative) and a shortage at the other (the positive). A constant p.d. is then applied to any circuit connected across their terminals.

The *p.d.* or *voltage* of the domestic mains supply is 240 volts and of a car battery 12 volts. In current electricity we deal with smaller p.d.s but larger charges than in electrostatics.

Energy changes and p.d.

In an electric circuit electrical energy is supplied from a source such as a battery and is changed into other forms of energy by devices in the circuit. A lamp produces heat and light.

Fig. 59.1

mains lamp (100 W)
a.c. ammeters (0–1 A)
car side-lamp (6 W)
240 V mains
12 V supply a.c.

If the circuits of Fig. 59.1 are connected up, it will be found from the ammeter readings that the current is about the same (0.4 A) in each lamp. However, the mains lamp with a p.d. of 240 V applied to it, gives much more light and heat than the car lamp with 12 V across it. In terms of energy, the mains lamp changes a great deal more electrical energy in a second than does the car lamp.

Evidently the p.d. across a device affects the rate at which it changes electrical energy. This gives us a way of defining the unit of p.d.—the volt.

Model of a circuit

It may help you to understand the definition of the volt, i.e. what a volt is, if you *imagine* that the current in a circuit is formed by 'drops' of electricity, each having a charge of 1 coulomb and carrying equal-sized 'bundles' of electrical energy. In Fig. 59.2, Mr. Coulomb represents one such 'drop'. As

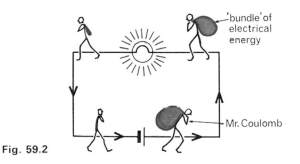

Fig. 59.2

'bundle' of electrical energy
Mr. Coulomb

a 'drop' moves round the circuit it gives up all its energy which is changed to other forms of energy. Note that electrical energy is 'used up', not charge or current.

In our imaginary representation, Mr. Coulomb travels round the circuit and unloads energy as he goes, most of it in the lamp. We think of him receiving a fresh 'bundle' every time he passes through the battery, which suggests he must be travelling very fast. In fact, as we saw earlier (p. 170), the electrons drift along quite slowly. As soon as the circuit is complete, energy is delivered at once to the lamp, not by electrons directly from the battery but from electrons that were in the connecting wires. The model is helpful but not an exact representation.

The volt

The demonstrations of Fig. 59.1 show that the greater the p.d. at the terminals of a supply, the larger is the 'bundle' of electrical energy given to each coulomb and the greater is the rate at which light and heat are produced in a lamp.

The p.d. between two points in a circuit is 1 volt if 1 joule of electrical energy is changed into other forms of energy when 1 coulomb passes from one point to the other.

That is, 1 volt=1 joule per coulomb (1 V= 1 J/C). If 2 J are given up by each coulomb, the p.d. is 2 V. If 6 J are changed when 2 C pass, the p.d. is 6 J/2 C=3 V. In general if W (joules) is the energy changed (i.e. the work done) when charge Q (coulombs) passes between two points, the p.d. V (volts) between the points is given by

$$V = W/Q \qquad \text{or} \qquad W = Q \times V$$

If Q is in the form of a steady current I (amperes) flowing for time t (seconds) then $Q = I \times t$ (p. 170) and

$$W = I \times t \times V$$

Cells and batteries

Greater p.d.s are obtained when cells are joined in series, i.e. + of one to − of next. In Fig. 59.3a the two 1.5 V cells give a p.d. of 3 V at the terminals A, B. Every coulomb in a circuit connected to this battery will have 3 J of electrical energy.

Fig. 59.3

If two 1.5 V cells are connected in parallel, Fig. 59.3b, the p.d. at terminals P, Q is still 1.5 V but the arrangement behaves like a larger cell and will last longer.

The cells in Fig. 59.3c are in opposition and the p.d. at X, Y is zero.

Experiment: measuring p.d.

A *voltmeter* is an instrument for measuring p.d. It looks like an ammeter but has a scale marked in volts. Whereas an ammeter is inserted *in series* in a circuit to measure the current, a voltmeter is connected across that part of the circuit where the p.d. is required, i.e. *in parallel*. (We will see later, p. 202, that a voltmeter should have a high resistance and an ammeter a low resistance.)

To prevent damage the + terminal (marked red) must be connected to the point at the higher potential, i.e. nearest the + of the battery.

174

Fig. 59.4

(a) Connect the circuit of Fig. 59.4a. The voltmeter gives the p.d. across the lamp. Read it.
(b) Connect the circuit of Fig. 59.4b. Measure:
    (i) the p.d. V between X and Y,
    (ii) the p.d. V_1 across lamp L_1,
    (iii) the p.d. V_2 across lamp L_2,
    (iv) the p.d. V_3 across lamp L_3.
How does the value of V compare with $V_1 + V_2 + V_3$?

Questions

Fig. 59.5

1. The p.d. across the lamp in Fig. 59.5 is 12 V. How many joules of electrical energy are changed into light and heat when
    (a) a charge of 1 C passes through it,
    (b) a charge of 5 C passes through it,
    (c) a current of 2 A flows through it for 10 s?
2. Three 2 V accumulators are connected in series and used as the supply for a circuit.
    (a) What is the p.d. at the terminals of the supply?
    (b) How many joules of electrical energy does 1 C gain on passing through (i) one accumulator, (ii) all three accumulators?
3. A set of Christmas tree lights consists of 20 identical lamps connected in series to a 240 V mains supply. What is the voltage (p.d.) across each lamp?
    A 12 V   B 20 V   C 240 V   D 4800 V   (E.A.)
4. The symbol for a 1.5 V cell is ⊣⊢ . Which of the arrangements in Fig. 59.6 would produce a battery with a p.d. of 6 V?   (W.M.)

Fig. 59.6

(a)   (b)   (c)   (d)   (e)   (f)

Fig. 59.7

5. The lamps and the cells in all the circuits of Fig. 59.7 are the same. If the lamp in *a* has its full, normal brightness, what can you say about the brightness of the lamps in *b*, *c*, *d*, *e* and *f*?

6. Three voltmeters V, V_1, V_2 are connected as in Fig. 59.8.

(*a*) If V reads 18 V and V_1 reads 12 V, what does V_2 read?

(*b*) If the ammeter A reads 0.5 A, how much electrical energy is changed to heat and light in L_1 in 1 minute?

(*c*) Copy Fig. 59.8 and mark with a +, the positive terminals of the ammeter and voltmeters for correct connection.

Fig. 59.8

60 Resistance

When the same p.d. is applied across different conductors, different currents flow depending on how easily electrons can move in them. The opposition of a conductor to current flow is called its *resistance*. A long thin wire has more resistance than a short thick one of the same material because a given p.d. causes a smaller current in it.

A good conductor has a low resistance and a poor conductor a high resistance. Silver is the best conducting material, but copper, the next best, is much cheaper and is used for connecting wire and cables in electric circuits. Good insulators for static electricity are also good for current electricity.

The ohm

If the current through a conductor is I when the p.d. across it is V, Fig. 60.1, its resistance R is defined by

$$R = \frac{V}{I}$$

Fig. 60.1

This is a reasonable way to measure resistance since the smaller I is for a given V, the greater is R. If V is in volts and I in amperes, R is in *ohms* (Ω: pronounced omega). For example, if $I = 2$ A when $V = 12$ V, then $R = 12/2 = 6\,\Omega$.

The ohm is the resistance of a conductor in which the current is 1 ampere when a p.d. of 1 volt is applied across it.

Resistors

Conductors intended to have resistance are called *resistors* (symbol ─▭─) and are made either from wires of special alloys or from carbon. Those in radio and television sets have values from a few ohms up to millions of ohms, Fig. 60.2a.

Variable resistors are used in electronics (and are then called *potentiometers*) as volume and other controls, Fig. 60.2b. Larger current versions are use-

(a)

(b)

Fig. 60.2

ful in laboratory experiments and consist of a coil of constantan wire (an alloy of 60% copper, 40% nickel) wound on a tube with a sliding contact on a metal bar above the tube, Fig. 60.3.

Fig. 60.3

There are two ways of using a variable resistor. It may be used as a *rheostat* for changing the current in a circuit; only one end connection and the sliding contact are then required. In Fig. 60.4a moving the sliding contact to the left reduces the resistance and increases the current. It can also act as a *potential divider* for changing the p.d. applied to a device, all three connections being used. In Fig. 60.4b any fraction from the total p.d. of the battery to zero can be tapped off by moving the sliding contact down.

Fig. 60.4

(a)

(b)

Experiment: measuring resistance

The resistance R of a conductor can be found by measuring the current I through it when a p.d. V is applied across it and then using $R = V/I$. This is called the *ammeter-voltmeter method*.

Fig. 60.5

Set up the circuit of Fig. 60.5 in which the unknown resistance R is 1 metre of S.W.G. 34 constantan wire. Altering the rheostat changes both the p.d. V and the current I. Record in a table, with three columns, five values of I (e.g. 0.10, 0.15, 0.20, 0.25 and 0.30 A) and the corresponding values of V.

Work out R for each pair of readings.

Repeat the experiment but instead of the wire use (*i*) a torch bulb (e.g. 2.5 V, 0.3 A), (*ii*) a semiconductor diode (e.g. 1N4001) connected first one way then the other way round, (*iii*) a thermistor (e.g. TH 7).

Ohm's law

Experiments show that for metallic conductors, so long as their temperature does not change, V/I always has the same value when V is varied and the corresponding value of I found. That is, the resistance of a metallic conductor is constant whatever the p.d. applied. Hence V/I is a constant or $I \propto V$. This means, for example, that doubling V doubles I and so on.

The current through a metallic conductor is directly proportional to the p.d. across its ends if the temperature and other physical conditions are constant.

This is *Ohm's law*. It applies to metals and some alloys, called ohmic conductors. Constantan is ohmic, semiconductor diodes, valves and transistors are non-ohmic. In symbols Ohm's law can be written

$$\frac{V}{I} = R \quad \text{or} \quad I = \frac{V}{R} \quad \text{or} \quad V = I \times R$$

The last one is easiest to remember; all are useful for calculations on ohmic conductors.

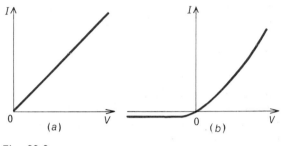

Fig. 60.6

For an ohmic conductor a graph of I against V is a straight line through the origin since $I \propto V$, Fig. 60.6*a*. Fig. 60.6*b* is for a semiconductor diode and shows that I is large in one direction but almost zero when V is reversed; this one-way property makes it useful as a *rectifier* for changing alternating current (a.c.) to direct current (d.c.) (p. 231).

Resistance and temperature

The resistance of a torch bulb increases when the filament gets hot. That is, V/I increases as I increases and a graph of I against V bends over, Fig. 60.7. The resistance of most thermistors decreases if their temperature rises.

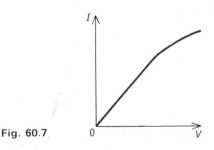

Fig. 60.7

In general, an increase of temperature increases the resistance of metals but decreases the resistance of carbon, non-metals and semiconductors. Certain alloys such as constantan (also called eureka) show very small changes of resistance with temperature.

Resistors in series

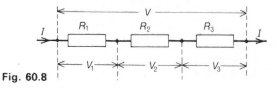

Fig. 60.8

The resistors in Fig. 60.8 are in series. The *same current I* flows through each and the total p.d. *V* across all three equals the separate p.d.s across them, i.e.

$$V = V_1 + V_2 + V_3$$

But $V_1 = IR_1$, $V_2 = IR_2$ and $V_3 = IR_3$. Also if R is the combined resistance, $V = IR$ and so

$$IR = IR_1 + IR_2 + IR_3$$

Dividing both sides by I

$$R = R_1 + R_2 + R_3$$

Resistors in parallel

The resistors in Fig. 60.9a are in parallel. The *p.d. V between the ends of each is the same* and the total current I equals the sum of the currents in the separate branches, i.e.

$$I = I_1 + I_2 + I_3$$

But $I_1 = V/R_1$, $I_2 = V/R_2$ and $I_3 = V/R_3$. Also if R is the combined resistance, $V = IR$ and so

$$\frac{V}{R} = \frac{V}{R_1} + \frac{V}{R_2} + \frac{V}{R_3}$$

Dividing both sides by V

$$\frac{1}{R} = \frac{1}{R_1} + \frac{1}{R_2} + \frac{1}{R_3}$$

For the simpler case of *two* resistors in parallel

$$\frac{1}{R} = \frac{1}{R_1} + \frac{1}{R_2} = \frac{R_2}{R_1 R_2} + \frac{R_1}{R_1 R_2}$$

$$\therefore \quad \frac{1}{R} = \frac{R_2 + R_1}{R_1 R_2}$$

Fig. 60.9 (a) (b)

178

Inverting both sides

$$R = \frac{R_1 R_2}{R_1 + R_2} = \frac{\text{product of resistances}}{\text{sum of resistances}}$$

Short circuit

In Fig. 60.9b if a short length of copper wire is connected across the battery (the dotted line), the lamp goes out. A large current flows in the copper wire which gets very hot. It acts as a 'short circuit' and provides an easy path for the current because of its low resistance. Short circuits are to be avoided (see p. 187).

Worked example

A p.d. of 24 V from a battery is applied to the network of resistors in Fig. 60.10a.

    (a) *What is the combined resistance of the 6 Ω and 12 Ω resistors in parallel?*

    (b) *What is the current in the 8 Ω resistor?*

    (c) *What is the p.d. across the parallel network?*

    (d) *What is the current in the 6 Ω resistor?*

Fig. 60.10

(a) Let R_1 = resistance of 6 Ω and 12 Ω in parallel

$$\therefore \quad \frac{1}{R_1} = \frac{1}{6} + \frac{1}{12} = \frac{2}{12} + \frac{1}{12} = \frac{3}{12}$$

$$\therefore \quad R_1 = \frac{12}{3} = 4\,\Omega$$

(b) Let R = *total* resistance of circuit = $4 + 8 = 12\,\Omega$. The equivalent circuit is shown in Fig. 60.10b and if I is the current in it then since $V = 24$ V

$$I = \frac{V}{R} = \frac{24}{12} = 2\,\text{A}$$

$\therefore$ Current in 8 Ω resistor = 2 A.

(c) Let V_1 = p.d. across parallel network

$$\therefore \quad V_1 = I \times R_1 = 2 \times 4 = 8\,\text{V}$$

(d) Let I_1 = current in 6 Ω resistor, then since V_1 = 8 V

$$I_1 = \frac{V_1}{6} = \frac{8}{6} = \frac{4}{3} \text{A}$$

Questions

1. What is the resistance of a lamp when a p.d. of 12 V across it causes a current of 4 A?

2. Calculate the p.d. across a 10 Ω resistor carrying a current of 2 A.

3. The p.d. across a 2 Ω resistor is 4 V. What is the current flowing (in ampere)?

A $\frac{1}{2}$　　**B** 1　　**C** 2　　**D** 6　　**E** 8

(*J.M.B./A.L./N.W.16+*) ·

Fig. 60.11

4. Three 5 Ω resistors are connected as shown in Fig. 60.11. Their effective total resistance is

A $\frac{3}{5}$ Ω　　**B** $1\frac{2}{3}$ Ω　　**C** 5 Ω　　**D** 15 Ω　　**E** 125 Ω

(*O./S.R.16+*)

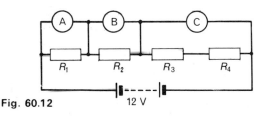

Fig. 60.12

5. The resistors R_1, R_2, R_3 and R_4 in Fig. 60.12 are all equal in value. What would you expect the voltmeters A, B and C to read, assuming that the connecting wires in the circuit have negligible resistance?

Fig. 60.13

6. Calculate the effective resistance between A and B in Fig. 60.13. (*E.M.*)

Fig. 60.14

7. What is the effective resistance in Fig. 60.14 between (*a*) A and B, (*b*) C and D?

Fig. 60.15

8. Fig. 60.15 shows three resistors. Their combined resistance in ohm is

A $1\frac{5}{7}$　　**B** 14　　**C** $1\frac{1}{5}$　　**D** $7\frac{1}{2}$　　**E** $6\frac{2}{3}$　　(*W.Y.*)

Fig. 60.16

9. Fig. 60.16 shows a 2 V cell connected to an arrangement of resistors part in series and part in parallel.

(*a*) What is the total resistance of the two 6 Ω resistors in parallel?

(*b*) What is the current flowing in the 1 Ω resistor?

(*c*) What is the current in one of the 6 Ω resistors? (*N.W.*)

10. A 4 Ω coil and a 2 Ω coil are connected in parallel. What is their combined resistance? A total current of 3 A passes through the coils. What current flows through the 2 Ω coil?

Fig. 60.17

11. In Fig. 60.17 the circles are either ammeters or voltmeters. State what each is and the reading it would show. (*E.A.*)

12. A boy is given a 12 V lamp and decides to measure the resistance of a lamp filament using the voltmeter-ammeter method. He decides to apply various voltages to the lamp and to measure the current in each case.

(*a*) Draw a circuit diagram, showing clearly where the voltmeter and ammeter are placed in the circuit.

(*b*) Two of the boy's results are given below:

voltmeter reading	2.0 V	12 V
ammeter reading	1.0 A	2.0 A

Calculate the resistance of the lamp filament in each case.

(*c*) Explain why the resistance of the lamp filament is different in the two cases. (*Mddx.*)

61 Electromotive force

E.M.F. and terminal p.d.

A voltmeter connected across the terminals of a cell measures the *terminal p.d.* of the cell. The reading depends on the current being supplied; it is greatest when the cell is on 'open circuit', i.e. not supplying current, Fig. 61.1a.

(a) Open circuit

Fig. 61.1
(b) Closed circuit

When a circuit is connected to the cell, it is on 'closed circuit' and the reading is less, Fig. 61.1b. It decreases as the current supplied increases. The terminal p.d. of a cell on open circuit is thus greater than its terminal p.d. on closed circuit.

If we look upon a cell as a device which *supplies* electrical energy, we can define its terminal p.d. on open circuit as the number of joules of electrical energy it gives to each coulomb. If a voltmeter across the cell reads 1.5 V then each coulomb is supplied with 1.5 J of electrical energy and the cell is said to have an *electromotive force* (e.m.f., denoted by E) of 1.5 V.

The e.m.f. of a source of electrical energy is its terminal p.d. on open circuit.

A high resistance voltmeter must be used to measure the e.m.f. of a cell. Otherwise appreciable current flows through the voltmeter and the terminal p.d. measured is not that on open circuit.

Like p.d., e.m.f. is stated in volts and it too is often called a 'voltage': it has the same value for all cells made of the same materials.

The term e.m.f. is misleading to some extent; it measures energy per unit charge and not force but

it does cause charges to move in the circuit. Electromotive energy would be better.

Internal resistance

The terminal p.d. of a cell on closed circuit is also the p.d. applied to the external circuit. For example, in Fig. 61.1b, the voltmeter reading is the same (i.e. 1.2 V) if it is connected across the lamp terminals instead of the cell terminals. (The resistance of the connecting wires from the cell to the lamp is negligible, as is the p.d. across them.)

In an external circuit electrical energy is *changed* into other forms of energy and we regard the terminal p.d. of a cell on closed circuit as being the number of joules of electrical energy changed by each coulomb in the external circuit. If the terminal p.d. on closed circuit is 1.2 V then each coulomb changes 1.2 J of electrical energy.

Not all the electrical energy supplied by a cell to each coulomb is changed in the external circuit. The 'lost' energy per coulomb is due to the cell itself having resistance. Each coulomb has to 'waste' some energy—0.3 joule in the above example—to get through the cell itself and so less is available for the external circuit. The resistance of a cell is called its *internal resistance* (r) and depends among other things on its size.

The circuit equation

Taking stock of the energy changes in a complete circuit, including the cell, we can say from the principle of conservation of energy:

energy supplied per coulomb by cell	=	energy changed per coulomb in external circuit	+	energy *wasted* per coulomb on cell resistance

Or, from the definitions of e.m.f. and p.d.,

$$\text{e.m.f.} = \text{useful p.d.} + \text{'lost' p.d.} \qquad (1)$$

Hence the e.m.f. in a circuit equals the p.d. across the external resistance + the p.d. across the internal resistance.

If E is the e.m.f. of a cell of internal resistance r,

(a)

(b)

Fig. 61.2

Fig. 61.2*a*, and V is its terminal p.d. when sending a current I through a resistor R, Fig. 61.2*b*, then from equation (1).

$$E = V + v \qquad (2)$$

where v is the 'lost' p.d. It is a quantity which cannot be measured directly by a voltmeter but is only found by subtracting V from E. In equation (2), called the *circuit equation*, we can write $V = IR$ and $v = Ir$ since the current all round the circuit is I.

Suppose $E = 1.5$ V, $V = 1.2$ V and $I = 0.30$ A, then replacing in (2),

$$1.5 = 1.2 + v \quad \therefore \quad v = 1.5 - 1.2 = 0.30 \text{ V}$$

But
$$v = Ir$$
$$\therefore \quad 0.30 = 0.30 \times r$$
$$\therefore \quad r = 1.0 \, \Omega$$

Also
$$V = IR$$
$$\therefore \quad 1.2 = 0.30 \times R$$
$$\therefore \quad R = 1.2/0.30 = 4.0 \, \Omega$$

The effect of internal resistance can be seen when a car starts with its lights on. Suppose the electric motor which starts the engine needs a current $I = 100$ A and is connected to a battery of e.m.f. $E = 12$ V and internal resistance $r = 0.040 \, \Omega$. The 'lost' p.d. $v = Ir = 100 \times 0.040 = 4.0$ V. The terminal p.d. of the battery when it sends 100 A through the starter motor $= V = E - v = 12 - 4.0 = 8.0$ V. If the lights are meant to

be fully bright when there is a p.d. of 12 V across them, they will be dim on 8.0 V, as is observed.

Questions

Fig. 61.3

1. (*a*) What current will flow in the circuit of Fig. 61.3?
(*b*) What is the p.d. across the 3 Ω resistor in this circuit?

Fig. 61.4

2. Fig. 61.4 shows a battery of e.m.f. 24 V and internal resistance 3 Ω in series with a resistor of resistance 9 Ω. The current will be

A $\frac{3}{8}$ A   B $\frac{1}{2}$ A   C 2 A   D $3\frac{2}{3}$ A   E 8 A   (*O./S.R.16+*)

Fig. 61.5

3. In Fig. 61.5, the cell has an e.m.f. of 1.5 V. The voltmeter reading is 1.35 V. The ammeter records the value of the current as 0.3 A. Calculate (*a*) the internal resistance of the cell. (*b*) the value of the resistance R.   (*J.M.B./A.L./N.W.16+*)

4. A high resistance voltmeter reads 3.0 V when connected across the terminals of a battery on open circuit and 2.6 V when the battery sends a current of 0.20 A through a lamp.
What is (*a*) the e.m.f. of the battery, (*b*) the terminal p.d. of the battery when supplying 0.20 A, (*c*) the p.d. across the lamp, (*d*) the 'lost' p.d., (*e*) the internal resistance of the battery and (*f*) the resistance of the lamp?

62 Further questions

Permanent magnets: magnetic fields

Fig. 62.1

1. A bar magnet with north and south poles marked N and S respectively and a bar of iron PQ are fixed a short distance apart as shown in Fig. 62.1. A compass needle is brought in turn to ends P, Q, N and S. Its N pole will point towards

    A both ends of the iron but only to the N pole of the magnet

    B both ends of the iron but only to the S pole of the magnet

    C end P only of the iron and only to the S pole of the magnet

    D end Q only of the iron and only to the N pole of the magnet

    E end Q only of the iron and only to the S pole of the magnet. *(O./S.R.16+)*

2. How could you use a solenoid to (*i*) magnetize a bar of steel so that its polarity is known, (*ii*) demagnetize a magnet?

Explain in terms of the simple domain theory of ferromagnetism, the process of magnetization to saturation. *(J.M.B.)*

3. A powerful bar magnet is placed horizontally with its poles in line with the magnetic meridian, and the two small regions are found on the axis of the magnet where a small plotting compass sets in a random manner. With the aid of a diagram on which the poles of the magnet are marked, account for this effect. On another diagram show how similar regions could be produced on a horizontal line through the mid-point of the magnet and perpendicular to its axis. *(L.)*

4. The angles of *dip* and *declination* in London are, at present (1974), 67° and 7° west respectively. Describe with diagrams what you understand by these data, stating the importance of giving the place and time. *(S.)*

5. A magnetic needle, free to turn in a vertical plane, is suspended first at the earth's south magnetic pole and then at a point on the magnetic equator. The respective angles between the needle and the horizontal are

    A 0° and 0°   **B** 70° and 70°   **C** 0° and 45°

    D 0° and 90°   **E** 90° and 0°   *(N.I.)*

Static electricity: more electrostatics: capacitors

6. In the process of induction in electrostatics

    A a conductor is rubbed with an insulator

    B a charge is produced by friction

    C negative and positive charges are separated

    D a positive charge induces a positive charge

    E electrons are 'sprayed' into an object.

    (J.M.B.)

7. Fig. 62.2 shows two similar small conducting spheres suspended by light insulating threads from a point P. The spheres carry equal negative charges.

Fig. 62.2

(*a*) Copy the figure and show by arrows drawn on it, the directions of the forces acting on sphere A.

(*b*) Against each arrow, write the name of the force it represents.

(*c*) If a large vertical earthed metal plate were placed between the spheres in the position MN, state and explain what would happen. *(O.)*

8. A large hollow can which is open at the top stands on the cap of a leaf electroscope whose case is earthed. The leaf shows no divergence. State and explain what is observed as the following steps are carried out.

(*a*) A positively charged insulated metal sphere is lowered slowly into the can until it is well inside but still freely suspended.

(*b*) The sphere is allowed to touch the bottom of the can and is then removed.

(*c*) Finally the sphere, which is still insulated, is allowed to touch the outside of the can. *(L.)*

9. (*a*) Draw a labelled diagram of an uncharged electrophorus. Describe how the electrophorus is used to obtain a charge and how successive charges may be transferred to a large, deep, insulated metal can.

(*b*) A movable insulated metal plate connected to the earth is parallel and close to a similar positively charged, insulated, fixed metal plate. Draw a diagram to show the distribution of charge on the plates and the electric field lines between them.

The distance between the plates is doubled by moving the 'earthed' plate. State and explain how you would expect this change to affect (*i*) the charges on the plates, and (*ii*) the potential of the fixed plate. (*J.M.B.*)

10. (*a*) A capacitor is marked $2\,\mu\mathrm{F}$. (*i*) What is its capacitance in farad? (*ii*) What is the charge on the capacitor at 12 V? (*iii*) At what voltage will it store a charge of $3\,\mu\mathrm{C}$?

(*b*) One paper capacitor is marked $0.01\,\mu\mathrm{F}$, 12 V and another $0.1\,\mu\mathrm{F}$, 250 V. (*i*) Describe the construction of a paper capacitor. (*ii*) Explain the difference in construction between the two.

(*O./S.R.16+*)

Electric current: potential difference: resistance

Fig. **62.3**

11. V_1, V_2, V_3 are the p.d.s across the $2\,\Omega$, $3\,\Omega$ and $4\,\Omega$ resistors respectively in Fig. 62.3 and the current is 5 A. Which one of the columns A to E shows the correct values of V_1, V_2 and V_3 measured in volts?

	A	B	C	D	E
V_1	2.0	10	0.4	2.5	3.0
V_2	3.0	15	0.6	1.6	2.0
V_3	4.0	20	0.8	1.25	1.0 (*J.M.B.*)

12. If two resistors of $5\,\Omega$ and $15\,\Omega$ are joined together in series and then placed in parallel with a $20\,\Omega$ resistor, the effective resistance in ohms of the combination is

A 0.1 B 10 C 20 D 40 E 400 (*N.I.*)

13. Two $4\,\Omega$ resistors are connected to a 2 V cell and an ammeter as shown in Fig. 62.4*a, b, c.* Find

Fig. **62.4**

the reading on the ammeter in each case. The resistance of the connecting wires, the meter and the cell may be neglected. (*E.A.*)

14. When a $6\,\Omega$ resistor is connected across the terminals of a 12 V battery, the number of coulombs passing through the resistor per second is

A 0.5 B 2 C 6 D 12 E 72 (*N.I.*)

15. (*a*) The graph in Fig. 62.5 illustrates how the p.d. across the ends of a conductor is related to the current flowing through it. (*i*) What law may be deduced from the graph? (*ii*) What is the resistance of the conductor?

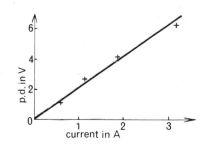

Fig. **62.5**

(*b*) Draw diagrams to show how six 2 V lamps could be lit to normal brightness when using (*i*) 2 V supply, (*ii*) 6 V supply and (*iii*) 12 V supply.

16. Two electric light bulbs, both marked 0.3 A, 4.5 V are connected (*a*) in parallel, (*b*) in series across a 4.5 V battery of negligible internal resistance. Assume that the resistance of the filament does not change. In each case (*a*) and (*b*), (*i*) state what might be seen, (*ii*) calculate the currents through each bulb, and (*iii*) calculate the current supplied by the battery. (*J.M.B.*)

Fig. 62.6

17. Resistors are connected as in Fig. 62.6 and a p.d. of 12 V is applied across them. S1 and S2 are switches. Calculate

(*a*) the total resistance when both switches S1 and S2 are closed,

(*b*) the total current supplied when both switches S1 and S2 are closed,

(*c*) the current in the 3 Ω resistor when switch S1 is closed and switch S2 open,

(*d*) the current supplied when both switches are open. (*W.*)

18. In the circuit of Fig. 62.7, C is a 2 V cell of negligible internal resistance. S_1 and S_2 are switches. The current taken by the voltmeter and the resistance of the ammeter can both be neglected.

Fig. 62.7

(*a*) Calculate the readings of the ammeter and the voltmeter when the switches are as shown with S_1 closed and S_2 open. Explain your calculations.

(*b*) What will the meters read when S_1 and S_2 are both closed? Explain.

(*c*) What will the meters read when S_1 and S_2 are both open? Explain. (*O.*)

19. In Fig. 62.8, what is the voltmeter reading if the ammeter reads 2 A and the resistance of the voltmeter is 900 Ω?

A 50 **B** 180 **C** 200 **D** 450 **E** 1800
(*N.I.*)

Fig. 62.8

184

20. Fig. 62.9 shows two ammeters X and Y arranged in parallel and connected to a battery and a resistor in order to determine the current supplied by the battery. Both give a full-scale deflection; Y reads 3.0 A, X reads 2.0 A.

Fig. **62.9**

(*a*) What is the current supplied by the battery?

(*b*) Explain why neither ammeter, used alone, is suitable for finding the current supplied.

Given that the resistance of Y is 0.04 Ω, calculate

(*c*) the p.d. between the points labelled P and Q,

(*d*) the resistance of X. (*C.*)

21. Describe with the aid of a circuit diagram how you would measure the resistance of a coil of wire using a voltmeter/ammeter method. What additional measurements would be necessary in order to determine the resistivity of the material of the coil? State also the required formula.

Calculate the combined resistance of 3 resistors, each 6 Ω, when connected (*a*) in series, (*b*) in parallel. Draw a sketch showing one other way in which these 3 resistors could be connected and calculate the combined resistance. (*Note.* For resistivity see p. 204.) (*S.*)

Electromotive force

22. A battery consists of 3 cells, each of *electromotive force* $E = 1.5$ V and *internal resistance* $r = 0.10\,\Omega$, connected in series. Explain the meaning of the terms in italics.

Is either of these affected by altering the dimensions of the cell?

A resistor of 1.48 Ω is put in series with the battery, and an ammeter of resistance 0.02 Ω is connected so as to measure the current through it. What is the ammeter reading?

Mention one advantage of a lead accumulator over a dry cell, for use in laboratory experiments. (*O. and C.*)

23. Describe, giving a circuit diagram, an experiment which would show whether a particular cell has an appreciable internal resistance. Indicate briefly what readings would be needed in order to estimate its value. (You are not required to derive the equation for this.)

Explain why a check against a short-circuit should be made when using secondary cells such as lead plate accumulators, whereas this is not so important when dry cells are used.

Resistances of $2\,\Omega$ and $3\,\Omega$ are connected in series with a cell. A high resistance voltmeter connected across the $3\,\Omega$ resistor reads 1.0 V but this increases to 1.2 V when an extra $2\,\Omega$ resistor is connected in parallel with the first $2\,\Omega$ resistor. Calculate the *electromotive force* and *internal resistance* of the cell.

(*L.*)

24. A cell in series with a $2\,\Omega$ resistor and a switch has a high-resistance voltmeter across it, Fig. 62.10.

Fig. 62.10

The voltmeter reads 1.5 V with the switch open, and 1.2 V with it closed.

(*a*) What is the electromotive force of the cell? Explain.

(*b*) What is the current through the $2\,\Omega$ resistor with the switch closed?

(*c*) A further resistor is added in series with the $2\,\Omega$ resistor making the current 0.25 A with the switch closed. Calculate its value.

(*d*) What current would flow if the cell were short-circuited?

(*e*) What would the voltmeter read if the cell were short-circuited? (*O./S.R.16+*)

63 Electric power

Power in electric circuits

Power was stated earlier (p. 78) to be the *rate at which energy is changed from one form to another.* The unit of power is the *watt* (W) and equals an energy change rate of 1 joule per second, i.e., $1 \text{ W} = 1 \text{ J/s}$. An electric lamp with a power of 100 W changes 100 J of electrical energy into heat and light each second. A larger unit is the kilowatt (kW): $1 \text{ kW} = 1000 \text{ W}$.

Consider the circuit of Fig. 63.1.

Ammeter reading = 2 A
Voltmeter reading = 6 V

Fig. 63.1

(*i*) The ammeter reads 2 A, therefore 2 coulombs pass through the lamp each second.

(*ii*) The voltmeter reads 6 V, therefore 6 J of electrical energy are changed to heat and light energy for every coulomb that passes.

(*iii*) Hence in each second $6 \times 2 = 12$ J of electrical energy are changed in the lamp, i.e., its power is $12 \text{ J/s} = 12 \text{ W}$.

In general, if a current I flows from one point to another when there is a p.d. V between them, the electrical energy changed per second, i.e. the power P, is

$$P = V \times I$$

In units,

$$\text{WATTS} = \text{VOLTS} \times \text{AMPERES}$$

If all the energy is changed to heat in a resistor of resistance R, then $V = IR$ and the rate of production of heat is given by

$$P = V \times I = IR \times I = I^2 R$$

That is, if the current is doubled, four times as much heat is produced per second. Also, $P = V^2/R$.

Experiment: measuring electric power

Fig. 63.2

(*a*) *Lamp.* Connect the circuit of Fig. 63.2. Note the ammeter and voltmeter readings and work out the electric power supplied to the bulb in watts.

(*b*) *Motor.* Replace the bulb by a small electric motor and find the power given to it.

Electric lighting

(*a*) *Filament lamps*, Fig. 63.3*a*. The filament is a small coiled coil of tungsten wire, Fig. 63.3*b*, which becomes white hot when current flows through it.

Fig. 63.3

The higher the temperature of the filament the greater is the proportion of electric energy changed to light and for this reason it is made of tungsten, a metal with a high melting point (3400 °C).

Most lamps are gas-filled and contain nitrogen or argon, not air. This reduces evaporation of the tungsten which would otherwise condense on the bulb and blacken it. The coiled coil, being compact, is cooled less by convection currents in the gas.

(*b*) *Fluorescent lamps.* A filament lamp changes only 10% of the electrical energy supplied into light; the other 90% becomes heat. Fluorescent lamps are three times as efficient and may last 3000 hours compared with the 1000 hour life of filament lamps. They cost more to install but running costs are less.

Fig. 63.4

electrodes

mercury vapour   glass tube   fluorescent powder

A simplified diagram of a fluorescent lamp is shown in Fig. 63.4. When the lamp is switched on, the mercury vapour emits ultraviolet radiation (invisible) which makes the powder on the inside of the tube fluoresce (glow), i.e. light (visible) is emitted. Different powders give different colours.

Electric heating

(*a*) *Heating elements*. In domestic appliances such as electric fires, cookers, kettles and irons the 'elements', Fig. 63.5, are made from Nichrome wire. This is an alloy of nickel and chromium which does not oxidize (and become brittle) when the current makes it red hot.

element

Cooker

Radiant fire

element

Kettle   Iron

Fig. 63.5

The elements in *radiant* electric fires are at red heat (about 900 °C) and the radiation they emit is directed into the room by polished reflectors. In *convector* types the element is below red heat (about 450 °C) and is designed to warm air which is drawn through the heater by natural or forced convection. In *storage* heaters the elements heat fire-clay bricks

during the night using 'off-peak' electricity. On the following day these cool down, giving off the stored heat to warm the room.

(*b*) *Three-heat switch*. This is sometimes used to control heating appliances. It has three settings and uses two identical elements. On 'high', the elements are in parallel across the supply voltage, Fig. 63.6*a*; on 'medium', current only passes through one, Fig. 63.6*b*; on 'low', they are in series, Fig. 63.6*c*.

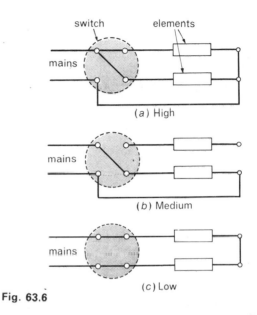

switch   elements

mains

(a) High

mains

(b) Medium

mains

(c) Low

Fig. 63.6

(*c*) *Fuses*. A fuse is a short length of wire of material with a low melting point (often tinned copper), which melts and breaks the circuit when the current through it exceeds a certain value. Two reasons for excessive currents are 'short circuits' due to worn insulation on connecting wires, and overloaded circuits. Without a fuse the wiring would become hot in these cases and could cause a fire.

fuse wire

symbol for a fuse

cartridge fuse

insulating holder

Fig. 63.7

Two types of fuse are shown in Fig. 63.7. *Always switch off before replacing a fuse.*

Fig. 63.8

House circuits

Electricity usually comes to our homes by an underground cable containing two wires, the *live* (L) and the *neutral* (N). The neutral is earthed at the local sub-station and so is at zero potential. The supply is a.c. (p. 212) and the live wire is alternately positive and negative. Study the modern house circuit shown in Fig. 63.8.

(*a*) *Circuits in parallel*. Every circuit is connected in parallel with the supply, i.e. across the live and neutral, and receives the full mains p.d. of 240 V.

(*b*) *Switches and fuses*. These are always in the live wire. If they were in the neutral, lamp and power sockets would be 'live' when switches were 'off' or fuses 'blown'. A shock (fatal) could then be obtained by, for example, touching the element of an electric fire when it was switched off.

(*c*) *Staircase circuit*. The lamp is controlled from two places by the two two-way switches.

(*d*) *Ring main circuit*. The live and neutral wires each run in two complete rings round the house, and the power sockets, each rated at 13 A, are tapped off from them. Thinner wires can be used since the current to each socket flows by two paths, i.e. in the whole ring. The ring has a 30 A fuse and if it has ten sockets all can be used so long as the total current does not exceed 30 A.

(*e*) *Fused plug*. Only one type of plug is used in a ring main circuit. It is wired as in Fig. 63.9 and has its own cartridge fuse, 3 A (blue) for appliances with powers up to 720 W and 13 A (brown) for those between 720 W and 3 kW.

Fig. 63.9

(*f*) *Earthing and safety*. A ring main has a third wire which goes to the top sockets on all power points, Fig. 63.8, and is earthed by being connected either to a *metal* water pipe in the house or to an earth connection on the supply cable. This third wire is a safety precaution to prevent electric shock should an appliance develop a fault.

The earth pin on a three-pin plug is connected to the metal case of the appliance which is thus joined to earth by a path of almost zero resistance. If then, for example, the element of an electric fire breaks or sags and touches the case, a large current flows to earth and 'blows' the fuse. Otherwise the case becomes 'live' and anyone touching it receives a shock *which might be fatal*, especially if they were 'earthed' by, say, standing on a concrete floor or holding a water tap.

Experiment: house circuits

On a circuit board connect up and investigate (*a*) the staircase circuit of Fig. 63.10*a* and (*b*) the ring main circuit of Fig. 63.10*b*.

Fig. 63.10

(*a*)   (*b*)

Paying for electricity

Electricity Boards charge for the *electrical energy* they supply. A joule is a very small amount of energy and a larger unit, the *kilowatt-hour* (kWh) is used.

A kilowatt-hour is the electrical energy used by a 1 kW appliance in 1 hour.

A 3 kW electric fire working for 2 hours uses 6 kWh of electrical energy—usually called 6 'units'.

Fig. 63.11

Electricity meters are marked in kWh: the reading on the one in Fig. 63.11 is 87939. When the pointer is between two figures the lower one is read, except when the figures are 9 and 0. At present a 'unit' costs about 5p.

Typical powers of some appliances are:

Lamps 60,	100 W	Fire	1, 2, 3 kW
Fridge	150 W	Kettle	2–3 kW
TV set	200 W	Immersion heater	3 kW
Iron	750 W	Cooker	8 kW

Questions

1. How much electrical energy in *joules* does a 100 watt lamp change in (*a*) 1 second, (*b*) 5 seconds, (*c*) 1 minute?

2. (*a*) What is the power of a lamp rated at 12 V 2 A?
(*b*) How many joules of electrical energy are changed per second by a 6 V 0.5 A lamp?

3. The largest number of 100 W bulbs which can safely be run from a 240 V supply with a 5 A fuse is

    A 2   **B** 5   C 10   D 12   E 20   (*W.Y.*)

4. What is the maximum power in kilowatts of the appliance(s) that can be connected safely to a 13 A 240 V mains socket?

5. A current of 2 A passes through a resistance of 4 Ω. Calculate (*a*) the p.d. between the ends of the resistance, (*b*) the power used by the resistance.   (*E.M.*)

6. A bulb is labelled 12 V 36 W. When used on a 12 V supply, (*a*) what current will it take, (*b*) what is its resistance?   (*A.L.*)

7. A 3 kW electric fire is designed to be run on a 250 V supply. Assuming it to be operating at the correct voltage, (*a*) what current will it draw from the supply, (*b*) what is the resistance of the element of the fire?   (*N.W.*)

8. Copy the diagrams of the electrical fitting of a domestic installation shown in Fig. 63.12. Connect up these fittings so that (*i*) the three lamps will be controlled separately, (*ii*) a supply is taken to the 13 A socket,

Fig. 63.12

9. If a 2 kW electric heater is used for 10 hours and electricity costs 3p per unit, (*a*) how many units (kWh) are used, (*b*) what is the cost?   (*A.L.*)

10. What is the cost of heating a tank of water with a 3000 W immersion heater for 80 minutes if electricity costs 3 p per kWh?

11. An electric cooker has an oven rated at 3 kW, a grill rated at 2 kW and two rings each rated at 500 W. The cooker operates from 240 V mains.
(*a*) Are the different heating elements connected in series or in parallel? Give a reason for your answer.
(*b*) Would a 30 A fuse be suitable for the cooker, assuming that all parts are switched on? Show clearly how you obtain your answer.
(*c*) What is the cost of operating all the parts for 30 minutes if electricity costs 3p per unit?   (*E.A.*)

12. (*a*) A lamp is marked 240 V 60 W. What exactly does this tell you about the bulb?
(*b*) A boy has a large number of 240 V 60 W coloured bulbs he wishes to use for decorations so that the bulbs operate normally.
    (*i*) How many can he connect to a 240 V supply through a 5 A fuse?
    (*ii*) What would be the total power of the circuit?
    (*iii*) Draw a diagram of the circuit he would employ.
(*c*) If electrical energy costs 3p per unit, what will be the cost of running the above circuit for 5 hours a night for 14 nights?   (*S.E.*)

64 Electrolysis and cells

Conduction in liquids

The apparatus of Fig. 64.1 can be used to find liquids that conduct electricity. There is no effect with distilled water; it is not a conductor. However if a little dilute sulphuric acid or common salt is added to the water the bulb lights up showing that current is flowing through the solution. Bubbles of gas appear at the copper strips and are evidence of chemical action. Tap water usually contains dissolved salts and allows a small current to flow.

Fig. 64.1

to 3 V battery
crocodile clip
beaker
liquid
bulb (1.25 V 0.25 A)
copper foil strips

The production of chemical action in a liquid by an electric current is called *electrolysis*. The liquid is an *electrolyte*. Solutions in water of acids, bases and salts are electrolytes. Mercury conducts electricity but no chemical change occurs and so it is not an electrolyte.

The two conductors (wires or plates) where current enters and leaves the liquid are *electrodes*. The one joined to the positive terminal of the battery at which the current (conventional) enters is the *anode*; the other is the *cathode*. The vessel in which the electrolysis occurs is called a *voltameter* (*not* voltmeter).

Electrolysis

(a) *Copper sulphate with copper electrodes.* The apparatus and circuit of Fig. 64.1 can be used with a strong copper sulphate solution (10 g to 100 cm³ water) in the beaker. No bubbles appear at the electrodes but if they are removed after a few minutes the cathode will be seen to be covered with a fresh layer of copper while the anode is dull. Weighing shows that the mass of copper lost by the anode (if it is pure) equals that gained by the cathode. Also,

the concentration of the copper sulphate solution is unchanged. It seems that copper is transferred from the anode to the cathode.

(b) *Acidified water with platinum electrodes.* A simple arrangement is shown in Fig. 64.2. The water contains a few drops of concentrated sulphuric acid to make it a better conductor. When current is passing, streams of bubbles rise from both electrodes and after a time the volume of gas from the cathode will be seen to be *twice* that from the anode.

Fig. 64.2

test tubes
water + few drops conc. H_2SO_4
platinum anode
platinum cathode
to 6 V battery and rheostat

If the tube above the cathode is removed and a light applied, there is an explosive 'pop' which is characteristic of hydrogen. The gas from the anode is oxygen and will relight a glowing splint.

The amount of acid stays constant and so it is water which is regarded as being electrolysed into hydrogen and oxygen.

Ionic theory

Current is considered to be carried in an electrolyte by *ions*. An ion is an atom or group of atoms which has *either* a positive charge due to losing one or more electrons *or* a negative charge due to gaining one or more electrons, Fig. 64.3a.

According to the ionic theory, in electrolysis, positive ions are attracted to the negative cathode and negative ions to the positive anode, Fig. 64.3b. In an electrolyte the charge carriers are therefore both positive and negative.

Copper sulphate solution contains copper ions and sulphate ions and since copper is deposited on the cathode during electrolysis, copper must be

electron

Normal atom

Positive ion

Negative ion

(a)

anode cathode

$\oplus\!\!\to$ positive ion

$\leftarrow\!\!\ominus$ negative ion

(b)

Fig. 64.3

positively charged. The negative sulphate ions go to the anode, where they form copper sulphate.

In general, metals and hydrogen form positive ions whilst non-metals and oxygen form negative ions.

Experiment: first law of electrolysis

The aim is to find how the mass of substance deposited depends on the charge that has passed.

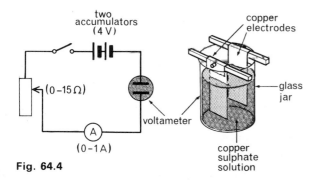

two accumulators (4 V)

$(0-15\,\Omega)$

A

$(0-1\,A)$

voltameter

copper electrodes

glass jar

copper sulphate solution

Fig. 64.4

Set up the circuit of Fig. 64.4 using a strong solution of copper sulphate containing a little sulphuric acid. Switch on and adjust the rheostat for a current of 0.5 to 1 A. (To obtain a hard coating of copper the current should not exceed $1/40\,A$ per cm^2 of immersed cathode surface.)

Switch off after 2 or 3 minutes, remove the cathode, wash it, rinse it in meths and dry it *well above* a non-luminous burner flame. Lightly clean the cathode with emery and find its mass m_1. Replace the cathode, switch on and pass the previous current I for time $t = 30$ min, occasionally checking the ammeter.

Remove the cathode, carefully wash it, rinse in meths, dry, then find its new mass m_2. The mass of copper deposited $m = m_2 - m_1$.

Record the results as shown below. The charge Q depositing mass m is given by $Q = I \times t$ where t is in seconds.

m_1 (g)	m_2 (g)	$m_2 - m_1$ $= m$ (g)	I (A)	t (s)	$Q = It$ (C)	m/Q

Either repeat the experiment with different values of I and t or use results obtained by others to fill in the table. Work out m/Q in each case.

The first law of electrolysis was discovered by Faraday and may be stated as follows.

The mass of substance liberated in electrolysis is proportional to the charge passed.

In symbols, $m \propto Q$ or $m/Q =$ a constant. The constant is called the *electrochemical equivalent* (e.c.e.) of the substance.

Electrolytes and Ohm's law

Fig. 64.5

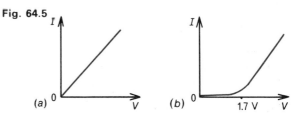

(a)

(b) 1.7 V

With copper sulphate solution and copper electrodes, the graph of I against V is a straight line through the origin, Fig. 64.5a, i.e. Ohm's law applies. With acidified water and platinum electrodes, Fig. 64.5b shows the I–V graph. I is practically zero until V exceeds 1.7 V; Ohm's law does not hold.

Uses of electrolysis

(a) *Electroplating.* Articles of one metal are often electrically plated with another to improve their appearance or to prevent rusting if they are made of iron or steel. Cutlery is often made of nickel, plated with silver. Steel car bumpers are chromium plated. The object to be plated is made the cathode in a voltameter with a salt of the plating metal as electrolyte, e.g. a silver salt for silver plating. Fig. 64.6 shows an industrial electroplating tank.

191

Fig. 64.6

(b) *Refining of metals.* In the case of copper the cathode is a thin sheet of copper, the electrolyte is copper sulphate solution and the anode, the impure copper to be refined. During electrolysis, *pure* copper is deposited on the cathode from the anode which slowly disappears. Impurities fall to the bottom of the voltameter.

Electrolysis is also used to make records and in the extraction of aluminium from its ores.

Electric cells

In a cell chemical energy becomes electrical energy. The process is the reverse of electrolysis where an electric current causes chemical change.

(a) *Simple cell*, Fig. 64.7. It has an e.m.f. of about 1.0 V but stops working after a short time due to 'polarization', i.e. the collection of hydrogen

bubbles on the copper plate. The cell is depolarized by adding potassium dichromate which oxidizes the hydrogen to water. A second defect is 'local action'. This is due to impurities in the zinc and results in the zinc being used up even when current is not supplied. The simple cell is no longer used.

(b) *Dry* (*Leclanché*) *cell*, Fig. 64.8. It is used in torches and transistor radios and has an e.m.f. of 1.5 V. The source of energy is chemical action between zinc and ammonium chloride, but as a result hydrogen is produced which collects at the carbon rod and 'polarizes' the cell. Manganese dioxide acts as the depolarizer (the carbon in the core reduces the

Fig. 64.7

zinc plate — copper plate
dilute sulphuric acid — glass jar

Fig. 64.8

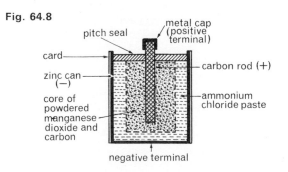

pitch seal — metal cap (positive terminal)
card
zinc can (−) — carbon rod (+)
core of powdered manganese dioxide and carbon — ammonium chloride paste
negative terminal

internal resistance to about $0.5\,\Omega$) and enables it to supply a steady current (e.g. 0.3 A) for some time.

(*c*) *Lead–acid accumulator*. It supplies much larger currents than a dry cell and is called a 'secondary' cell because it can be recharged by passing a current through it in the opposite direction. Simple and dry cells are 'primary' cells. A 12 V car battery consists of six accumulators in series, Fig. 64.9.

Fig. 64.9

The positive plate is lead dioxide (brown) and the negative one is lead (grey), with sulphuric acid as the electrolyte. During discharge both plates change to lead sulphate (white) and the acid becomes more dilute. When fully charged the relative density of the acid (measured by a hydrometer, p. 92) is 1.25, which falls to 1.18 at full discharge.

A charging circuit is shown in Fig. 64.10. The supply must be d.c. of greater e.m.f. than that of the accumulators to be charged. The *positive* of the supply is joined to the *positive* of the battery and

Fig. 64.10

the current is adjusted by the rheostat to the recommended value. Before charging, the accumulators should be 'topped up' with distilled water.

The internal resistance of an accumulator is less than $0.01\,\Omega$ and for currents of a few amperes, the 'lost' p.d. is negligible.

The capacity of an accumulator is stated in *ampere-hours* (A h) for a 10-hour discharge time. A 30 A h accumulator would supply 3 A for 10 hours but whilst 1 A would be supplied for more than 30 hours, 6 A would not flow for 5 hours.

Questions

1. (*a*) (*i*) When a current flows through a solution what is the name of the particles which move? (*ii*) How does the particle mentioned in (*i*) differ from an atom?

(*b*) If you wished to copper plate a piece of metal by an electrical method, explain why you would not use an a.c. supply.

(*c*) Describe and explain what happens to the lamp when the carbon rods of the apparatus in Fig. 64.11 are dipped into a beaker of (*i*) distilled water, (*ii*) dilute salt solution, (*iii*) mercury. (*W.M.*)

Fig. 64.11

2. Part of a circuit for electroplating a spoon with silver is shown in Fig. 64.12.

(*a*) Copy the diagram and include a battery with its polarity marked.

(*b*) What liquid could be used?

(*c*) If electrode X is made of silver, what happens to it during the electroplating?

Fig. 64.12

3. If 0.000 33 g of copper are deposited in a voltameter when a current of 1 A flows for 1 s, how much will be deposited after 10 min by a current of 4 A?

4. (*a*) Two small lamps are connected in series with a battery of dry cells. At first the lights shine brightly. Explain why they gradually become dimmer.

(*b*) The battery is disconnected for half an hour. Explain why the lamps again shine brightly when the battery is reconnected.

(*c*) Explain how, by altering the circuit, you could increase the brilliance of the lamps, and state what effect this change would have upon the life of the battery.

65 Electromagnets

Oersted's discovery

In 1819 Oersted accidentally discovered the magnetic effect of an electric current. His experiment can be repeated by holding a wire over and parallel to a compass needle which is pointing N and S, Fig. 65.1. The needle moves when the current is switched on. Reversing the current causes the needle to point in the opposite direction.

Fig. 65.1

Evidently around a wire carrying a current there is a *magnetic field*. As with the field due to a permanent magnet, we represent the field due to a current by *field lines* or *lines of force*. Arrows on the lines show the direction of the field, i.e. the direction in which a N pole points.

Different field patterns are given by differently shaped conductors.

Field due to a straight wire

If a straight vertical wire passes through the centre of a piece of card held horizontally and a current is passed through the wire, iron filings sprinkled on

Fig. 65.2

the card set in concentric circles when the card is tapped, Fig. 65.2.

Plotting compasses placed on the card set along the field lines and show the direction of the field at different points. When the current direction is reversed, the compasses point in the opposite direction showing that the direction of the field reverses when the current reverses.

If the current direction is known, the direction of the field can be predicted by the *Right-hand screw rule*.

If a right-handed screw moves forward in the direction of the current (conventional), the direction of rotation of the screw gives the direction of the field.

Field due to a circular coil

Fig. 65.3

The field pattern is shown in Fig. 65.3. At the centre of the coil the field lines are straight and at right angles to the plane of the coil. The Right-hand screw rule again gives the direction of the field at any point.

Field due to a solenoid

A solenoid is a long cylindrical coil. It produces a field similar to that of a bar magnet; in Fig. 65.4, end A behaves like a N pole and end B like a S pole. The polarity is found as before by applying the Right-hand screw rule to a short length of one turn of the solenoid. Alternatively the *Right-hand grip rule* can be used (p. 155).

The field inside a solenoid can be made very strong if it has a large number of turns and a large current flows. Previously we used it to magnetize

solenoid   field line

A   B

← current direction →

Fig. 65.4

materials (p. 154): permanent magnets are now made by allowing the molten metal to solidify in such fields.

Experiment: simple electromagnet

An electromagnet is a coil of wire wound on a soft iron core. A 5 cm iron nail and 3 m of rayon covered copper wire (SWG 26) are needed.

(*a*) Leave about 25 cm at one end of the wire (for connecting to the circuit) and then wind about 50 cm as a single layer on the nail. *Keep the turns close together and always wind in the same direction.* Connect the circuit of Fig. 65.5, setting the rheostat at its *maximum* resistance.

electromagnet   wooden stand

Fig. 65.5

paper clips

Ⓐ
(0–2A)   (0–15Ω)   (2–3 V)

Find the number of paper clips the electromagnet can support when known currents between 0.25 and 2.0 A pass through it. Record the results in a table. How does the 'strength' of the electromagnet depend on the current?

(*b*) Wind another two layers of wire on the nail in the *same direction* as the first layer. Repeat the experiment. What can you say about the 'strength' of an electromagnet and the number of turns of wire?

(*c*) Place the electromagnet on the bench under a sheet of paper. Sprinkle iron filings on the paper, tap it gently and observe the field pattern. How does it compare with that given by a bar magnet?

(*d*) Use the Right-hand screw (or grip) rule to predict which end of the electromagnet is a N pole. Check with a plotting compass.

Electromagnets

The magnetism of an electromagnet is *temporary* and can be switched on and off, unlike that of a permanent magnet. It has a core of *soft iron* which is magnetized only when current flows in the surrounding coil.

The strength of an electromagnet increases if

(*i*) the current in the coil increases,
(*ii*) the number of turns on the coil increases,
(*iii*) the poles are closer together.

In C-core (or horseshoe) electromagnets condition (*iii*) is achieved, Fig. 65.6. Note that the coil is wound in *opposite* directions on each limb of the core.

Fig. 65.6   coil   soft iron core

S

field line

N

current direction

Apart from being used as a crane to lift iron objects, Fig. 65.7, scrap iron, etc., an electromagnet is an essential part of many electrical devices.

Fig. 65.7

Electric bell: door chimes

(a) *Bell*, Fig. 65.8. When the circuit is completed, current flows in the coils of the electromagnet which becomes magnetized and attracts the soft iron bar (the armature). The hammer hits the gong but the circuit is now broken at the point C of the contact screw.

bell push
springy metal strip
soft iron armature
C
contact screw
electromagnet
hammer
gong

Fig. 65.8

The electromagnet loses its magnetism and no longer attracts the armature. The springy metal strip is then able to pull the armature back, remaking contact at C and so completing the circuit again. This cycle is repeated so long as the bell push is depressed and continuous ringing occurs.

wooden striker
spring
brass tube
metal chime plate
coil
soft iron rod
metal chime plate
wooden striker
push switch
to electrical supply

Fig. 65.9

(b) *Chimes*. The circuit is shown in Fig. 65.9. Work out what happens when the push switch is (i) pressed, (ii) released.

Relay: reed switch

(a) *Relay*. This is a switch worked by an electromagnet. It is useful if we want one circuit to control another, especially if the current is large in the

insulator
springy metal
Fig. 65.10
D
E
C
pivot
iron armature
A
B
coil   soft iron core

second circuit (see Qn. 10, p. 215). Fig. 65.10 shows a typical relay. When current flows in the coil from the circuit connected to AB, the soft iron core is magnetized and attracts the L-shaped iron armature. This rocks on its pivot and closes the contacts at C in the circuit connected to DE. The relay is then 'energized' or 'on'.

(b) *Reed switch*. One is shown in Fig. 65.11a. When current flows in the coil, the magnetic field produced magnetizes the strips (called 'reeds') of magnetic material. The ends become opposite poles and one reed is attracted to the other so completing the circuit connected to AB. The reeds separate when the current in the coil is switched off.

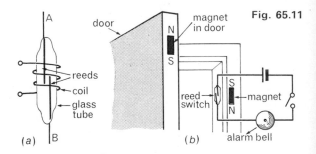

A
door
magnet in door
Fig. 65.11
N
S
reeds
coil
glass tube
reed switch
S
N
magnet
(a)   B
(b)
alarm bell

Reed switches are also operated by permanent magnets. Fig. 65.11b shows the use of a normally open reed switch as a burglar alarm. How does it work?

Telephone

A telephone contains a microphone at the speaking end and a receiver at the listening end.

(a) *Carbon microphone*, Fig. 65.12. When someone speaks, sound waves cause the diaphragm to move backwards and forwards. This varies the pressure on the carbon granules between the front carbon block which is attached to the diaphragm and the back one which is fixed. When the pressure in-

Fig. 65.12

creases, the granules are squeezed closer together and their electrical resistance decreases. A decrease of pressure has the opposite effect. If there is a current passing through the microphone (from a battery), this too will vary in a similar way to the sound wave variations.

(*b*) *Receiver.* A microphone changes sound energy into electrical energy which travels along the telephone cables and is changed back into sound by the receiver, Fig. 65.13.

Fig. 65.13

The varying current from the microphone passes through the coils of an electromagnet. This pulls the diaphragm towards it, by a distance which depends on the current. As a result, the diaphragm moves in and out and produces sound waves that are a copy of those that entered the microphone.

Crystal microphones and crystal earphones work on different principles from the above devices.

Questions

1. The vertical wire in Fig. 65.14 is at right angles to the card. In what direction will a plotting compass at A point when (*a*) there is no current in the wire, (*b*) current flows upwards?

Fig. 65.14

2. Fig. 65.15 shows a solenoid wound round a core of soft iron. Will the end A be a N pole or a S pole when the current (conventional) flows in the direction shown?

(*J.M.B./A.L./N.W.16+*)

Fig. 65.15

3. A small electromagnet, used for lifting and then releasing a small steel ball, is made in the laboratory, Fig. 65.16.

Fig. 65.16

(*a*) Explain why soft iron is a better material than steel to use for the core.

(*b*) In order to lift a slightly larger ball it is necessary to make a stronger electromagnet. State TWO ways in which an electromagnet could be made more powerful. (*Met.*)

4. You are asked to carry out an experiment to find how the lifting power of a horseshoe electromagnet depends upon the current flowing through the coils.

(*a*) Draw a clear diagram of the circuit you would use showing clearly the direction of the current, the direction of the winding of the coils of the electromagnet and the polarity of one end of the magnet.

(*b*) Eventually when the current has reached a certain value any further increase in the current does not result in a further increase in the lifting power. Why is this? (*E.M.*)

5. Fig. 65.17 shows an arrangement for lighting three lamps, A, B and C, only one of which is controlled directly by the switch.

Fig. 65.17

(*a*) Which of the lamps is directly controlled by the switch?
(*b*) What is the name given to this use of an electromagnet?
(*c*) Which lamps can be on at once?
(*d*) Explain how lamp C comes on. (*S.R.*)

66 Electric motors

Electric motors form the heart of a whole host of electrical devices ranging from domestic appliances such as vacuum cleaners and washing machines to electric locomotives and lifts. In a car the windscreen wipers are usually driven by one and the engine is started by another.

The motor effect

A wire carrying a current in a magnetic field experiences a force. If the wire can move it does.

Fig. 66.1

motion

flexible wire

to low voltage high current supply

(a) *Demonstration.* In Fig. 66.1 the flexible wire is loosely supported in the strong magnetic field of a C-shaped magnet (permanent or electro). When the switch is pressed, current flows in the wire which jumps upwards as shown. If either the direction of the current or the direction of the field is reversed, the wire moves downwards. What happens if both are reversed?

(b) *Explanation.* Fig. 66.2a is a side-view of the magnetic field lines due to the wire and the magnet. Those due to the wire are circles and we will suppose their directions are as shown. The dotted lines

Fig. 66.2

force on wire

wire
(a)

wire
(b)

represent the field lines of the magnet and their direction is to the right.

The resultant field obtained by combining both fields is shown in Fig. 66.2b. There are more lines below than above the wire since both fields act in the same direction below but in opposition above. If we *suppose* the lines are like stretched elastic, those below will try to straighten out and in so doing will exert an upwards force on the wire.

Fleming's left-hand rule

The direction of the force or thrust on the wire can be predicted by this rule which is also called the 'Motor rule', Fig. 66.3.

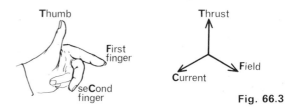

Thumb

First finger

seCond finger

Thrust

Current

Field

Fig. 66.3

*Hold the thumb and first two fingers of the left hand at right angles to each other with the **F**irst finger pointing in the direction of the **F**ield and the se**C**ond finger in the direction of the **C**urrent, then the **Th**umb points in the direction of the **Th**rust.*

If the wire is not at right angles to the field, the force is smaller and is zero if it is parallel to the field.

Simple d.c. electric motor

A simple motor to work from direct current (d.c.) consists of a rectangular coil of wire mounted on an axle which can rotate between the poles of a C-shaped magnet, Fig. 66.4. Each end of the coil is connected to half of a split ring of copper, called the *commutator*, which rotates with the coil. Two carbon blocks, the *brushes*, are pressed lightly against the commutator by springs. The brushes are connected to an electrical supply.

If Fleming's left-hand rule is applied to the coil in the position shown, we find that side *ab* experiences an upward force and side *cd* a downward

Fig. 66.4

b coil c

N S

a d

brush (fixed) + brush (fixed)

commutator (rotates with coil)

force. (No forces act on *ad* and *bc* since they are parallel to the field.) These two forces form a *couple* which rotates the coil in a clockwise direction until it is vertical.

The brushes are then in line with the gaps in the commutator and the current stops. However, because of its inertia, the coil overshoots the vertical and the commutator halves change contact from one brush to the other. This reverses the current through the coil and so also the directions of the forces on its sides. Side *ab* is on the right now, acted on by a downward force, whilst *cd* is on the left with an upward force. The coil thus carries on rotating clockwise.

Experiment: a model motor

The motor is shown in Fig. 66.5 and is made from a kit of parts.

1. Wrap Sellotape round one end of the metal tube which passes through the wooden block.
2. Cut two rings off a piece of narrow rubber tub-

ing; slip them onto the Sellotaped end of the metal tube.
3. Remove the insulation from one end of a $1\frac{1}{2}$ metre length of SWG 26 PVC-covered copper wire and fix it under both rubber rings so that it is held tight against the Sellotape. This forms one end of the coil.
4. Wind 10 turns of the wire in the slot in the wooden block and finish off the second end of the coil by removing the PVC and fixing this too under the rings but on the *opposite* side of the tube from the first end. The bare ends act as the *commutator*.
5. Push the axle through the metal tube of the wooden base so that the block spins freely.
6. Arrange two $\frac{1}{2}$ metre lengths of wire to act as *brushes* and leads to the supply, as shown. Adjust the brushes so that they are vertical and each touches one bare end of the coil when the plane of the coil is horizontal. *The motor will not work if this is not so.*
7. Slide the base into the magnet with *opposite poles facing.* Connect to a 3 V battery (or other low voltage d.c. supply) and a slight push of the coil should set it spinning at high speed.

Practical motors

Practical motors have:

(*a*) *a coil of many turns wound on a soft-iron cylinder or core* which rotates with the coil. This makes it more powerful. The coil and core together are called the *armature.*

Fig. 66.5

Fig. 66.6

paper cone attached to the coil moves with it and sets up sound waves in the surrounding air, Fig. 66.7b.

Questions

1. A wire carries a current horizontally between the magnetic poles N and S which face each other on a table, Fig. 66.8. The direction of the force on the wire due to the magnets is

  A from N to S
  B from S to N
  C opposite to the current direction
  D in the direction of the current
  E vertically upwards   (*O./S.R.16+*)

Fig. 66.8

2. In Fig. 66.9 AB is a copper wire hanging from a pivot at A and dipping in mercury in a copper dish at B so that it hangs between the poles of a powerful magnet.

Fig. 66.9

(*b*) *several coils* each in a slot in the core and each having a pair of commutator segments. This gives increased power and smoother running. The motor of an electric drill is shown in Fig. 66.6.

(*c*) *an electromagnet* (usually) to produce the field in which the armature rotates.

Most electric motors used in industry are *induction motors*. They work off a.c. (alternating current) on a different principle to the d.c. motor.

Moving coil loudspeakers

Varying currents from a radio, record-player etc. pass through a short cylindrical coil whose turns are at right angles to the magnetic field of a magnet with a central pole and a surrounding ring pole, Fig. 66.7a.

A force acts on the coil which, according to Fleming's left-hand rule, makes it move in and out. A

(*a*) Copy the diagram and mark in the lines of force representing the field between the poles.

(*b*) Mark in the direction of the conventional current flow in AB when the switch is closed.

(*c*) What else will happen when the switch is closed? (*S.E.*)

3. In the simple electric motor of Fig. 66.10, will the coil rotate clockwise or anticlockwise as seen by the eye from the position X? The arrows on the diagram indicate the direction of the conventional current flow.   (*J.M.B./A.L./N.W.16+*)

Fig. 66.10

4. An electric motor is a device which converts

  A mechanical energy into electrical energy
  B heat energy into electrical energy
  C electrical energy into heat only
  D heat energy into mechanical energy
  E electrical energy into mechanical energy and heat.
                                      (*W.Y.*)

Fig. 66.7

casing
ring pole
END-ON VIEW
central pole
coil
paper cone
coil on tube

(a)   (b)

67 Electric meters

Moving coil galvanometer

A galvanometer detects small currents or small p.d.s, often of the order of milliamperes (mA) or millivolts (mV). (1 mA = 1/100 A = 0.001 A = 10^{-3} A.) Some are even more sensitive.

In the moving coil *pointer-type* meter, a coil is pivoted on jewelled bearings between the poles of a permanent magnet, Fig. 67.1a. Current enters and leaves the coil by hair springs above and below it. When current flows, a couple acts on the coil (as in an electric motor), causing it to rotate until stopped by the springs. The greater the current the greater the deflection which is shown by a pointer attached to the coil.

Fig. 67.1

The soft iron cylinder at the centre of the coil is *fixed* and along with the concave poles of the magnet it produces a *radial* field, Fig. 67.1b, i.e. the field lines are directed to the centre of the cylinder. The scale on the meter is then even or linear, i.e. all divisions are the same size.

The sensitivity of a galvanometer is increased by having

(*i*) more turns on the coil,
(*ii*) a stronger magnet,
(*iii*) weaker hair springs or a wire suspension,

(*iv*) as a pointer, a long beam of light reflected from a mirror on the coil.

The last two are used in *light-beam* meters which have a full scale deflection of a few microamperes (μA). (1 μA = 10^{-6} A.)

A moving coil galvanometer measures d.c. not a.c. unless it is used with a rectifier (p. 212).

Ammeters and shunts

A galvanometer can be modified for use as an ammeter. Suppose a moving coil meter has resistance 5 Ω (due largely to the coil) and gives a full scale deflection (f.s.d.) when 1 mA (0.001 A) passes through it.

To convert it to an ammeter to read 0–1 A, a resistor of low value is connected in parallel with it as a by-pass. The resistor is called a *shunt* and, when the current to be measured is 1 A, it must allow only 0.001 A to go through the meter and the rest, i.e. 0.999 A, must flow through the shunt, Fig. 67.2.

Fig. 67.2

The meter and shunt are in parallel, and so,

$$\text{p.d. across meter} = \text{p.d. across shunt}$$
$$\therefore \quad 0.001 \times 5 = 0.999 \times S$$

where S is the resistance of the shunt in Ω.

$$\therefore \quad S = \frac{0.001 \times 5}{0.999} = \frac{5}{999} = 0.005 \ \Omega$$

Shunts consist of short lengths of thick manganin wire or strip. Manganin is an alloy whose resistance does not change when it is warmed by the current.

An ammeter is placed in *series* in a circuit and must have a *low resistance* compared with the rest of the circuit, otherwise it changes the current to be measured. The combined resistance of this meter and shunt is below 0.005 Ω.

Voltmeters and multipliers

A moving coil galvanometer of resistance $5\,\Omega$ and f.s.d. 1 mA can be converted to a voltmeter to read 0–1 V by connecting a resistor of high value in series with it.

The resistor is called a *multiplier* and it must be such that when a p.d. of 1 V is applied across it and the meter together, the current is 0.001 A, i.e., the meter records a f.s.d., Fig. 67.3.

Fig. 67.3

If M is the resistance of the multiplier in Ω, then since it is in series with the meter,

p.d. across multiplier and meter at f.s.d.
$$= 0.001 \times (M + 5) = 1$$
$$\therefore \; M + 5 = 1/0.001 = 1000$$
$$\therefore \; M = 995\,\Omega$$

Multipliers consist of long lengths of insulated manganin wire wound on a bobbin. A moving coil galvanometer with shunts and multipliers is shown in Fig. 67.4.

A voltmeter is placed in *parallel* with the part of the circuit across which the p.d. is to be measured. It should have a *high resistance* compared with the resistance across which it is connected. Otherwise the total resistance of the whole circuit is reduced so changing the current and the p.d. required. The ideal voltmeter has an infinite resistance.

Note. When a galvanometer with a resistance of

Fig. 67.4

$5\,\Omega$ gives a f.s.d. of 1 mA, the p.d. across it must be $0.001 \times 5 = 0.005\,\text{V} = 5$ millivolts (mV). It could be used as a millivoltmeter reading 0–5 mV.

Moving iron meters

(a) *Repulsion type*, Fig. 67.5a. When current flows in the coil the two small soft iron rods P and Q are magnetized in the same direction. They repel. Q is fixed but P is attached to a pivoted pointer and moves away from Q until stopped by the hair spring. The larger the current the greater the repulsion.

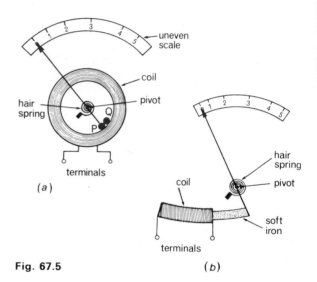

Fig. 67.5　　　　　　　　　　　　　(b)

(b) *Attraction type*, Fig. 67.5b. Work out from the diagram how it operates.

Both types can be used as ammeters or voltmeters with suitable shunts or multipliers. They work whichever way current passes and so will measure a.c. or d.c. A disadvantage is their uneven scale; it is closer at the start.

Definition of the ampere

A wire carrying a current in a magnetic field experiences a force (p. 198). In Fig. 67.6 currents are flowing in each wire and each is in the field created by the other. A force therefore exists between them, which according to Fleming's left-hand rule, should be one of attraction if the currents are in the same direction.

The forces set up between current carrying wires are used to define and measure the ampere accurately.

Fig. 67.6

metal hook

wooden bar

10 A

50 cm copper wire

low voltage d.c. supply

1 cm

mercury

The ampere is the current which, if flowing in each of two infinitely long parallel straight wires placed 1 metre apart in a vacuum, produces a force between them of 2×10^{-7} newton per metre of wire.

(The choice of 2×10^{-7} newton was made to keep the value of the ampere defined in this way close to its previous value which was defined in terms of the chemical effect.)

The measurement is made by a large, expensive *current balance* in which the force between two coils is measured. The current is thus found by weighing. Fig. 67.7 shows the instrument used at the National Physical Laboratory to check ammeters.

Questions

1. In Fig. 67.8a a moving coil meter is placed in series with a high resistance, R, which is very much greater in value than the resistance of the meter itself.

In Fig. 67.8b the same meter is shown placed in parallel with a small resistance, r, which is very much smaller in value than the resistance of the meter itself.

Fig. 67.8

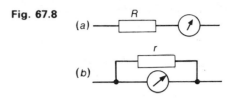

(a)

(b)

R

r

(a) For what purpose, or, as what sort of measuring instrument would (i) the arrangement in Fig. 67.8a be used, (ii) the arrangement in Fig. 67.8b be used?

(b) What is the effect on the range of the instrument (i) in Fig. 67.8a, if the value of R is greatly increased, (ii) in Fig. 67.8b, if the value of r is greatly increased?   (J.M.B./A.L./N.W.16+)

2. An ammeter, of resistance R and reading up to 5 A, is to be converted to one reading up to 10 A. This can be done by connecting

    A a resistance R/2 in series
    B a resistance R in parallel
    C a resistance R in series
    D a resistance 2R in parallel
    E a resistance 2R in series   (O./S.R.16+)

3. A galvanometer has a resistance of $20\,\Omega$ and gives a full scale reading for a current of 0.20 A.

(a) What is the voltage across the galvanometer coil?

(b) Draw a diagram showing how you would connect a low resistance to the galvanometer to convert it into an ammeter.

(c) If the galvanometer is converted to an ammeter which can read up to 1.0 A, what size current must pass through the low resistance when 0.20 A are passing through the coil?

(d) What is the size of this extra low resistance?   (W.M.)

4. A galvanometer of internal resistance $20\,\Omega$ gives a full scale deflection with a current of 50 mA.

How should the galvanometer be modified for use as (a) a 1.0 A ammeter, (b) a 100 V voltmeter?   (E.M.)

5. Fig. 67.9 shows an end section of two rods 1 and 2 placed close together in a long solenoid. When a direct current is passed round the solenoid the rods move apart. When the current is switched off the rods return to their original position.

Fig. 67.9

(a) What has happened to the rods to cause them to move apart?

(b) What are the rods made of?

(c) If alternating current is used, what effect, if any, will this have on the experiment?   (E.M.)

68 Electrical measurements

Wheatstone bridge

A Wheatstone bridge enables resistance to be measured more accurately than by the ammeter-voltmeter method (p. 177). It involves making adjustments until there is no deflection on a galvanometer and so, being a 'null' method, it does not depend on the accuracy of an instrument.

Fig. 68.1

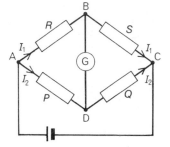

Four resistors P, Q, R, S are joined as in Fig. 68.1. If R is the unknown resistor, S must be known as must the values of P and Q or their ratio. A galvanometer G and a dry cell are connected as shown. One or more of P, Q and S are adjusted until there is no deflection on G. The bridge is then 'balanced' and we can show that

$$\frac{R}{S} = \frac{P}{Q}$$

enabling R to be found. The proof is as follows.

At balance, no current flows through G, the p.d. across BD must then be zero and so

p.d. across AB = p.d. across AD

Also, current through R = current through $S = I_1$ and, current through P = current through $Q = I_2$. Therefore

$$I_1 \times R = I_2 \times P \qquad (1)$$

Similarly, p.d. across BC = p.d. across DC. Hence

$$I_1 \times S = I_2 \times Q \qquad (2)$$

Dividing (1) by (2),

$$\frac{R}{S} = \frac{P}{Q} \quad \text{or} \quad R = S \times \frac{P}{Q}$$

Metre bridge

This is a practical version of the Wheatstone bridge, Fig. 68.2. Resistors P and Q consist of a wire AC of uniform cross-section area, 1 m long, with a resistance of several ohms and often made of constantan.

Fig. 68.2

The ratio of P to Q is altered by changing the position on the wire of the movable contact or 'jockey' D. The other arm of the bridge contains the unknown resistor R and a known resistor S. Thick copper strips of low resistance connect the various parts.

The position of D is adjusted until there is no deflection on G, then

$$\frac{R}{S} = \frac{P}{Q} = \frac{\text{resistance of AD}}{\text{resistance of DC}}$$

Since the wire is uniform, its resistance will be proportional to its length and therefore

$$\frac{R}{S} = \frac{\text{AD}}{\text{DC}} = \frac{l_1}{l_2} \quad \text{or} \quad R = S \times \frac{l_1}{l_2}$$

Two practical points should be noted. First, the value of S should be chosen to give a balance point near the centre of the wire, say between 30 and 70 cm. This gives a more accurate result. Second, after obtaining a balance, R and S should be interchanged and a second pair of values of l_1 and l_2 obtained. The average values are then used to calculate the result.

Resistivity

Experiments show that the resistance R of a wire is

(*i*) directly proportional to its length l, i.e. $R \propto l$.

(ii) inversely proportional to its cross-section area A, i.e. $R \propto 1/A$ (doubling A, halves R).

Combining these two results, we get

$$R \propto l \times \frac{1}{A}$$

This can be written as an equation if we insert a constant

$$\therefore \quad R = \rho \frac{l}{A}$$

where ρ is a constant, called the *resistivity* of the material.

If we put $l = 1$ m and $A = 1$ m^2 in the equation, then $\rho = R$.

The resistivity of a material is numerically equal to the resistance of a 1 m length of it of cross-section area 1 m^2.

The unit of resistivity is the *ohm metre* (Ω m) as can be seen by rearranging the equation in the form $\rho = RA/l$. Knowing ρ for a material, the resistance of any sample of it may be calculated.

Experiment: resistivity of constantan

Connect up a metre bridge as in Fig. 68.2 with 1 m of constantan wire as the unknown resistance. Measure its resistance R as described before.

Using a micrometer screw gauge, find the average diameter d of the wire by taking several readings along its length. The cross-section area A (in metres) is given by

$$A = \pi \, (\text{radius})^2 = \pi \left(\frac{\text{diameter}}{2} \right)^2 = \frac{\pi d^2}{4}$$

The resistivity ρ is then found in ohm metre from

$$\rho = \frac{AR}{l} = \frac{\pi d^2 R}{4l}$$

Slide-wire potentiometer

A potentiometer is a device for measuring p.d.s more accurately than by a voltmeter. It consists of a resistance wire AB of *uniform* cross-section area, on a ruler and with a *steady* current passing through it from an accumulator, Fig. 68.3.

Part of the p.d. across AB is tapped off and used to balance the unknown p.d. If AB is 1 m and the p.d. across it is 2.0 V, then if C is 75 cm from A, there will be a p.d. between A and C of 3/4 of $2.0 = 1.5$ V. The unknown p.d. is connected to X and Y *with the polarity shown* and the jockey moved along the wire

Fig. 68.3

until the galvanometer is not deflected. If this occurs at C, the unknown p.d. is 1.5 V.

No current is supplied by the unknown p.d. *at balance* and if it is a cell then the p.d. measured is its e.m.f., i.e. the potentiometer behaves as a voltmeter of infinite resistance.

Questions

Fig. 68.4

1. Fig. 68.4 shows a Wheatstone bridge circuit in which Q and R are both $15\,\Omega$ resistors, S is a length of platinum wire. P is a thermistor and G is a galvanometer.
   (a) Why is the Wheatstone bridge a more accurate method for measuring resistance than the voltmeter-ammeter method?
   (b) Why is a galvanometer used in a Wheatstone bridge rather than an ordinary ammeter?
   (c) What relation is satisfied when the bridge is balanced?
   (d) Find the resistance of the wire S given that its length and area of cross-section are 300 m and 1 mm^2 respectively (resistivity of platinum wire is $10^{-7}\,\Omega$ m).
   (e) The table below indicates the variation with temperature of the resistance of the thermistor P. Plot a graph to determine the thermistor temperature at which the bridge is balanced.

$X\,(\Omega)$	17	9.0	5.4	2.3	1.2
$T\,(\text{K})$	310	330	350	370	390

(N.I.)

Fig. 68.5

2. In the circuit of Fig. 68.5, PQ is a coil of resistance wire and the sliding contact J is slowly moved towards P. What is the effect on the brightness of the lamps L_1, L_2?
   A Both become brighter.
   B Both become dimmer.
   C There is no change in the brightness of either lamp.
   D L_1 becomes dimmer and L_2 brighter.
   E L_1 becomes brighter and L_2 dimmer.

(O./S.R.16+)

69 Generators

An electric current creates a magnetic field. The reverse effect of producing electricity from magnetism was discovered in 1831 by Faraday and is called *electromagnetic induction*. It led to the construction of generators (dynamos) for producing electrical energy in power stations.

Electromagnetic induction

Two ways of investigating the effect follow.

Fig. 69.1

magnet

wire

sensitive centre-zero galvanometer

(*a*) *Straight wire and U-shaped magnet*, Fig. 69.1. First the wire is held at rest between the poles of the magnet and the galvanometer observed. It is then moved in each of the six directions shown. Only *when it is moving* upwards (direction 1) or downwards (direction 2) is there a deflection on the galvanometer, indicating an induced current in the wire. The deflection is in opposite directions in each case and only lasts while the wire is in motion.

(*b*) *Bar magnet and coil*, Fig. 69.2. The magnet is pushed into the coil, one pole first, then held still

sensitive centre-zero galvanometer

coil (600 turns)

bar magnet

Fig. 69.2

inside it. It is next withdrawn. The galvanometer shows that current is induced in the coil in one direction as the magnet *moves in* and in the opposite direction as it is *removed*. There is no deflection when the magnet is at rest. The results are the same if the coil is moved instead of the magnet, i.e. only *relative motion* is needed.

Faraday's law

To 'explain' electromagnetic induction Faraday suggested that an e.m.f. is induced in a conductor whenever it 'cuts' magnetic field lines, i.e. moves *across* them, but not when it moves along them or is at rest. If the conductor forms part of a complete circuit, an induced current is also produced.

Faraday found, and it can be shown with apparatus like that in Fig. 69.2, that the induced e.m.f. increases with increases of

(*i*) the speed of motion of the magnet or coil,
(*ii*) the number of turns on the coil,
(*iii*) the strength of the magnet.

These facts led him to state a law.

The size of the induced e.m.f. is directly proportional to the rate at which the conductor cuts magnetic field lines.

Lenz's law

The direction of the induced current can be predicted by a law due to the Russian scientist, Lenz.

The direction of the induced current is such as to oppose the change causing it.

In Fig. 69.3*a* the magnet approaches the coil, north pole first. According to Lenz's law the in-

Fig. 69.3

(*a*)   (*b*)

duced current should flow in a direction which makes the coil behave like a magnet with its top a north pole. The downward motion of the magnet will then be opposed.

When the magnet is withdrawn, the top of the coil should become a south pole, Fig. 69.3b, and attract the north pole of the magnet, so hindering its removal. The induced current is thus in the opposite direction to that when the magnet approaches.

Lenz's law is an example of the principle of conservation of energy. If the currents caused opposite poles to those that they do, electrical energy would be created from nothing. As it is, mechanical energy is provided by whoever moves the magnet, to overcome the forces that arise.

For a straight wire moving at right angles to a magnetic field a more useful form of Lenz's law is *Fleming's right-hand rule* (the 'Dynamo rule'), Fig. 69.4.

Fig. 69.4

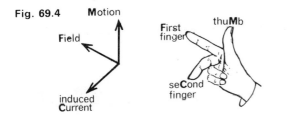

Hold the thumb and first two fingers of the right hand at right angles to each other with the First finger pointing in the direction of the Field and the thuMb in the direction of Motion of the wire, then the seCond finger points in the direction of the induced Current.

Simple a.c. generator (alternator)

The simplest alternating current (a.c.) generator consists of a rectangular coil between the poles of a C-shaped magnet, Fig. 69.5a. The ends of the coil

are joined to two *slip rings* on the axle and against which carbon *brushes* press.

When the coil is rotated it cuts the field lines and an e.m.f. is induced in it. Fig. 69.5b shows how the e.m.f. varies over one complete rotation.

As the coil moves through the vertical position with *ab* uppermost, *ab* and *cd* are moving along the lines (*bc* and *da* do so always) and no cutting occurs. The induced e.m.f. is zero.

During the first quarter rotation the e.m.f. increases to a maximum when the coil is horizontal. Sides *ab* and *dc* are then cutting the lines at the greatest rate.

In the second quarter rotation the e.m.f. decreases again and is zero when the coil is vertical with *dc* uppermost. After this, the direction of the e.m.f. reverses because, during the next half rotation, the motion of *ab* is directed upwards and *dc* downwards.

An alternating e.m.f. is generated which acts first in one direction and then the other; it would cause a.c. to flow in a circuit connected to the brushes. The *frequency* of an a.c. is the number of complete cycles it makes each second (c/s) and is measured in *hertz* (Hz), i.e. 1 c/s = 1 Hz. If the coil rotates twice per second, the a.c. has frequency 2 Hz. The mains supply is a.c. of frequency 50 Hz.

Simple d.c. generator

An a.c. generator becomes a direct current (d.c.) one if the slip rings are replaced by a *commutator* like that in a d.c. motor, Fig. 69.6a.

The brushes are arranged so that as the coil goes through the vertical, changeover of contact occurs from one half of the split ring of the commutator to the other. In this position the e.m.f. induced in the coil reverses and so one brush is always positive and the other negative.

The e.m.f. at the brushes is shown in Fig. 69.6b; although varying in value, it never changes direc-

Fig. 69.5

(a)

(b)

207

Fig. 69.6

(a)

(b) coil vertical   coil horizontal

tion and would produce a direct current (d.c.) in an external circuit.

In construction the simple d.c. dynamo is the same as the simple d.c. motor and one can be used as the other. When an electric motor is working it acts as a dynamo and creates an e.m.f., called a *back e.m.f.*, opposing and nearly equal to the applied p.d. The current in the coil is therefore much less once the motor is running.

Practical generators

In actual generators several coils are wound in evenly-spaced slots in a soft iron cylinder and electromagnets usually replace permanent magnets.

In power station alternators the electromagnets rotate (the *rotor*), whilst the coils and their core are at rest (the *stator*). This has the advantage that only the relatively small direct current needed for the electromagnets is fed through the rotating slip rings whilst the large p.d.s (e.g. 25 000 V) and currents induced in the coils are then led away through stationary cables. The rotor is driven by a steam or water turbine which also powers a small d.c. dynamo (the *exciter*) for supplying the electromagnets.

Fig. 69.7

A power station turbo-alternator-exciter set is shown in Fig. 69.7.

Fig. 69.8

In a cycle dynamo, Fig. 69.8, the rotor is a permanent magnet and the e.m.f. is induced in the coil which is at rest.

Questions

1. (*a*) A coil of copper wire is connected to a centre-zero galvanometer. Explain what would be observed if a bar magnet was pushed into the coil so that the north pole of the magnet entered first.

(*b*) What would be observed if the magnet was
 (*i*) held at rest inside the coil?
 (*ii*) pulled out again?
 (*iii*) pushed in faster than before?
 (*iv*) pushed in so that the south pole entered first?   (*E.A.*)

Fig. 69.9

2. A simple generator is shown in Fig. 69.9.
 (*a*) What are A and B called and what is their purpose?
 (*b*) What changes can be made to increase the e.m.f. generated?

70 Transformers

Mutual induction

When the current in a coil is switched on or off or changed, an e.m.f. and current are induced in a neighbouring coil. The effect, called *mutual induction*, is an example of electromagnetic induction not using a permanent magnet and can be shown with the arrangement of Fig. 70.1. Coil A is the *primary* and coil B the *secondary*.

Fig. 70.1

Switching on the current in the primary sets up a magnetic field and as its field lines 'grow' outwards from the primary they 'cut' the secondary. An e.m.f. is induced in the secondary until the current in the primary reaches its steady value. When the current is switched off in the primary, the magnetic field dies away and we can imagine the field lines cutting the secondary as they collapse, again inducing an e.m.f. in it. Changing the primary current by *quickly* altering the rheostat has the same effect.

The induced e.m.f. is increased by having a soft iron rod in the coils, or better still, by using coils wound on a complete iron ring. More field lines then cut the secondary due to the magnetization of the iron.

Experiment: mutual induction with a.c.

An alternating current is changing all the time and if it flows in a primary coil, an alternating e.m.f. and current are induced in a secondary coil.

Connect the circuit of Fig. 70.2. The 1 V high current power unit supplies a.c. to the primary and the lamp detects the secondary current.

Fig. 70.2

Find the effect on the brightness of the lamp of

(*i*) pulling the C-cores apart slightly,
(*ii*) increasing the secondary turns to 15,
(*iii*) decreasing the secondary turns to 5.

Transformer equation

A transformer transforms (changes) an *alternating p.d.* (voltage) from one value to another of greater or smaller value. It has primary and secondary coils wound on a complete soft iron core, either one on top of the other, Fig. 70.3a, or on separate limbs of the core, Fig. 70.3b.

Fig. 70.3

An alternating voltage applied to the primary induces an alternating voltage in the secondary whose value can be shown to be given by

$$\frac{\text{secondary voltage } (V_s)}{\text{primary voltage } (V_p)} = \frac{\text{secondary turns } (t_s)}{\text{primary turns } (t_p)}$$

A 'step-up' transformer has more turns on the secondary than the primary and V_s is greater than V_p, Fig. 70.4a. For example, if the secondary has twice as many turns as the primary, V_s is about twice V_p. In a 'step-down' transformer there are fewer turns on the secondary than the primary and V_s is less than V_p, Fig. 70.4b.

Fig. 70.4

(a) Step-up: $V_s > V_p$ (b) Step-down: $V_s < V_p$

Fig. 70.5

Energy losses in a transformer

If the p.d. is stepped-up in a transformer the current is stepped-down in proportion. This must be so if we assume that all the electrical energy given to the primary appears in the secondary, i.e. that energy is conserved and the transformer is 100% efficient (many approach this). Then

power in primary = power in secondary
$$V_p \times I_p = V_s \times I_s$$

where I_p and I_s are the primary and secondary currents respectively.

$$\therefore \quad \frac{I_s}{I_p} = \frac{V_p}{V_s}$$

So, in theory, if the p.d. is doubled the current is halved. In practice, it is more than halved due to small energy losses in the transformer arising from three causes.

(a) *Resistance of windings*. The windings of copper wire do have some resistance and heat is produced by the current in them.

(b) *Eddy currents*. The iron core is in the changing magnetic field of the primary and currents, called eddy currents, are induced in it which cause heating. These are reduced by using a *laminated* core made of sheets, insulated from each other to have a high resistance.

(c) *Leakage of field lines*. All the lines produced by the primary may not 'cut' the secondary, especially if the core has an air-gap or is badly designed.

A large transformer like that in Fig. 70.5 has to be oil-cooled to prevent overheating.

Fig. 70.6

The stepping-up of current can be demonstrated with the 100:1 *step-down* transformer of Fig. 70.6 in which the nail melts spectacularly.

Transmission of electrical power

(a) *Grid system*. This is a network of cables, most supported on pylons, which connect over 200 power stations throughout the country to consumers. In the largest modern stations, electricity is generated at 25 000 V (25 kilovolts = 25 kV) and stepped up at once in a transformer to 275 or 400 kV to be sent over long distances on the Supergrid. Later, the p.d. is reduced by sub-station transformers for distribution to local users, Fig. 70.7.

At the Area Control Centres engineers direct the flow and re-route it when breakdown occurs.

Fig. 70.7

This makes the supply more reliable, and cuts costs by enabling smaller, less efficient stations to be shut down at off-peak periods.

(b) *Use of high alternating p.d.s.* If 400 000 W of electrical power has to be sent through cables it can be done as 400 000 V at 1 A or 400 V at 1000 A (since watts = amperes × volts). But the amount of electrical energy changed to unwanted heat (due to the resistance of the cables) is proportional to the *square of the current* and so the power loss (I^2R) is less if transmission occurs at high voltage (high tension) and low current. On the other hand high p.d.s need good insulation. The efficiency with which transformers step alternating p.d.s up and down accounts for the use of a.c. rather than d.c.

VILLAGE END
20:1 step–down transformer
2400-turn coil
12 V 24 W
power line (1m eureka wire SWG 28)
POWER STATION END
120-turn coil
1:20 step-up transformer
12 V 24 W
12 V a.c.
2400-turn coil
120-turn coil

Fig. 70.8

The advantages of 'high' alternating p.d. power transmission may be shown as in Fig. 70.8, first without the transformers, then with them.

Car ignition system

A transformer does not work off d.c. but the *induction coil*, which uses the same principle, does. It is used in a car to produce the high voltage that causes the sparking plug to spark and ignite the mixture of petrol vapour and air.

The primary circuit is broken when the rotating

Fig. 70.9

ignition switch
coils
distributor
PRIMARY CIRCUIT
SECONDARY CIRCUIT
12 V
capacitor
rotor arm
to sparking plugs
'points' rotating cam
car body

cam, Fig. 70.9, separates the 'points'. A high p.d. is induced in the secondary which is applied at the right time to each plug in turn by the rotor arm of the distributor. When the 'points' open, the capacitor acts as a reservoir and stops sparking at them which would cause 'pitting'. It also ensures that the primary current falls rapidly, so giving a larger induced e.m.f. in the secondary.

Questions

1. Two coils of wire, A and B, are placed near one another, Fig. 70.10. Coil A is connected to a switch and battery. Coil B is connected to a centre-reading moving coil galvanometer.

Fig. 70.10

A   B

(a) If the switch connected to coil A were closed for a few seconds and then opened, the galvanometer connected to coil B would be affected. Explain and describe, step by step, what would actually happen.

(b) What changes would you expect if a bundle of soft iron wires were placed through the centre of the coils? Give a reason for your answer.

(c) What would happen if more turns of wire were wound on the coil B?

2. The main function of a step-up transformer is to

A increase current
B increase voltage
C change a.c. to d.c.
D change d.c. to a.c.
E increase the resistance of a circuit   (*S.E.*)

3. (a) Calculate the number of turns on the secondary of the step-down transformer, which would enable a 12 V bulb to be used with a 240 V a.c. mains power, if there are 480 turns on the primary.

(b) What current will flow in the secondary when the primary current is 0.50 A? Assume there are no energy losses.   (*N.W.*)

4. The block diagram in Fig. 70.11 represents the generation and distribution of electricity.

(a) T is a 'step-up' transformer which has a core made up of 'laminations'.

  (i) Explain what is meant by a 'step-up' transformer.
  (ii) What is meant by 'laminations'?
  (iii) What material is used for the laminations?
  (iv) Why is the core built in this way?

(b) If the transformer T has 1000 turns on its primary coil, how many turns must it have on its secondary coil? (Assume that there are no losses in the transformer.)

(c) Why is it an advantage to transmit electric power at high voltage?

(d) What will be the main item of equipment in the sub-stations A and B?   (*Mddx.*)

Fig. 70.11

generator
11000 V
T
grid
132 000 V
sub-stations
A
11 000 V
B
240 V

71 Alternating current

Difference between d.c. and a.c.

In a direct current (d.c.) the electrons flow in one direction only. Graphs for steady and varying direct currents are shown in Fig. 71.1. In an alternating current (a.c.) the direction of flow reverses regularly, Fig. 71.2. The sign for a.c. is $\sim$.

Fig. 71.1

Fig. 71.2

The pointer of a moving coil meter is deflected one way by d.c.; a.c. makes it move to and fro about the zero if the changes are slow enough, otherwise there is no deflection. Batteries give d.c.; generators can produce either d.c. or a.c. The mains supply is a.c.

For heating and lighting a.c. and d.c. are equally satisfactory but radio and television sets need d.c., as do processes such as battery charging and electroplating. a.c. can be *rectified* to give d.c. (p. 231).

Frequency of a.c.

The number of complete alternations or cycles in 1 second is the *frequency* of the a.c. The unit of frequency is the *hertz* (Hz) (formerly the cycle per second, c/s). The frequency of the a.c. in Fig. 71.2 is 2 Hz.

The mains supply in many countries including Britain has frequency 50 Hz. There are therefore 50 cycles in a second and one cycle lasts $1/50 = 0.02$ s.

Root mean square values

An alternating voltage or current is measured by its *effective* or *root mean square* (r.m.s.) value. This is *the steady direct voltage or current which would give the same heating effect*.

Fig. 71.3

For example, if the lamp in Fig. 71.3 is lit first by a.c. and its brightness noted, then if 0.3 A d.c. produces the same brightness, the r.m.s. value of the a.c. is 0.3 A. It can be shown that

$$r.m.s.\ value = 0.7 \times peak\ value$$

The r.m.s. voltage of the mains supply is 240 V; the peak value is therefore $240/0.7 = 340$ V.

Meters for a.c.

Most a.c. meters are marked in r.m.s. values.
(*a*) *Rectifier meter.* A rectifier (e.g. a germanium diode, p. 230) allows current to pass in one direction only. When connected to an a.c. supply it produces pulses of varying d.c., Fig. 71.4*a*, and in a rectifier meter these cause a deflection in a moving coil meter, Fig. 71.4*b*.

Fig. 71.4

(*b*) *Moving iron meter.* This type was described earlier (p. 202).

Capacitors in a.c. circuits

A capacitor stops d.c. but lets a.c. pass. In Fig. 71.5a the supply is d.c. and the bulb does not light; in Fig. 71.5b the supply is a.c. and the bulb lights.

Fig. 71.5

In the d.c. circuit there is a brief flow of current which charges the capacitor. In the a.c. circuit the capacitor is charged, discharged, charged in the opposite direction and discharged again, 50 times a second. No current actually passes through the capacitor (its plates are separated by an insulator) but electrons flow on and off the plates so rapidly that it seems to do so. The result is just as if it did and an a.c. ammeter would give a reading.

The larger the capacitor the easier does a.c. flow 'through' it.

Capacitor networks

(a) *Parallel*. Capacitors connected in parallel behave like one capacitor with larger plates. In Fig. 71.6a the combined capacitance C can be shown to be given by

$$C = C_1 + C_2 + C_3$$

(a)

(b)

Fig. 71.6

(b) *Series*. In Fig. 71.6b the combined capacitance C is less than that of the smallest capacitor and is found from

$$\frac{1}{C} = \frac{1}{C_1} + \frac{1}{C_2} + \frac{1}{C_3}$$

Inductors in a.c. circuits

An *inductor* or *choke* is a coil of wire with an air, or an iron core. It opposes or 'chokes' a changing current and is said to have *inductance*.

Fig. 71.7

In Fig. 71.7 R is adjusted to have the same resistance as the iron-cored inductor L. When the current is switched on, the lamp in series with L lights up a second or two *after* that in series with R. L delays the rise of the d.c. to its steady value.

If the 3 V d.c. supply is replaced by a 3 V a.c. supply, the lamp in series with L never lights (the current is changing all the time), unless the inductance of L is reduced by removing the iron core.

The use of capacitors and inductors in electronic circuits is described in Topics 76 and 77.

Questions

1. (a) How does a.c. differ from d.c.?
(b) Name a source of (i) d.c., (ii) a.c.
(c) Name a device which (i) only works on a.c., (ii) works equally well on a.c. or d.c.

2. Sketch a graph of current value against time for two complete cycles of an alternating current of peak value 0.5 A and frequency 50 Hz. Label your axes and make a correct scale of values on these axes (you must calculate the time for one cycle in order to mark the time axis).
Indicate with a horizontal line on the graph the approximate value of the r.m.s. current. (*J.M.B./A.L./N.W.16+*)

3. An a.c. supply lights a lamp with the same brightness as does a 12 V battery. What is (a) the r.m.s. voltage, (b) the peak voltage, of the a.c. supply?

supply

Fig. 71.8

4. Fig. 71.8 shows a circuit containing a capacitor, an inductor and two lamps. Explain what happens when the circuit is connected to (i) a.c., (ii) d.c. (*E.A.*)

72 Further questions

Electric power

1. (*a*) Below is a list of wattages of various appliances. State which is most likely to be the correct one for each of the appliances named.

60 W   250 W   750 W   1.5 kW   3 kW
(*i*) Immersion heater (for a bath)
(*ii*) Table lamp
(*iii*) Iron.

(*b*) What current will be taken by a 1 kW appliance if the supply voltage is 250?
$$(J.M.B./A.L./N.W.16+)$$

2. A heating coil has a resistance of $4\,\Omega$ and is connected to a 12 V supply. It is placed in a container holding 100 g of water at $20\,°C$. Calculate (*a*) the current, (*b*) the power of the circuit, (*c*) the energy produced in 5 minutes, (*d*) the rise in the temperature of the water, assuming no heat is lost. (Specific heat capacity of water is $4200\,J/kg\,°C$ or $4.2\,J/g\,°C$.) (*E.A.*)

3. A 2 kW electric fire is used for 10 hours each week and a 100 W lamp is used for 10 hours each day. Find the total energy consumed each week and the total cost for each week if 1 kWh of electricity costs 3p. (*J.M.B.*)

4. (*a*) Fig. 72.1*a* represents a simple lighting circuit. (*i*) What is wrong with this circuit? (*ii*) Explain why this is dangerous.

live

neutral
(*a*)   (*b*)

Fig. 72.1

(*b*) Fig. 72.1*b* represents an incomplete two-way lighting circuit. Copy and complete the circuit in such a way that the lamp would be lit with the circuit working correctly. (*J.M.B./A.L./N.W.16+*)

5. Two precautions usually taken when using electrical equipment connected to the mains are to (*a*) earth the case (if metal), (*b*) put a fuse in the circuit.

Explain clearly why each of these precautions is desirable. (*L.*)

Electrolysis and cells

6. State the relationship between the mass of a substance liberated during electrolysis and the charge passed. Describe an experiment by which this relationship can be established for a metal such as copper.

An ammeter and a copper voltameter are placed in series in a circuit and after 20 minutes the mass of copper deposited is 0.36 g. The ammeter reads 0.80 A. What can you deduce about the ammeter reading? (Assume mass of copper deposited = 0.000 30 g/C.) (*L.*)

7. (*a*) A 6 V d.c. supply is connected through a key (switch) to a voltameter containing dilute sulphuric acid and platinum electrodes. Describe what happens in the voltameter when the key is closed and indicate the energy changes which take place.

(*b*) Describe briefly two different industrial applications of electrolysis.

(*c*) A current of 0.75 A is passed through a copper voltameter depositing copper on both sides of a rectangular central cathode which measures $15\,cm \times 6\,cm$. Find the thickness of the deposit when the current has been flowing for 1 hour. (1 C deposits $3.3 \times 10^{-7}\,kg$ of copper; density of copper $= 8900\,kg/m^3$.) (*N.I.*)

8. Describe the structure of a secondary cell (i.e. a lead-acid or alkali cell). Name two advantages which such a cell possesses over a primary cell.

Name two checks you could make to decide if a given secondary cell needed charging. Explain how you would connect the cell to a supply so as to charge it. What kind of supply is required?

What action would you take if the level of the acid in a car battery became low? (*L.*)

Electromagnets

9. Figs. 72.2*a* to *d* show identical vertical insulated coils with many turns of wire and the same large direct current passing through each. The pieces of iron and steel are attached as shown. When the current is switched off what will happen to each piece of iron and steel? (*W.M.*)

iron core	iron core	steel core	steel core
iron 'A'	steel 'A'	iron 'B'	steel 'B'
(a)	(b)	(c)	(d)

Fig. 72.2

10. Part of the electrical system of a car is shown in Fig. 72.3.

Fig. 72.3

(a) Why are connections made to the car body?
(b) There are *two* circuits in parallel with the battery. What are they?
(c) Why is wire A thicker than wire B?
(d) Why is a relay used?

11. Fig. 72.4 represents a coil of copper wire XY connected to a small battery, fixed to a cork and floating in a bowl of water.

Fig. 72.4

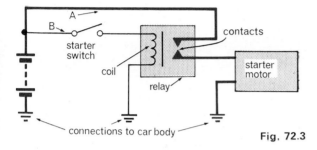

Sketch the form of the magnetic field produced by the coil. Indicate the direction of the field.

How would you use this arrangement to find the direction of magnetic north? (*L.*)

Electric motors

12. (a) Draw a labelled diagram of the essential components of a simple direct current electric motor. Explain clearly how continuous rotation is produced and show how the direction of rotation is related to the direction of the current.

(b) State what would happen to the direction of rotation of the motor you have described if (i) the current were reversed, (ii) the magnetic field were reversed, (iii) both current and field were reversed simultaneously.

(c) Why is a lead-acid accumulator preferred to a Leclanché (dry) battery in motor cars? (*J.M.B.*)

13. (a) In Fig. 72.5, AB is a copper rod resting on two horizontal copper bars between the poles of a horseshoe magnet. Describe and account for what will happen to AB when the key K is closed.

Fig. 72.5

(b) A working electric motor takes a current of 1.5 A when the p.d. across its terminals is 250 V. Determine the efficiency of the motor if the power output is 200 W.

If the resistance of the armature of the motor is about 1 Ω why is the current as little as 1.5 A when the motor is running? (*L.*)

(*Note.* Efficiency = power output/power input. For last part, see p. 208.)

Electric meters

14. A galvanometer has a resistance 10 Ω, and needs a current of 15 mA to give a full-scale deflection.

(a) Why is it an advantage of the galvanometer to have many turns?

(b) What design features account for the scale being linear, Fig. 72.6?

Fig. 72.6

215

(*c*) What voltage is the galvanometer measuring at full-scale deflection?

(*d*) If the galvanometer were of the centre-zero type, how would it respond to current which alternated very slowly or rapidly?

The galvanometer is used with a 290 Ω resistor in series to make a voltmeter.

(*e*) What current is needed to produce a full-scale deflection? Explain.

(*f*) What is the voltage across the 290 Ω resistor at full-scale deflection?

(*g*) What is the range of the voltmeter?

(*h*) Explain why a high-quality voltmeter needs to have a high resistance and state what design changes would need to be made to allow for this. (*O./S.R.16+*)

15. The current in a circuit is maintained constant. It is shown by a milliammeter to be 15 mA. When the milliammeter has a resistance of 0.90 Ω connected across it, the reading drops to 10 mA. Explain this and calculate the resistance of the milliammeter. (*O. and C.*)

16. With the aid of a large clear diagram describe and explain the structure and action of a moving coil ammeter.

A milliammeter has a full-scale reading of 0.01 A and has resistance 20 Ω. Show how a suitable resistor may be connected in order to use this instrument as a voltmeter reading up to 10 V. (*S.*)

Electrical measurements

17. If a wire of resistance 30 Ω were uniformly stretched until its diameter were halved, what would its new resistance be, assuming that no change in resistivity occurred? (*O. and C.*)

18. Fig. 72.7*a* shows a simple circuit in which a 2 V cell of no resistance drives a current through a 1 Ω resistor and a metre wire of resistance 3 Ω.

(*a*) What is the total resistance of the circuit?

(*b*) Is the current the same at all points in the circuit. Explain.

(*c*) Calculate the current through the 1 Ω resistor.

(*d*) Calculate the voltage across the 1 Ω resistor.

(*e*) Draw a diagram to show how the total resistance of the circuit could be *decreased* with the help of an additional resistor?

Another cell C is connected at one end of the metre wire and through a galvanometer to a point 80 cm along the wire, at which the meter shows no current, Fig. 72.7*b*.

(*f*) Calculate the e.m.f. of the new cell C.

(*g*) Would the balance length be altered if the new cell had a high internal resistance? Explain.

(*h*) Does the new cell with the slider at the balance point make any change to the current along the metre wire? Explain. (*O./S.R.16+*)

Generators

19. A thick straight copper wire XY is connected to the terminals of a sensitive centre zero galvanometer. XY is placed in between the poles of a horseshoe magnet perpendicular to the magnetic field and made to vibrate vertically as shown by the arrows in Fig. 72.8.

Fig. 72.8

Describe and explain the deflections seen on the galvanometer, G. (*A.E.B.*)

20. In a simple a.c. generator a rectangular coil is rotated in a uniform magnetic field about an axis which is perpendicular to the field. The diagrams in Fig. 72.9 show end-on views of the coil which rotates about an axis through O in a uniform magnetic field produced between the poles of the permanent magnet N–S.

In each of the questions following select the coil position which corresponds to the situation described in the question. Each position may be used once, more than once or not at all.

(*a*) The induced e.m.f. is at its peak value.

(*b*) The induced e.m.f. is between zero and its peak value and is *increasing*.

(*c*) The induced e.m.f. is between its peak value and zero and is decreasing.

(a)

(b)

Fig. 72.7

Fig. 72.9

(*d*) When the external circuit is completed, the direction of the e.m.f. induced in the coil is such as to give a current in YX *from Y to* X.   (*N.I.*)

21. Describe, with the aid of a labelled diagram, a simple form of dynamo. Explain how it may be used to generate (*a*) an alternating current, (*b*) a direct current.

In the case of (*a*) sketch a graph of the variation with time of the p.d. between the ends of the coil. Use the same axes to show clearly the effects of:

(*i*) doubling the number of turns of the coil and keeping the rotation speed and the magnetic field constant,

(*ii*) doubling the speed of rotation and keeping the number of turns and the magnetic field constant.   (*W.*)

Transformers

22. A transformer has 2000 turns on the primary coil. The voltage applied to the primary coil is 240 V a.c. How many turns are on the secondary coil if the output voltage is 48 V a.c.?

A 40   **B** 400   **C** 4000   **D** 5000
E 10 000   (*O./S.R.16+*)

23. (*a*) (*i*) Draw a labelled diagram showing the essential features of a voltage step-down transformer. Explain how the transformer works.

(*ii*) State one source of energy loss in the transformer and say how it may be reduced.

(*b*) A transformer designed to operate a 12 V lamp from a 240 V supply has 1200 turns on the primary coil. Assuming that the transformer is 100% efficient, calculate (*i*) the number of turns on the secondary coil, (*ii*) the current passing through the primary coil when the 12 V lamp has a current of 2 A flowing through it.   (*J.M.B.*)

24. A transformer is used on the 240 V a.c. supply to deliver 9.0 A at 80 V to a heating coil. If 10% of the energy taken from the supply is dissipated in the transformer itself, what is the current in the primary winding?   (*O. and C.*)

25. A generator with a power output of 20 kW at 4 kV distributes power to a workshop along cables having a total resistance of 16 Ω. Calculate (*a*) the current in the cables, (*b*) the power loss in the cables and (*c*) the potential drop between the ends of the cables.

How could the power supplied to the workshop be increased?   (*A.E.B.*)

Alternating current

26. The two circuits in Fig. 72.10 show a parallel plate capacitor in an a.c. circuit and in a d.c. circuit. What would happen to the bulb and ammeter in each circuit when the switch is closed?   (*A.L.*)

Fig. 72.10

27. (*a*) One capacitor has a value of 10 μF, a second has a value of 15 μF. Calculate the total capacitance of the two in parallel.

Fig. 72.11

(*b*) Calculate the value of X in Fig. 72.11 if the total value of the three components is 15 μF.
    (*J.M.B./A.L./N.W.16+*)

73 Electrons

The discovery of the electron was a landmark in physics and led to great technological advances. Evidence for its existence will now be considered.

Thermionic emission

The evacuated bulb in Fig. 73.1 contains a small coil of wire, the *filament*, and a metal plate called the *anode* because it is connected to the positive of the 400 V d.c. power supply. The negative of the supply is joined to the filament which is also called the *cathode*. The filament is heated by current from a 6 V supply (a.c. or d.c.).

Fig. 73.1

With the circuit as shown, the meter deflects, indicating current flow in the circuit containing the gap between anode and cathode. The current stops if *either* the 400 V supply is reversed to make the anode negative, *or* the filament is not heated.

This demonstration supports the view that negative charges, in the form of electrons, escape from the filament when it is hot. The process is known as *thermionic emission*. The electrons are attracted to the anode if it is positive and are able to reach it because there is a vacuum in the bulb.

Cathode rays

Streams of electrons moving at high speed are called *cathode rays*. Their properties can be studied using two special cathode ray tubes.

(*a*) *Maltese cross tube*, Fig. 73.2. Electrons emitted by the hot cathode are accelerated towards the anode but most pass through the hole in it and

Fig. 73.2

travel on along the tube. Those that miss the cross, cause the screen to fluoresce with a green light and cast a shadow of the cross on it. The cathode rays evidently travel in straight lines.

If the N pole of a magnet is brought up to the neck of the tube, the rays (and the fluorescent shadow) move upwards. The rays are deflected by a magnetic field and, using Fleming's left-hand rule (p. 198), we see that they behave like conventional current (positive charge flow) travelling from anode to cathode, i.e. like negative charge moving from cathode to anode.

The optical shadow of the cross due to the light also emitted by the cathode, is unaffected by the magnet.

Fig. 73.3

(*b*) *Deflection tube*, Fig. 73.3. Electrons from a hot cathode strike a fluorescent screen S set at an angle. A p.d. applied across two horizontal metal plates Y_1Y_2 creates a *vertical* electric field which deflects the rays upwards if Y_1 is positive (as shown) and downwards if it is negative.

When current flows in the two coils X_1X_2 (in series) outside the tube, a *horizontal* magnetic field is produced across the tube. It can be used instead of a magnet to deflect the rays, or to cancel the deflection due to an electric field.

Specific charge *e/m*

The ratio of the charge *e* of an electron to its mass *m* is called its *specific charge e/m* and can be found from experiments in which cathode rays are deflected by electric and magnetic fields. This was first done by J. J. Thomson in 1897 using a deflection-type tube. His work is regarded as proving the existence of the electron as a negatively charged particle of very small mass and not, as some scientists thought, a form of electromagnetic radiation like light.

The modern value of *e/m* for an electron is 1.76×10^{11} C/kg and when compared with the specific charge of other atomic particles it gives interesting results. When water is electrolysed, 9.6×10^7 C set free 1 kg of hydrogen. Assuming the charge carriers are hydrogen ions, the specific charge of such an ion is thus 9.6×10^7 C/kg. Comparing this with the electron value, we get

$$\frac{\text{specific charge of electron}}{\text{specific charge of hydrogen ion}}$$
$$= \frac{1.76 \times 10^{11}}{9.6 \times 10^7} = 2000 \text{ (approximately)}$$

Two alternative conclusions might be that, compared with a hydrogen ion, an electron has

(*i*) the same mass but a *charge* 2000 times *greater*,
(*ii*) the same charge but a *mass* 2000 times *smaller*.

If a hydrogen ion is formed when an electron is removed from a hydrogen atom, the charges on an electron and a hydrogen ion must be equal (and opposite). It follows that (*ii*) is correct.

Thermionic diode valve

This is an evacuated glass bulb G, Fig. 73.4, with an *anode* A in the form of a hollow metal cylinder,

Fig. 73.4

surrounding a smaller metal cylinder, the *cathode* C, which is heated when current passes through an insulated wire (the *heater* HH) inside it. Connections are made to an external circuit by pins at the base.

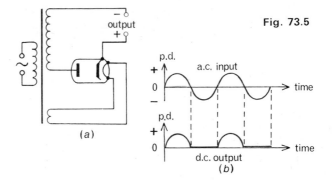

Fig. 73.5

(a)

(b)

If an alternating p.d. is applied between the anode and cathode, say from the secondary of a step-up transformer, Fig. 73.5a, electrons only flow from cathode to anode during the half cycles when the anode is positive. The output is a series of pulses in the same direction, Fig. 73.5b. The diode behaves like a *valve* allowing current in one direction; it converts a.c. to d.c., i.e. it is a *rectifier*.

The semiconductor diode (p. 230) has now replaced the thermionic diode except as a very high voltage rectifier.

Cathode ray oscilloscope (C.R.O.)

The C.R.O. is one of the most important scientific instruments ever to be developed. It contains, like a television set, a cathode ray tube which has three main parts, Fig. 73.6.

(*a*) *Electron gun.* This consists of a *heater* H, a *cathode* C, another electrode called the *grid* G and two or three *anodes* A. G is at a negative potential with

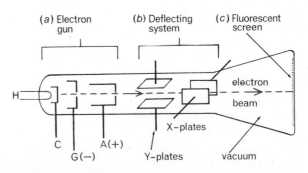

Fig. 73.6

respect to C and controls the number of electrons passing through its central hole from C to A; it is the *brightness* control. The anodes are at high positive potentials relative to C; they accelerate the electrons along the highly evacuated tube and also *focus* them into a narrow beam.

(*b*) *Deflecting system.* Beyond A are two pairs of deflecting plates to which p.d.s can be applied. The *Y-plates* are horizontal but create a vertical electric field which deflects the beam vertically. The *X-plates* are vertical and deflect the beam horizontally.

(*c*) *Fluorescent screen.* A bright spot of light is produced on the screen where the beam hits it.

The C.R.O. is often used as a 'graph-plotter' to display a waveform showing how a p.d. changes with time. The p.d. is applied to the Y-plates and a circuit is switched on in the C.R.O., called the *time base*, which generates a p.d. across the X-plates. This sweeps the spot steadily and horizontally across the screen until it 'flies back' very rapidly to the left of the screen and repeats the motion. Fig. 73.7 shows traces for (*a*) time base on X only, (*b*) a.c. on Y only and (*c*) a.c. on Y and time base on X.

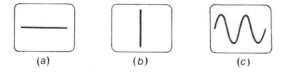

Fig. 73.7

Experiment: using a C.R.O.

The instructions refer to the C.R.O. in Fig. 73.8.

(*a*) *Preliminary adjustments.* Before switching on, set the controls as follows.

> BRIGHTNESS—to OFF; FOCUS—mid position
> TIME BASE RANGE switch—to OFF
> A.C.–D.C. switch to D.C.; Y-SHIFT—mid position
> Y-GAIN—fully anticlockwise (minimum).

Switch on at the BRIGHTNESS control and after 30 s, turn it clockwise till the spot appears. Centralize it with the Y-SHIFT.

Adjust BRIGHTNESS and FOCUS to give a small, sharp spot but *do not have it too bright* when the time base is off or the screen will be damaged.

(*b*) *Measuring p.d.s.* Connect a 1.5 V cell to the input (marked HIGH and LOW) and adjust the Y-GAIN so that the spot is deflected 1.5 divisions on the scale. Now apply two cells in series (3 V) and note the de-

Fig. 73.8

flection. Repeat with three cells (4.5 V). The C.R.O. is now calibrated as a voltmeter.

Disconnect the cells and apply 1 V a.c. to the INPUT. The length of the trace is twice the peak p.d. What is the value of the peak p.d.?

(*c*) *Studying waveforms.* With 1 V a.c. still applied to the INPUT, set the TIME BASE RANGE to '2' and increase Y-GAIN to obtain a wave-trace. See the effect of changing the TIME BASE VARIABLE control.

Disconnect the 1 V a.c. and connect a crystal microphone. Set the Y-GAIN fully clockwise and observe the waveforms when you speak or whistle.

Photoelectric emission

Electrons are also emitted by certain metals when electromagnetic radiation of small enough wavelength falls on them. The effect is called *photoelectric emission* and is given by zinc exposed to ultra-violet as may be shown with the apparatus of Fig. 73.9*a*.

The zinc plate must be *cleaned thoroughly* with emery cloth. If the electroscope is charged positively, it is unaffected when the zinc is exposed to u.v. It discharges if charged negatively but a sheet of glass between the lamp and the plate halts the discharge.

When the plate and electroscope are negatively charged the plate repels the emitted electrons and the electroscope discharges, Fig. 73.9*b*. With a positive charge on the plate, the emitted electrons are attracted back to the plate which therefore keeps its charge, Fig. 73.9*c*. The glass stops most of the u.v. but transmits violet light (also emitted by the lamp) and shows that zinc does not give the effect with it.

Photocells and their uses are studied later (p. 232).

Fig. 73.9 (a) (b) (c)

Leaf falls

No change in leaf

X-rays

X-rays are produced when fast-moving electrons are stopped by matter.

Fig. 73.10

(a) *Production.* In an X-ray tube, Fig. 73.10, electrons from a hot filament are accelerated across a vacuum to the anode by a large p.d. (up to 100 kV). The anode is a copper block with a 'target' of a high melting-point metal such as tungsten on which the electrons are focused by the concave cathode. The tube has a lead shield with a small exit for the X-rays. Less than $\frac{1}{2}\%$ of the k.e. of the electrons becomes X-rays, the rest heats the anode which has to be cooled.

High p.d.s give short wavelength, very penetrating (*hard*) X-rays. Less penetrating (*soft*) rays, of longer wavelength are obtained with lower p.d.s. A more *intense* beam of rays is produced if the rate of emission of electrons is raised by increasing the filament current.

(b) *Properties and nature.* They

   (*i*) readily penetrate matter; up to 1 mm of lead,

   (*ii*) are *not* deflected by electric or magnetic fields,

   (*iii*) ionize a gas, making it a conductor, e.g. a charged electroscope discharges when the X-rays pass through the surrounding air,

   (*iv*) affect a photographic film,

   (*v*) cause fluorescence,

   (*vi*) give interference and diffraction effects.

These facts (and others) indicate that X-rays are electromagnetic waves of very short wavelength.

(c) *Uses.* These were considered earlier (p. 45).

Questions

1. Cathode rays consist of
   A beams of fast moving electrons
   B fluorescent particles
   C light rays from a screen
   D light rays from a hot filament
   E infrared rays from a hot filament.   *(O./S.R.16+)*

2. (*a*) In a thermionic diode, what does the current consist of?
   (*b*) Why do these current carriers leave the cathode?
   (*c*) Why do they move to the anode?
   (*d*) Why is a thermionic diode called a valve?   *(E.A.)*

Fig. 73.11   (a)   fluorescent screen   screen seen from front   (b)

3. (*a*) Fig 73.11*a* shows a cathode ray tube fitted with one pair of plates. (*i*) What name is given to part P? (*ii*) What does part P produce?
   (*b*) With switch S off a spot is seen in the centre of the screen as shown in Fig. 73.11*b*. (*i*) What happens to this spot when switch S is closed? (*ii*) What would happen to the spot if the e.m.f. of the battery were increased? (*iii*) What would you *see* on the screen if a low frequency alternating e.m.f. of about 1 Hz were connected to the plates Q and R? (*iv*) What would you *see* on the screen if a higher frequency alternating e.m.f. of about 50 Hz were connected to the plates Q and R?
   (*c*) Describe another way in which the spot can be made to behave exactly as it does when the switch S is closed as in (*b*)(*i*). Illustrate your answer with a diagram.   *(S.E.)*

4. (*a*) State two important facts about X-rays, other than that they can penetrate matter. Do *not* give uses of X-rays.
   (*b*) How is the penetrating power of X-rays affected by a reduction in their wavelength?
   (*c*) How does the penetrating power of X-rays depend on the voltage applied across the X-ray tube.

(J.M.B./A.L./N.W.16+)

74 Radioactivity

The discovery of radioactivity in 1896 by the French scientist Becquerel was accidental. He found that uranium compounds emitted radiation which (*i*) affected a photographic plate even when wrapped in black paper and (*ii*) ionized a gas. Soon afterwards Madame Curie discovered radium. Today radioactivity is used widely in industry, medicine and research.

We are all exposed to *background* radiation caused partly by radioactive materials in rocks, the air and our bodies, and partly by cosmic rays from outer space.

Ionizing effect of radiation

A charged electroscope discharges when a lighted match or a radium source (*held in forceps*) is brought near the cap, Fig. 74.1*a, b*.

Fig. 74.1

In the first case the flame knocks electrons out of surrounding air molecules; in the second case radiation causes the ionization. The resulting positive air ions are attracted to the cap if it is negatively charged; if it is positively charged the electrons are attracted. As a result, the charge on the electroscope is neutralized, i.e. it loses its charge.

Radiation detectors

The ionizing effect is used to detect radiation.

(*a*) *Spark counter*, Fig. 74.2. A p.d. is applied between the wire and gauze till sparking occurs. It is then reduced until it *just* stops (usually about 4.5 kV).

When a radium source is held (*in forceps*) 1 or 2 cm above the gauze, sparks are seen and heard at irregular intervals due to the radiation ionizing the air between the gauze and the wire. The range

Fig. 74.2

of the radiation can be found by raising the source till sparking stops.

(*b*) *Geiger-Müller* (*G-M*) *tube*, Fig. 74.3. When radiation enters the tube, either through a thin end-window made of mica, or, if it is very penetrating,

Fig. 74.3

through the wall, it creates argon ions and electrons. These are accelerated towards the electrodes and cause more ionization by colliding with other argon atoms.

On reaching the electrodes, the ions produce a current pulse which is amplified and fed either to a *scaler* or a *ratemeter*. A scaler counts the pulses and shows the total received in a certain time. A ratemeter has a meter marked in 'counts per second (or minute)' from which the average pulse-rate can be read. It usually has a loudspeaker which gives a 'click' for each pulse.

Alpha, beta, gamma rays

Experiments to study the penetrating power, ionizing ability and behaviour in magnetic and electric fields, show that a radioactive substance emits one

Fig. 74.4

4 mm plug

ratemeter

radium source

G–M tube

lead sheet with 1 mm hole to prevent overloading of G–M tube

or more of three types of radiation—called alpha (α), beta (β) and gamma (γ) rays.

Penetrating power can be investigated as in Fig. 74.4 by observing the effect on the count-rate of placing in turn between the G-M tube and the lead, a sheet of (i) thick paper (the radium source, lead and tube must be *close together* for this part), (ii) aluminium 2 mm thick and (iii) lead 2 cm thick. Other sources can be tried, e.g. plutonium, americium, strontium and cobalt.

(a) *Alpha rays* are stopped by a thick sheet of paper and have a range in air of a few cm. They cause intense ionization in a gas and are deflected by electric and *strong* magnetic fields in a direction and by an amount which suggests they are helium atoms minus two electrons, i.e. *helium ions with a double positive charge*. From a particular substance, they are all emitted with the same speed (about 1/20th of that of light).

Plutonium (Pu 239) and americium (Am 241) may be used as pure α sources.

(b) *Beta rays* are stopped by a few mm of aluminium and some have a range in air of several metres. Their ionizing power is much less than that of α particles. As well as being deflected by electric fields, they are more easily deflected by magnetic fields and measurements show they are streams of *high-energy electrons*, like cathode rays, emitted with a range of speeds, up to that of light.

Strontium (Sr 90) emits β rays only.

The magnetic deflection of β particles can be shown as in Fig. 74.5. With the G-M tube at A and

strontium source

magnet

ratemeter

β

A

G–M tube

lead plates

B

Fig. 74.5

without the magnet, the count-rate is noted. Inserting the magnet reduces the count-rate but it increases again when the G-M tube is at B.

(c) *Gamma rays* are the most penetrating and are stopped only by many cm of lead. They ionize a gas even less than β particles and are not deflected by electric and magnetic fields. They give interference and diffraction effects and are *electromagnetic radiation* travelling at the speed of light. Their wavelengths are those of very short X-rays from which they differ only because they arise *in* atomic nuclei whereas X-rays come from energy changes in the electrons *outside* the nucleus.

Cobalt (Co 60) is a pure γ source. Radium (Ra 226) emits α, β and γ rays.

A G-M tube detects β and γ rays and energetic α particles; a spark counter detects α only, as does a charged electroscope. All three types of rays cause fluorescence.

Cloud chambers

When air containing vapour, e.g. alcohol, is cooled enough, saturation occurs. If ionizing radiation passes through the air, further cooling causes the saturated vapour to condense on the air ions created. The resulting white line of tiny liquid drops shows up as a track when illuminated.

LIGHT

glass

radium source

Fig. 74.6

black felt soaked with alcohol

to 1 kV

to bicycle pump

black plate

(a) *Expansion type*, Fig. 74.6. A rapid expansion is produced by withdrawing *quickly* the piston of a bicycle pump having the leather washer reversed so that it removes air. As a result the alcohol vapour in the chamber is cooled and condensation occurs on the ions produced by a weak radium source in the chamber. A high p.d. (e.g. 1 kV) between the top and bottom of the chamber provides an electric field which clears away unwanted ions. The tracks seen are therefore those of rays that leave the source as the expansion occurs.

(b) *Diffusion type*, Fig. 74.7. Vapour from alcohol in the felt ring diffuses downwards, is cooled by the 'dry ice' (solid carbon dioxide at −78 °C) in the

Fig. 74.7

Fig. 74.8a

Fig. 74.8b

lower section and condenses near the floor on air ions formed by radiation from the source in the chamber. Tracks are produced continuously which are sharp if an electric field is created by frequently rubbing the plastic lid of the chamber with a cloth.

α particles give straight, thick tracks, Fig. 74.8a. Very fast β particles produce thin, straight tracks; slower ones give short, twisted, thicker tracks, Fig. 74.8b. γ rays eject electrons from air molecules: the electrons behave like β particles and produce their own tracks spreading out from the γ rays.

The *bubble chamber*, in which the radiation leaves a trail of bubbles in liquid hydrogen, has now replaced the cloud chamber in research work.

Radioactive decay: half-life

Radioactive atoms change or *decay* into atoms of different elements when they emit α or β particles (p. 227). These changes are spontaneous and cannot be controlled; also, it does not matter whether the material is pure or combined chemically with something else.

The *rate of decay* is unaffected by temperature but every radioactive element has its own definite decay rate, expressed by its *half-life*. This is *the time for half the atoms in a given sample to decay*. It is difficult to know when a substance has lost all its radioactivity, but the time for its activity to fall to half its value can be found more easily.

Half-lives vary greatly. For radium it is 1600 years so that starting with 1 g of pure radium, $\frac{1}{2}$ g remains as radium after 1600 years, $\frac{1}{4}$ g after 3200 years and so on.

The half-life of the α-emitting gas *thoron* can be found as in Fig. 74.9a by squeezing the thoron bottle 3 or 4 times to transfer some thoron to the flask. The clips are then closed, the bottle removed and the stopper replaced by a G-M tube so that it seals the top, Fig. 74.9b.

Fig. 74.9

(a)

(b)

When the ratemeter reading has reached its maximum and started to fall, the count-rate is noted every 15 s for 2 minutes and then every 60 s for the next few minutes. (The G-M tube is left in the flask for at least 1 hour until the radioactivity has decayed.)

A graph of *count-rate* (from which the background count-rate, found separately, has been subtracted) against *time* is plotted and the half-life (52 s) estimated from it.

Uses of radioactivity

Radioactive substances, called· *radioisotopes* (p. 227), are now made in nuclear reactors (p. 229) and have many uses.

(*a*) *Thickness gauge.* If a radioisotope is placed on one side of a moving sheet of material and a G-M tube on the other, the count-rate decreases if the thickness increases. This technique is used to control automatically the thickness of paper, plastic and metal sheets during manufacture, Fig. 74.10.

(*b*) *Tracers.* The progress of a small amount of a weak radioisotope injected into a system can be 'traced' by a G-M tube or other detector. The method is used in medicine to detect brain tumours, in agriculture to study the uptake of fertilizers by plants and in industry to measure fluid flow in pipes.

(*c*) *Radiotherapy.* Gamma rays from strong cobalt radioisotopes are replacing X-rays in the treatment of cancer (p. 45).

(*d*) *Archaeology.* A radioisotope of carbon, present in the air, is taken in by plants and trees and is used to date archaeological remains of wood and linen.

Dangers and safety

The danger from α particles is small unless the source enters the body. β and γ rays can cause radiation burns (i.e. redness and sores on the skin) and delayed effects such as cancer and eye cataracts. Fall-out from atomic explosions contains highly active elements (e.g. strontium), with long half-lives, that are absorbed by the bones.

The weak sources used at school *should always be lifted with forceps, never held near the eyes and should be kept in their boxes when not in use.* In industry sources are handled by long tongs and transported in thick lead containers. Workers are protected by lead and concrete walls.

Fig. 74.10

Questions

1. Which type of radiation from radioactive materials
   (*a*) has a positive charge?
   (*b*) is the most penetrating?
   (*c*) is easily deflected by a magnetic field?
   (*d*) consists of waves?
   (*e*) causes the most intense ionization?
   (*f*) has the shortest range in air?
   (*g*) has a negative charge?
   (*h*) is not deflected by an electric field?
2. What is the effect of radiation on
   (*a*) a charged electroscope?
   (*b*) a photographic film?
   (*c*) a fluorescent screen?
3. (*a*) What do you understand by 'background radiation'? State two sources of this radiation.
   (*b*) State three safety precautions to be observed when using radioactive sources.
   (*c*) Describe briefly two uses of radioactive sources.
   (*d*) How would you test to distinguish between two radioactive sources, one of which emits only alpha particles and the other which emits only beta particles? (*A.L.*)
4. A radioactive sample has a mass of 16 g and a half-life of 10 days. What mass of the original sample remains after (*a*) 10 days, (*b*) 20 days, (*c*) 40 days?
5. If the half-life of a radioactive gas is 2 minutes, then after 8 minutes the activity will have fallen to a fraction of its initial value. This fraction is

   A $\frac{1}{4}$ **B** $\frac{1}{6}$ **C** $\frac{1}{8}$ **D** $\frac{1}{16}$ **E** $\frac{1}{32}$ (*W.Y.*)

75 Atomic structure

The discovery of the electron and of radioactivity seemed to indicate that atoms contained negatively and positively charged particles and were not indivisible as was previously thought. The questions then were 'how are the particles arranged inside an atom', and 'how many are there in the atom of each element?'

An early theory, called the 'plum-pudding' model, regarded the atom as a positively charged sphere in which the negative electrons were distributed in sufficient numbers to make the atom electrically neutral. There were doubts about this model.

Nuclear model

Whilst investigating radioactivity Rutherford noticed that not only could α particles pass straight through very thin metal foil as if it wasn't there but also that some were deflected from their initial direction. With the help of Geiger (of tube fame) and Marsden, Rutherford investigated this in detail at Manchester University using the arrangement in Fig. 75.1. The fate of the α particles after striking the gold foil was detected by the scintillations (flashes of light) they produced on a glass screen coated with zinc sulphide and fixed to a rotatable microscope.

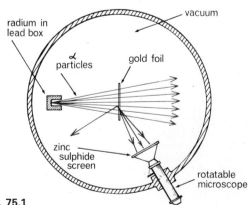

Fig. 75.1

They found that most of the α particles were undeflected, some were scattered by appreciable angles and a few (about 1 in 8000) surprisingly 'bounced' back. To explain these results Rutherford proposed in 1911 a nuclear model of the atom in which *all the positive charge* and *most of the mass of an atom* formed a dense core or *nucleus*, of very small size compared with the whole atom. The electrons surrounded the nucleus some distance away.

He derived a formula for the number of α particles deflected at various angles, assuming that the electrostatic force of repulsion between the positive charge on an α particle and the positive charge on the nucleus of a gold atom obeyed an inverse square law (i.e. the force increases four times if the separation is halved). Geiger and Marsden's results completely confirmed Rutherford's formula and supported the view that an atom is mostly empty space. In fact the nucleus and electrons occupy about one million millionth of the volume of an atom. Putting it another way, the nucleus is like a sugar lump in a very large hall and the electrons a swarm of flies in the hall.

Fig. 75.2

The paths of three α particles are shown in Fig. 75.2. ① is clear of all nuclei and passes straight *through* the gold atoms. ② suffers some deflection. ③ approaches a gold nucleus so closely as to be violently repelled by it and 'rebounds', appearing to have had a head-on 'collision'.

Protons and neutrons

We now believe as a result of other experiments, in some of which α and other high-speed particles were used as atomic probes, that atoms contain three basic particles—protons, neutrons and electrons.

A *proton* is a hydrogen atom minus an electron, i.e. a positive hydrogen ion. Its charge is equal in size but opposite in sign to that of an electron but its mass is about 2000 times greater.

A *neutron* is uncharged with almost the same mass as a proton.

Protons and neutrons are in the nucleus and are called *nucleons*. Together they account for the mass of the nucleus (and most of that of the atom); the protons account for its positive charge. In a neutral atom the number of protons equals the number of electrons surrounding the nucleus.

Table 1 shows the particles in some atoms. Hydrogen is simplest with 1 proton and 1 electron. Next is the inert gas helium with 2 protons, 2 neutrons and 2 electrons. The soft white metal lithium has 3 protons and 4 neutrons.

Table 1

	Hydrogen	Helium	Lithium	Oxygen	Copper
Protons	1	2	3	8	29
Neutrons	0	2	4	8	34
Electrons	1	2	3	8	29

The atomic or proton number Z of an atom is the number of protons in the nucleus. It is also the number of electrons in the atom. The electrons determine the chemical properties of an atom and if you take chemistry you will know that when the 104 elements (89 natural and 15 man-made) are arranged in atomic number order in the Periodic table, they fall into chemical families.

The mass or nucleon number A of an atom is the number of nucleons in the nucleus.

Atomic *nuclei* are represented by symbols. Hydrogen is written $_1^1$H, helium $_2^4$He, lithium $_3^7$Li and in general atom X is written $_Z^A$X where A is the mass number and Z the atomic number.

Note. The *mass number A* of an atom is not the same as its *relative atomic mass* A_r (formerly the *atomic weight*) which is defined by

$$A_r = \frac{\text{mass of atom}}{\frac{1}{12} \text{ mass of } _6^{12}\text{C atom}}$$

Atomic masses used to be compared by taking the mass of the hydrogen atom as 1. Since 1960 the carbon 12 ($_6^{12}$C) scale has been adopted.

Isotopes

Isotopes of an element are atoms which have the same number of protons but different numbers of neutrons. That is, their atomic numbers are the same but not their mass numbers.

Isotopes have identical chemical properties since they have the same number of electrons and occupy the same place in the Periodic table. (In Greek, *isos* means same and *topos* means place.)

Few elements consist of identical atoms; most are mixtures of isotopes. Chlorine has two isotopes; one has 17 protons and 18 neutrons (i.e. $Z = 17$, $A = 35$) and is written $_{17}^{35}$Cl, the other has 17 protons and 20 neutrons (i.e. $Z = 17$, $A = 37$) and is written $_{17}^{37}$Cl. They are present in ordinary chlorine in the approximate ratio of three atoms of $_{17}^{35}$Cl to one atom of $_{17}^{37}$Cl, giving chlorine an average atomic mass of 35.5.

Hydrogen has three isotopes. $_1^1$H with 1 proton, *deuterium* $_1^2$D with 1 proton and 1 neutron and *tritium* $_1^3$T with 1 proton and 2 neutrons. Ordinary hydrogen contains 99.99 per cent of $_1^1$H atoms. Water made from deuterium is called heavy water (D_2O); it has a density of $1.108 \, \text{g/cm}^3$, it freezes at $3.8\,°\text{C}$ and boils at $101.4\,°\text{C}$.

Radioactive decay

The emission of an α or β particle from a nucleus produces an atom of a different element, called the *decay* product, which may itself be unstable. After a series of changes a stable end-element is formed.

(*a*) *Alpha decay.* An α particle is a helium nucleus having 2 protons and 2 neutrons and when an atom decays by α emission, its mass number decreases by 4 and its atomic number by 2. For example, when radium of mass number 226 and atomic number 88 emits an α particle, it decays to radon of mass number 222 and atomic number 86. The change is written:

$$_{88}^{226}\text{Ra} \rightarrow \ _{86}^{222}\text{Rn} + \ _2^4\text{He}$$

(*b*) *Beta decay.* Here a neutron changes to a proton and an electron. The proton remains in the nucleus and the electron is emitted as a β particle. The new nucleus has the same mass number, but its atomic number increases by one since it has one more proton. Radioactive carbon, called carbon 14, decays by β emission to nitrogen.

$$_6^{14}\text{C} \rightarrow \ _7^{14}\text{N} + \ _{-1}^0\text{e}$$

(*c*) *Gamma emission.* After emitting an α or β particle some nuclei are left in an 'excited' state. Rearrangement of the protons and neutrons occurs in the nucleus and a burst of γ rays is released. Radium 226 does this.

Models of the atom

(a) *Rutherford–Bohr model.* Shortly after Rutherford proposed his nuclear model of the atom, Bohr, a Danish physicist, developed it to explain how an atom emits light. He suggested that the electrons circled the nucleus at high speed being kept in *certain orbits* by the electrostatic attraction of the nucleus for them. He pictured atoms as miniature solar systems. Fig. 75.3 shows the models for hydrogen, helium and lithium.

Fig. 75.3

- $\oplus$ proton
- $\bullet$ neutron
- $\ominus$ electron

Normally the electrons remain in their orbits but if the atom is given energy, e.g. by being heated, electrons may jump to an outer orbit. The atom is then said to be *excited*. Very soon afterwards the electrons return to an inner orbit and as they do, they emit energy in the form of bursts of electromagnetic radiation (called *photons*), e.g. as light, infrared, ultraviolet or X-rays, Fig. 75.4. The wavelength of the radiation emitted depends on the two orbits between which the electrons jump.

Fig. 75.4

If an atom gains enough energy for an electron to escape altogether, the atom becomes an ion and the energy needed to achieve this is called the *ionization energy* of the atom. It can be found from experiments in which gas or vapour atoms are bombarded by electrons accelerated by p.d.s to known energies which cause ionization.

(b) *Modern model.* Although it is still useful for some purposes, the Rutherford–Bohr model has now been replaced by a *mathematical model* which is not easy to picture. The best we can do, without using advanced mathematics, is to say that the atom consists of a nucleus surrounded by a hazy cloud of electrons. Regions of the atom where the mathematics predicts electrons are likely to be found, are represented by dense shading, Fig. 75.5.

Fig. 75.5

The modern theory does away with the idea of electrons moving in definite orbits and replaces them by *energy levels*. When an electron jumps from one level, say E_3 in Fig. 75.6, to a lower one E_1,

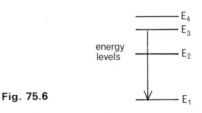

Fig. 75.6

a photon of electromagnetic radiation is emitted with energy equal to the difference in energy of the two levels.

Nuclear energy

(a) $E = mc^2$. Einstein predicted that if the energy of a body changes by an amount E, its mass changes by an amount m given by the equation

$$E = mc^2$$

where c is the speed of light (3×10^8 m/s). The implication is that any reaction in which there is a decrease of mass, called a *mass defect*, is a source of energy. The energy and mass changes in physical and chemical changes are very small; those in some nuclear reactions, e.g. radioactive decay, are millions of times greater.

(b) *Fission.* The heavy metal uranium is a mixture of isotopes of which $^{235}_{92}U$, called uranium 235, is the most important. Some atoms of this isotope decay quite naturally, emitting high-speed neutrons. If one of these hits the nucleus of a neigh-

228

bouring uranium 235 atom (being uncharged the neutron is not repelled by the nucleus), this may break (*fission*) into two nearly equal radioactive nuclei, often of barium and krypton, with the production of two or three more neutrons.

$$\underset{\text{neutron}}{^{235}_{92}U} + \underset{}{^{1}_{0}n} \rightarrow \underset{\text{fission fragments}}{^{144}_{56}Ba + ^{90}_{36}Kr} + \underset{\text{neutrons}}{2^{1}_{0}n}$$

The mass defect is large and appears mostly as k.e. of the fission fragments. These fly apart at great speed, colliding with surrounding atoms and raising their average k.e., i.e. their temperature. Heat is therefore produced.

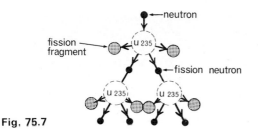

Fig. 75.7

If the fission neutrons split other uranium 235 nuclei, a *chain reaction* is set up, Fig. 75.7. In practice some fission neutrons are lost by escaping from the surface of the uranium before this happens. The ratio of those escaping to those causing fission decreases as the mass of uranium 235 increases. This must exceed a certain *critical* value for a chain reaction to start.

(*c*) *Nuclear reactor.* In a nuclear power station a nuclear reactor produces the steam for the turbines instead of a coal- or oil-burning furnace. Fig. 75.8 is a simplified diagram of a reactor.

The chain reaction occurs at a steady rate which is controlled by inserting or withdrawing neutron-absorbing rods of boron among the uranium rods. The graphite core is called the *moderator* and slows down the fission neutrons: fission of uranium 235 occurs more readily with slow than with fast neutrons. Carbon dioxide gas is pumped through the core and carries off heat to the heat exchanger where steam is produced. The concrete shield gives protection from γ rays and neutrons.

In an *atomic bomb* an increasing uncontrolled chain reaction occurs when two pieces of uranium 235 come together and exceed the critical mass.

(*d*) *Fusion.* The union of light nuclei into heavier ones can also lead to a loss of mass and, as a result, the release of energy. At present, research is being done on the controlled fusion of isotopes of hydrogen (deuterium and tritium) to give helium. Temperatures of about 100 million °C are required. Fusion is believed to be the source of the sun's energy.

Questions

1. What are the particles you would expect to find in an atom? Give some idea of their relative masses and state what electrical charge, if any, each kind has. (*S.E.*)

2. (*a*) An atom of cobalt has an atomic number of 27 and a mass number of 59. Describe simply the structure of the cobalt atom.
(*b*) What are isotopes?
(*c*) Why are isotopes difficult to separate by chemical methods? (*W.M.*)

3. Uranium 238 and uranium 235 are 'isotopes' of uranium and have the same atomic number, 92.
(*a*) What do the numbers 238 and 235 represent?
(*b*) (*i*) What does the number 92 tell you about the nucleus of either of these two atoms?
(*ii*) What else does the number 92 tell you about the atom as a whole?
(*c*) In what way does the nucleus of uranium 238 differ from the nucleus of uranium 235? (*J.M.B./A.L./N.W.16+*)

4. What changes, if any, occur in the atomic number of a radioactive atom if the nucleus emits (*a*) an α particle, (*b*) a β particle, (*c*) a γ ray? (*E.A.*)

5. Atomic bombs and atomic reactors both provide large quantities of energy through chain reactions.
(*a*) Explain what is meant by a chain reaction.
(*b*) Explain how the reaction, which is violent in the case of a bomb, is slowed down in the reactor. (*E.A.*)

Fig. 75.8

76 Electronics

Electronics is being used more and more in our homes, factories, offices, banks, shops and hospitals. The development of semiconductor devices such as transistors and integrated circuits ('chips') has given us, among other things, pocket calculators that are also clocks and musical instruments, Fig. 76.1*a*, heart pacemakers, Fig. 76.1*b*, microcomputers, robots, TV games, machines for teaching spelling and arithmetic and even for recognizing signatures.

Semiconductors

These are neither very good conductors nor very good insulators. Silicon and germanium are the two best known. They are used to make electronic devices because their conductivity can be increased by adding tiny but controlled amounts of other substances (called 'impurities')—a process known as 'doping'.

Two types of semiconductor material are obtained in this way. In *n*-type, conduction is by *n*egative electrons; in *p*-type it is by *p*ositive charges called 'holes'.

If semiconductors are heated their conductivity increases rapidly and may no longer be controllable. Working temperatures have to be limited, more so for germanium than silicon.

Junction diode

When *p*-type and *n*-type materials are brought together, a *p–n junction diode* is formed. If the posi-

(a) Forward bias   (b) Reverse bias

Fig. 76.2

tive of a battery is joined to the *p*-type and the negative to the *n*-type, the diode conducts due to 'holes' moving from *p* to *n* and electrons from *n* to *p*; it is said to be *forward biased*, Fig. 76.2*a*. Connecting the battery the other way, *reverse biases* the diode and little or no current flows, Fig. 76.2*b*. The current-p.d. graph for a semiconductor diode was given earlier (p. 177, Fig. 60.6*b*).

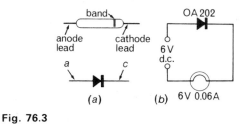

Fig. 76.3

A diode and its symbol are shown in Fig. 76.3*a*; the arrow is in the direction of conventional current flow, i.e. from anode *a* to cathode *c*.

Fig. 76.1   (*a*)   (*b*)

The one-way action of a diode can be shown with the circuit of Fig. 76.3b. The bulb lights only when the diode is forward biased.

Rectification and smoothing

A semiconductor diode (like a thermionic diode, p. 219) rectifies, i.e. converts a.c. to d.c.

(a) *Half-wave rectification*, Fig. 76.4a. The diode removes the negative half-cycles of a.c. to give a varying but one-way (direct) p.d. across R, the 'load' requiring a d.c. supply, Fig. 76.4b. Many loads require steady d.c.

Fig. 76.4

(b) *Smoothing.* The 'humps' in the d.c. are smoothed by connecting (with correct polarity) a large electrolytic capacitor C across R, Fig. 76.4c. On the positive half-cycles of the a.c. supply the diode conducts, current flows through R *and* also into C.

On the negative half-cycles when the diode is reverse biased and non-conducting, C partly discharges through R. The charge-storing action of C thus maintains current in R and a steadier p.d. across it, Fig. 76.4d.

(c) *Full-wave rectification.* Both half-cycles of the a.c. to be rectified are used. In the *bridge circuit* of Fig. 76.5a, the current follows the solid arrows when

X is positive and Y negative and the broken arrows on the negative half-cycles when the polarities of X and Y are reversed. During both half-cycles current flows in R and in the *same* direction giving a p.d. like that in Fig. 76.5b which can be smoothed as before.

Transistor

(a) *Description.* A transistor is a semiconductor sandwich with a very thin 'filling' of either p- or n-type material called the *base*. The outside layers, known as the *collector* and *emitter*, are of a different material to the base, but both are the same.

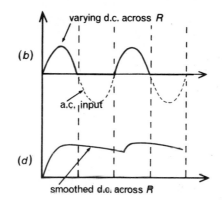

There are two kinds, n-p-n and p-n-p, Fig. 76.6. The arrow on the emitter in the symbol indicates the direction of conventional current in the transis-

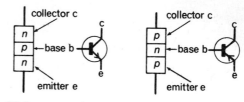

Fig. 76.6

tor and shows its type. Silicon n-p-n types are now commonest.

Fig. 76.5   (a)   (b)

Transistors are damaged if they get too hot; some have 'heat sinks' (e.g. metal discs) to prevent this happening. *Correct battery connections are also essential* and so the leads need to be known. Three transistors are shown in Fig. 76.7. In some types the

BC 108
(*npn* Si)

tag

c
e
b
(from below)

c b e

ZTX 300
(*npn* Si)

c b e

c b e
(from below).

OC 71
(*pnp* Ge)

dot

e b c
(from below)

e b c

Fig. 76.7

emitter lead is identified by a tag on the case or by the shape of the case. In others the collector lead is spaced farther from the base lead than the emitter lead or is sometimes marked by a dot on the case.

(*b*) *Action.* In the circuit of Fig. 76.8 the transistor is an *n-p-n* type so the collector goes to the positive of the battery and the emitter to the negative. The 1 kΩ resistor in the base lead limits the base current and prevents damage to the transistor.

When Y is connected to X, Y is at a 'high' voltage (6 V), L_c lights but not L_b. If L_b is unscrewed, L_c goes off. When Y is joined to Z (dotted line), Y is at a 'low voltage' (0 V) and L_c and L_b are both out.

We can conclude that the collector current I_c is

| Tr BC108 or ZTX 300 | L_b 6 V 0.06 A |
| R 1 kΩ | L_c 6 V 0.06 A |

Fig. 76.8

larger than the base current I_b and only flows if I_b is not zero. More accurate experiments with ammeters show that I_c may be about 100 times greater than I_b, e.g. if $I_b = 0.5$ mA, $I_c = 50$ mA. If we regard I_b as the 'input' and I_c as the 'output', then a small input current controls a large output current and small changes in the input cause greater changes in the output. The transistor acts as a *current amplifier*. In this example, *current gain* $= I_c/I_b = 50$ mA$/0.5$ mA $= 100$.

Other semiconductor devices

(*a*) *Photocell or light dependent resistor (l.d.r.).* It is made of cadmium sulphide, whose resistance depends on the light intensity. In the dark it may be 10 MΩ (10 megohms = 10 million ohms) and in daylight 1 kΩ. Fig. 76.9*a* shows a cell, its symbol and a circuit which shows its action. When light (from a lamp) shines on the cell, the bulb comes on.

(*b*) *Thermistor.* When heated, directly or by current in it, its resistance decreases. It contains semi-conducting metallic oxides. Fig. 76.9*b* shows a

l.d.r.

ORP 12

(*a*) 6 V
d.c.

6V 0.06A

thermistor

TH3

(*b*) 6 V
d.c.

6V 0.06A

thyristor THY 1A/50

cathode

anode   gate

S

1 kΩ   6 V
0.06 A

6 V d.c.

c   g

a
(from below)

(*c*)

Fig. 76.9

232

thermistor, its symbol and a circuit to show its action. Heating the thermistor with a match lights the bulb.

(*c*) *Thyristor or silicon controlled rectifier (s.c.r.).* This is a silicon diode with a third connection called the *gate*. When forward biased, it does not conduct until a small gate current enters it. Conduction continues even if the gate current is removed; it stops only if the battery to the diode itself is disconnected or if the diode current falls below a certain value. Fig. 76.9*c* shows a thyristor, its symbol and a circuit which demonstrates its action when S is closed.

Transistor as a switch

Transistors can act as *very sensitive*, fast-acting switches which are turned on and off electrically. When used with devices such as photocells, thermistors and microphones (called *transducers* because they change one form of energy to another) they respond to small changes of light, temperature and sound respectively. They can switch on lamps, bells, motors and relays.

A simple way to control a transistor is to vary the *base current*. This may be shown with the circuit of Fig. 76.10*a*. Decreasing *R* increases the base current which, when it is large enough, 'turns on' the collector current and this lights the lamp. If *R* is replaced by a photocell, in the dark the base current (and the collector current) is small (why?) and the lamp is off. In daylight the lamp is on.

A better way to control the transistor is by the *base voltage* using a potential divider as in Fig. 76.10*b*. The base voltage is the p.d. V_s across S and this depends on the resistance of S compared with that of *R*. (See Qn 3, p. 235.) When V_s exceeds about 1 V the transistor 'switches on' and the lamp lights.

Other useful switching actions can be obtained if a transistor is used with a capacitor or a thyristor, as we will see shortly.

Experiment: transistor switching circuits

The components can be assembled on an S-DeC[1], Fig. 76.11*a*. Fig. 76.11*b* shows how to lengthen transistor leads and also how to make connections (without soldering) to components that have 'tags', e.g. variable resistors, relays.

Fig. 76.11

(*a*)

(*b*)   SWG 22 tinned copper connecting wire

(*a*) *Light-operated.* Connect the circuit of Fig. 76.12 with the photocell as part of a potential divider. The lamp comes *on* when the photocell is shielded due to more of the battery voltage being dropped across the increased resistance of the photocell and less

[1] From Roden Products, 5 High March, Daventry, Northants. NN11 4QE.

(*a*)

Fig. 76.10

(*b*)

Fig. 76.12

R 10 kΩ

1 kΩ

ORP 12

BC 108
or
ZTX 300

6 V
0.06 A

6 V

Lamp ON in dark

across *R*. Hence in the dark, the base voltage increases (i.e. the p.d. between base and emitter) as does the base current and so also the collector current. If *R* is replaced by a 10 kΩ variable resistor the light level at which the lamp comes on can be adjusted.

This circuit could be used as an automatic *car parking light*.

If the photocell and *R* are interchanged in Fig. 76.12 the lamp goes off in the dark. Why?

(b) Heat-operated. Set up the circuit of Fig. 76.13. The diode protects the transistor from damage because, on switching off the relay, a high e.m.f. is induced in its coil (see p. 209). The diode is connected in reverse bias and provides an easy path for the current this e.m.f. produces.

relay (magnetic 185 Ω or reed 700 Ω)

TH3

OA
202

contacts
normally
open

1 kΩ

electric
bell

6 V

BC108
or
ZTX 300

R 10 kΩ

Fig. 76.13

The collector current in the small transistor used here is too small to ring a bell but it will operate a relay. The bell is connected to a pair of 'normally open' contacts on the relay and obtains the larger current it requires directly from the battery.

Adjust *R* till the bell just stops ringing. Heat the thermistor with a match; this reduces its resistance, increases the transistor base voltage and makes the bell ring again. The circuit behaves as a *fire alarm*. (For your purpose it may be more convenient to use a lamp instead of a bell.)

(c) Time-operated. Set up the circuit in Fig. 76.14. When S_1 is closed, L comes on and *C* starts to charge up through *R*. Eventually the charge will be high enough for some of the current to flow to the

relay
(magnetic 185 Ω or reed 1 kΩ)

contacts
normally
closed

10 kΩ

R OA 202

c
a

S_1

S_2

1 kΩ

+
C
1000 μF

BC 108
or
ZTX 300

L

6 V

6 V
0.06 A

Fig. 76.14

base of the transistor and switch it on. The relay contacts then open, switching off L. To re-set the circuit, S_1 is opened and S_2 closed to let *C* discharge. What would be the effect on L of increasing *R*?

In photography, colour films are exposed, during development, to a lamp controlled by a *timer* such as this.

(d) Sound-operated with latching. Connect the circuit of Fig. 76.15. If you tap the crystal microphone on the bench it produces enough base current to switch on the transistor. The collector current pass-

Fig. 76.15

BC108
or
ZTX 300

6 V
0.06 A

crystal
microphone
or earphone

THY 1A/50

6 V

ing through it to the emitter provides gate current which triggers the thyristor and allows current to flow through the lamp. The lamp should stay on till the battery is disconnected. The thyristor acts as a latching switch.

Using a relay and bell instead of a lamp (as in Fig. 76.13) the circuit could form the basis of a sound-operated *burglar alarm*.

Fig. 76.16

(a)

magnetic earphone(1 kΩ)

R_B 100 kΩ

C 10 μF

BC 108

6V

crystal microphone or earphone

(b)

crystal earphone (10 MΩ)

1 kΩ

10 μF 100 kΩ

BC 108

6V

microphone

Transistor amplifier

A transistor amplifies a small a.c. signal (e.g. from a microphone) applied as the input to its base-emitter circuit if there is a suitable 'load' (e.g. a *magnetic* earphone of resistance 1 kΩ) in its collector circuit. It should also be correctly *biased*, i.e. when there is no input signal the base current must have a suitable value.

In the simple amplifying circuit of Fig. 76.16a the steady base current is determined by the resistance of R_B which should be about 100 times greater than the resistance of the 'load'. Capacitor C stops d.c. from the battery passing through the microphone (and upsetting the biasing) but allows the a.c. signal from the microphone to pass to the base. With a *crystal* earphone (resistance 10 MΩ) the circuit of Fig. 76.16b is used.

Practical amplifiers have several transistors. The radio receiver of Fig. 77.10 (p. 240) has a two-stage amplifier in which the output from the collector of the first transistor is fed via a 2.2 μF capacitor to the base of the second transistor.

The transistors in Fig. 76.16 are in *common-emitter* connection, i.e. the emitter is common to both the collector and base circuits.

Questions

1. Fig. 76.17a shows a lamp, semiconductor diode and a cell connected in series. The lamp lights when the diode is connected in this direction. Say what happens to each of the lamps in b, c and d. Give reasons for your answer. (*S.E.*)

Fig. 76.17

(a) D L

(b) D₁ L₂ L₁ D₂

(c) E₁ D L₁ E₂ L₂

(d) E₁ D₁ L₁ E₂ D₂ L₂

2. Fig. 76.18 shows a circuit demonstrating an important use of a transistor. State the action in the circuit when the resistance of the variable resistor is decreased. State the importance of this action. (*E.A*)

Fig. 76.18

M M + − − +

3. What are the readings on the high resistance voltmeters V_1 and V_2 in the potential divider circuit of Fig. 76.19 if (a) $R_1 = R_2 = 10$ kΩ, (b) $R_1 = 10$ kΩ, $R_2 = 50$ kΩ and (c) $R_1 = 20$ kΩ and $R_2 = 10$ kΩ?

Fig. 76.19

R_1 R_2

V_1 V_2

6V

4. Fig. 76.20 shows an incomplete electronic circuit.

(a) Copy the diagram and make the following additions.

(i) In the circle draw the symbol for an *n-p-n* transistor.

(ii) Add the symbol for a battery, correctly connected between B and D.

(iii) Draw the symbol for a thermistor between points A and X.

(iv) Draw the symbol for a variable resistor between points X and C.

(v) Draw the symbol for a lamp in the collector circuit.

(vi) Connect the base and emitter of the transistor to the correct places in the circuit.

(b) As the circuit is arranged the lamp will not light. If there is a rise in temperature the lamp will light. Explain this.

Fig. 76.20

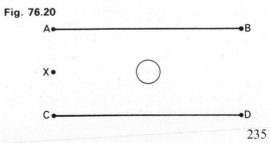

A B

X

C D

(c) A simple rearrangement of this circuit would make the lamp light when the temperature falls. Explain what changes should be made, and how they will affect the working of the circuit.

(d) In the original circuit, instead of a variable resistor, a fixed resistor could have been used between points X and C. Explain why it might have been considered desirable to use a variable resistor for these two circuits.   (J.M.B./A.L./N.W.16+)

5. A simple moisture warning circuit is shown in Fig. 76.21 in which the moisture detector is two closely-spaced copper rods.

(a) Describe how the circuit works when the detector gets wet.

(b) Warning lamps are often placed in the collector circuit of a transistor. Why is a relay used here?

(c) If the relay operates with a current of 30 mA and the current

Fig. 76.21

gain of the transistor is 60, what base current is needed for the relay to work?

(d) What is the function of D?

77 Radio and television

Radio waves

Radio waves are electromagnetic radiation (pp. 43 and 44) which vary in wavelength from a few mm to several km. Typical values are given below.

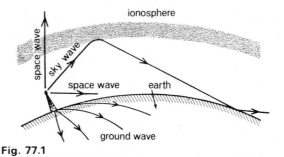

Fig. 77.1

Waves →	Long	Medium	Short	v.h.f.	u.h.f.	Micro
Wave-length	1500 m	300 m	30 m	3 m	30 cm	3 cm
Fre-quency	200 kHz	1 MHz	10 MHz	10^2 MHz	10^3 MHz	10^4 MHz
Use	←	Radio	→	← T.V. →		Radar

They can travel in the three ways shown in Fig. 77.1. *Ground waves* follow the earth's surface and have a limited range, being greatest (1500 km) for long waves and only a few km for v.h.f. (very high frequency) waves. *Sky waves* are bounced back from the ionosphere (p. 44) and are used in long-distance communication by long, medium and short waves. *Space waves* travel in straight lines and can penetrate the ionosphere. v.h.f., u.h.f. (ultra high frequency) and microwaves travel in this way.

Fig. 77.2 shows the Goonhilly Downs, Cornwall, aerial for receiving high frequency waves relayed across the Atlantic by a synchronous satellite (i.e. one which travels round the earth in 24 hours and appears to be at rest).

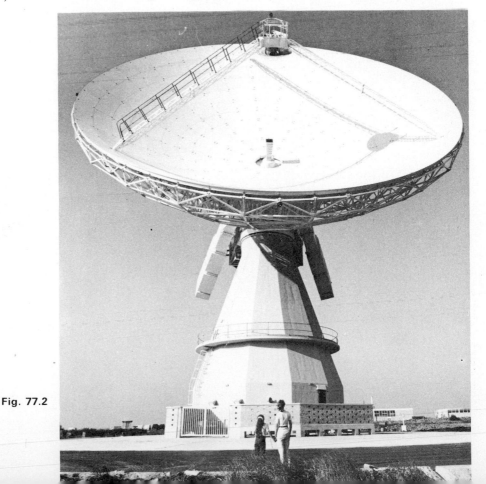

Fig. 77.2

Outline of radio

Radio waves are emitted by aerials when a.c. flows in them but the length of the aerial must be comparable with the wavelength of the wave produced for the radiation to be appreciable. A 50 Hz a.c. corresponds to a wavelength of 6×10^6 m (since $v = f\lambda$ where $v = 3 \times 10^8$ m and $f = 50$ Hz).

Alternating currents with frequencies below about 20 kHz are called *audio frequency* (a.f.) currents; those with frequencies greater than this are *radio frequency* (r.f.) currents. Therefore, so that aerials are not too large, they are supplied with r.f. currents. However, speech and music generate a.f. currents and so some way of combining a.f. with r.f. is required if they are to be sent over a distance.

(*a*) *Transmitter*. In this an *oscillator* produces an r.f. current which would cause an aerial connected to it to send out an electromagnetic wave, called a *carrier wave*, of constant amplitude and having the same frequency as the r.f. current. If a normal receiver picked up such a signal nothing would be heard. The r.f. signal has to be modified or *modulated* so that it 'carries' the a.f. This is done in various ways.

In *amplitude modulation* (a.m.) the amplitude of the r.f. is varied so that it depends on the a.f. current from the microphone, the process occurring in a *modulator*. This type of transmitter is used for medium and long-wave broadcasting in Britain: Fig. 77.3*a* is a block diagram for one.

In *frequency modulation* (f.m.), which is used in v.h.f. broadcasts, the frequency of the carrier is altered at a rate equal to the frequency of the a.f. but the amplitude remains constant, Fig. 77.4. This kind of signal is fairly free from electrical interference.

r.f. carrier modulated by 1 cycle of a.f.

Fig. 77.4

(*b*) *Receiver*. A block diagram of a simple a.m. receiver is shown in Fig. 77.3*b*. The *tuning circuit* selects the wanted signal from the *aerial*. The *detector* (or demodulator) separates the a.f. (speech or music) from the r.f. carrier. The *amplifier* then boosts the a.f. which produces sound in the loudspeaker.

Electrical oscillations

The production of r.f. currents is impossible with mechanical generators (p. 207) but is readily achieved electrically.

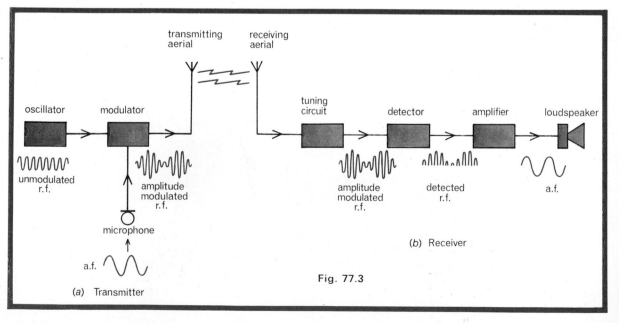

Fig. 77.3

(a) *Oscillatory circuit*. It contains a capacitor C and a coil L, Fig. 77.5a. If C is charged and then discharges through L, current flows backwards and forwards round the circuit, alternately discharging

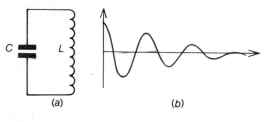

Fig. 77.5

and charging C, first one way then the other. The frequency of the a.c. produced depends on C and L; the smaller they are the higher is the frequency and each circuit has a *natural frequency* of oscillation. Due to the resistance of the coil, the current eventually stops and a decaying or damped oscillation is obtained, Fig. 77.5b.

Fig. 77.6

Slow damped oscillations (about 2 Hz) can be shown using the circuit of Fig. 77.6 with the C.R.O. on its slowest time base speed.

Fig. 77.7

(b) *Transistor oscillator*. To obtain oscillations that do not die away, energy has to be fed into the L-C circuit at the right time. This can be done using a transistor as in Fig. 77.7. The coil L_1, by being near L, feeds the energy needed into the input (base-emitter) circuit of the transistor.

Tuning circuit

Different transmitting stations send out radio waves of different frequencies. Each induces a signal in the aerial of a radio receiver but if the aerial is connected to an *L-C* circuit, Fig. 77.8, only the signal

Fig. 77.8

whose frequency equals the natural frequency of the *L-C* circuit is selected. If the value of C is varied (p. 168, Fig. 57.10) different stations can be 'tuned in'.
　　This is an example of *electrical resonance* (p. 50).

Detection

In *detection* or *demodulation* the a.f. which was 'added' to the r.f. in the transmitter is recovered in the receiver.
　　Suppose the amplitude modulated r.f. signal V of Fig. 77.9a is applied to the detector circuit of Fig. 77.9d. The diode produces rectified pulses of r.f. current I, Fig. 77.9b. These charge up C during the

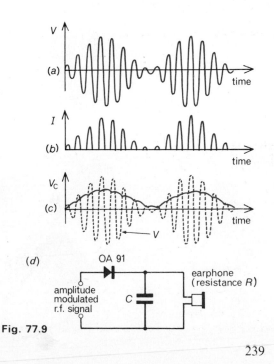

Fig. 77.9

positive half-cycles as well as flowing through the earphone. During the negative half-cycles when the diode is non-conducting, C *partly* discharges through the earphone.

The p.d. V_c across C (and the earphone) varies as in Fig. 77.9c if C and R have the correct values. Apart from the slight r.f. ripple, V_c has the same frequency and shape as the modulating a.f. and produces the original sound in the earphone.

Germanium diodes are used as detectors. If a loudspeaker is to be operated, the detector is followed by several stages of a.f. amplification (p. 235). A suitable resistor then replaces the earphone.

Experiment: simple radio receiver

as high as you can; making an earth connection to a water tap will improve reception, Fig. 77.11b.

You should be able to tune in one or two stations (depending on your location) by altering the variable capacitor.

Note. If a crystal earphone is used instead of a magnetic one, the circuit has to be modified as in Fig. 76.16b, p. 235.

Television

(*a*) *Black and white.* A TV receiver is basically a C.R.O. with two time bases. The horizontal or *line time base* acts as in the C.R.O. The vertical or *frame time base* operates at the same time and draws the

Fig. 77.10

Connect the circuit of Fig. 77.10 on an S-DeC, Fig. 77.11a. The transistor leads can be lengthened and connections made to the 'tags' on the variable capacitor as in Fig. 76.11b, p. 233.

The resistor colour code is given on p. 244.

For an aerial, support a length of wire (e.g. 10 m)

spot at a much slower rate down to the bottom of the screen and then returns it almost at once to the top. The spot thus 'draws' a series of parallel lines of light (625) which cover the screen, Fig. 77.12.

A picture is produced by the incoming signal altering the number of electrons which travel from

Fig. 77.11 (*a*)

(*a*)

Fig. 77.11

(*b*)

water tap
crocodile clip
wire to 'earth' on receiver

Fig. 77.12

the electron gun to the screen. The greater the number the brighter the spot. The brightness of the spot varies from white through grey to black as it sweeps across the screen. A complete picture appears every 1/25 s, but because of the persistence of vision we see the picture as continuous. If each picture is just slightly different from its predecessor, the resultant effect is that of a 'movie' and not a sequence of 'stills'.

When a triangle of dots is struck it may be that the red and green electron beams are intense but not the blue. The triangle will emit red and green light strongly and appear yellowish (see p. 27). The triangles of dots are struck in turn, and since the dots are so small and the scanning so fast, we see a continuous colour picture.

Questions

1. (*a*) (*i*) Draw a labelled diagram of the electromagnetic spectrum showing how radio waves fit in with other types of electromagnetic radiation. What do all these radiations have in common?

(*ii*) A radio station broadcasts on a frequency of 100 MHz. Assuming the speed of light to be 3×10^8 m/s what will be the wavelength of the radio frequency carrier wave from this station?

(*b*) What is meant by the terms (*i*) audio frequencies, (*ii*) radio frequencies? Illustrate your answer by reference to sound waves and carrier waves. (*N.W.*)

Fig. 77.13

metal shadow mask

dots emitting blue, red and green light

electron guns blue, red, green

electron beam

glass face plate

hole

(*b*) *Colour.* A colour TV has three electron guns and the screen is coated with about a million tiny light-emitting 'dots' arranged in triangles. One 'dot' in each triangle emits red light when hit by electrons, another green light and the third blue light.

As the three electron beams scan the screen, an accurately placed 'shadow mask' consisting of a perforated metal plate with about one-third of a million holes ensures that each beam strikes only dots of one 'colour', e.g. electrons from the 'red' gun strike only 'red' dots, Fig. 77.13.

Fig. 77.14

earphone

2. Fig. 77.14 shows the circuit of a simple radio receiver.

(*a*) State the names of the parts labelled A, B, C.

(*b*) What is the purpose of the part labelled D?

78 Further questions

Electrons

1. Draw a labelled diagram of a cathode ray tube. Explain how the electrons are made available, how they are accelerated and how they may be deflected.

Describe how you would use an oscilloscope to compare the magnitudes of two alternating voltages.
(*J.M.B.*)

2. An electron starting from rest and accelerated through a p.d. V volts acquires a kinetic energy eV joules where e is the charge on the electron in coulombs. If when the accelerating p.d. is 1000 volts, the electron acquires a velocity of 1.88×10^7 m/s, determine the value of e/m in C/kg where m is the mass of the electron.
(*N.I.*)

3. What are X-rays? What is the difference between hard and soft X-rays?

Explain the action of a simple X-ray tube with the help of a labelled diagram.

How do the properties of X-rays make them suitable for *either* medical *or* industrial photography?

Radioactivity

4. Describe simple experiments (details of instruments are not expected) to show the difference between α and β radiation when (*a*) passed through a magnetic field, and (*b*) appropriate sheets of material are placed in their paths.

What are the essential differences in nature and properties between the above types of radiation and γ radiation?

State, with a reason, an essential precaution which is necessary when using equipment known to emit γ radiation or X-rays.

A radioactive substance has a half-life of 1 minute. By what factor would you expect the level of activity to drop after 4 minutes?
(*S.*)

5. Explain what is meant by *half-life, background radiation*.

At a certain instant the corrected count-rate registered on a detector placed close to an α-particle emitter is 200 per second and this falls to 50 per second in 12 minutes. Determine the half-life of the source.
(*L.*)

Atomic structure

6. Which of the following statements most correctly represents the important deductions from experiments on the scattering of alpha particles by matter?

  A Alpha particles are nuclei of helium atoms.
  B Atoms are composed of protons, neutrons and electrons.
  C Atoms consist of positively and negatively charged matter.
  D Electrons move in orbits round the nucleus of atoms.
  E Atoms have a small nucleus carrying a positive charge
(*J.M.B.*)

7. The following represents part of a radioactive series in which the chemical symbols have been replaced by letters.

$$\overset{(i)}{} \qquad \overset{(ii)}{} \qquad \overset{(iii)}{}$$
$$^{234}_{90}A \longrightarrow {}^{234}_{91}B \longrightarrow {}^{234}_{92}C \longrightarrow {}^{230}_{90}D$$

Name the particles emitted in the three changes.

Write down the two letters which represent isotopes.
(*W.*)

Electronics

8. (*a*) Draw a diagram to show the construction of a junction diode.

(*b*) Explain the differences between a conductor and a semiconductor.

(*c*) Why are some semiconductors called '*p*' type and others '*n*' type?

Fig. 78.1

(*d*) A puzzle box, Fig. 78.1, contains two lamps and other simple components connected so that, when terminal T_1 is connected to the positive pole of a cell, lamp L_1 lights, but when terminal T_2 is connected to the positive, lamp L_2 lights. Suggest what is in the puzzle box and how the connections are made.
(*W.Y.*)

9. (*a*) Sketch a graph to show what is meant by half-wave rectification.

(*b*) Sketch a graph to show what is meant by full-wave rectification.

(*c*) Draw a diagram of a *bridge circuit* using four semiconductor diodes which would produce full-wave rectification. Mark on your diagram where the input voltage is applied and where the output voltage is produced.

(*d*) What is the purpose of a smoothing capacitor? (*E.M.*)

10. Fig. 78.2 shows a *p-n-p* transistor in a circuit with ammeters M_1 and M_2.

Fig. 78.2

(*a*) Why is the circuit called a 'common emitter circuit'?

(*b*) Which meter measures the base current?

(*c*) Which junction is reverse biased?

(*d*) As the potentiometer *R* is varied, the meter reading of M_1 will vary. Explain briefly how you would use this circuit to demonstrate current amplification by a transistor. Indicate the sort of results that you would expect to obtain.

(*e*) Draw a circuit diagram of a simple amplifier which uses one transistor. (*Mddx.*)

11. Fig. 78.3 is a diagram of a simple safety circuit.

(*a*) (*i*) Name component A. (*ii*) Name component B.

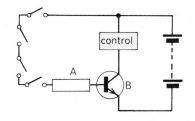

Fig. 78.3

(*b*) (*i*) What is the name of the terminal of component B to which component A is connected? (*ii*) Why is component A usually needed in this part of this type of circuit?

(*c*) (*i*) How many contacts must be closed to operate this circuit? (*ii*) Explain exactly what happens in the circuit when the required number of contacts is closed.

Fig. 78.4

Fig. 78.4 is a diagram of a simple security circuit.

(*d*) (*i*) Component C is known by two names, in addition to its abbreviation. Give BOTH full names. (*ii*) What is the name of the terminal of component C to which component A is connected?

(*e*) (*i*) How many contacts have to be closed to operate this circuit? (*ii*) Explain exactly what happens when the required number of contacts is closed.

(*f*) (*i*) Explain why component C (Fig. 78.4) is more useful than component B (Fig. 78.3) in a warning circuit. (*ii*) Explain how the circuit in Fig. 78.4 may be returned to its normal state after operation. (*J.M.B./A.L./N.W.16+*)

12. Fig. 78.5 is designed to switch on the beacon automatically when daylight fades.

Fig. 78.5

(*a*) (*i*) What is the full name of component A? (*ii*) What is the abbreviation of its name? (*iii*) What changes the value of this component? (*iv*) Explain fully how the properties of the component change.

(*b*) Name component B.

(*c*) Component D is the coil of a reed switch: (*i*) Why has this coil no metal core? (*ii*) What is the function of the coil?

(*d*) (*i*) Explain how the transistor circuit works, mentioning the function of each component. (*ii*) Explain how the transistor circuit controls the operation of the beacon.

(*e*) The beacon operates on a.c. Explain why this supply cannot be used for the transistor circuit. (*J.M.B./A.L./N.W.16+*)

Radio and television

13. (*a*) Explain the meaning of the terms *audio frequency* and *radio frequency*.

(*b*) What is a synchronous communications satellite? Explain why such satellites are used to transmit television signals across the Atlantic ocean.

(*c*) Radio signals travel at a speed of 300 000 km/s. How long would it take a signal from the USA to reach this country if the total path was 6000 km? (*E.A.*)

14. The circuit of a very simple radio receiver is shown in Fig. 78.6. It can be divided into three parts along the dotted lines.

(*a*) Name part X and state what it does.

(*b*) Name part Y and state what each of the *three* components does.

(*c*) Name part Z and state its function.

(*d*) Draw three diagrams to show the colour coding on the 1 kΩ, 10 kΩ and 100 kΩ resistors. (See the Resistor Colour Code below.)

Fig. 78.6

Resistor Colour Code

Black	0	Green	5
Brown	1	Blue	6
Red	2	Violet	7
Orange	3	Grey	8
Yellow	4	White	9

- 1st figure (eg. yellow = 4)
- 2nd figure (eg. violet =7)
- no. of zeros (eg. red = 00)
- tolerance

value = 4700 Ω = 4.7 kΩ

4th band = tolerance: gold = ± 5%, silver = ± 10%, no colour = ± 20%

Revision questions

In both types of question the order of topics follows the *Contents* on pp. 6–7.
Take $g = 10 \, \text{m/s}^2$ or $10 \, \text{N/kg}$

(a) Short types (1 to 10 minutes each)

1. An optician's test card is fixed 80 cm behind the eyes of a patient, who looks into a plane mirror 300 cm in front of him, as shown in Fig. 1. The distance from his eyes to the image of the card is

   A 300 cm   **B** 380 cm   **C** 600 cm   **D** 680 cm
   E 760 cm   *(L.)*

Fig. 1

2. State where an object must be placed so that the image formed by a concave mirror is
   (*i*) erect and virtual,   (*ii*) at infinity,
   (*iii*) the same size as the object.   *(W.)*

3. Fig. 2*a* shows a ray of light PQ incident normally on a rectangular glass block, so that the emergent ray RS is neither displaced nor deviated from the original direction. The block is then turned in an anticlockwise direction to a new position. Which one of the diagrams in Fig. 2*b* best illustrates what happens to the emergent ray RS?   *(N.I.)*

Fig. 2

4. A ray of light is incident on the plane surface of a transparent material at such an angle that the reflected and refracted rays are at right angles to each other. Draw a diagram to illustrate this and calculate the refractive index if the angle of incidence is 60°.   *(S.)*

5. A 45° right-angled prism ABC, made of glass of refractive index 1.5, is used to turn light through 90°.

Fig. 3

   (*a*) Copy Fig. 3, continue the paths of the two rays until they emerge into the air again.
   (*b*) Why does no light emerge from face AC?
   (*c*) By referring to the two rays, explain what is meant by lateral inversion.
   (*d*) Why are the rays which leave face CB slightly fainter than those which enter face AB?
   (*e*) Calculate the critical angle for a material of refractive index 1.25. If the prism were made of this material, would it reflect light in the same way?
                                    (O.)

6. A converging lens is used to form an image of a bright object on a white screen. If the lower half of the lens is covered with a sheet of metal, as shown in Fig. 4, then

   A the image disappears entirely
   B the lower half of the image disappears
   C the upper half of the image disappears
   D the brightness of the image is reduced
   E the image is unchanged.   *(N.I.)*

Fig. 4

245

7. A translucent white plastic bottle has green printing on it. An electric lamp with red glass is suspended inside the bottle and switched on in a darkened room. The green printing on the bottle will appear to be

   A black **B** blue **C** magenta **D** red
   E yellow   (*L.*)

8. State whether the following waves are transverse or longitudinal *and* progressive or stationary:

(*a*) the vibrations of a stretched wire (which is fixed at both ends) when plucked;

(*b*) the sound from the above wire to an observer;

(*c*) a ripple on a large pond;

(*d*) the vibrations of an air column in a long test tube.   (*S.*)

9. Fig. 5 represents a plan view of a horizontal ripple tank. Two dippers, A and B, vibrate in-phase with the same frequency. At a point P constructive interference is observed, and at a nearby point Q destructive interference is observed.

(*a*) On the same axes sketch two graphs of displacement against time for the vibration of the water at P, one for the waves from A, the other for

Fig. 5

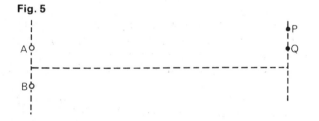

the waves from B. On the same axes sketch a third graph showing the displacement of the water at P due to both sets of waves arriving at P together.

(*b*) In exactly the same way, sketch three graphs of displacement against time for the water at Q, one for waves from A, another for waves from B and the third for both sets of waves arriving at Q together.

(*c*) (*i*) State a relationship between the distances AP and BP.

(*ii*) State a relationship between the distances AQ and BQ.   (*J.M.B.*)

10. Fig. 6 illustrates crests of circular wave-fronts radiating from a point source O. If the time taken for a wavefront to travel from P to Q is 10 s, and the wavelength of the waves is 2 m, the speed of the waves, in m/s, is

   A 0.20 **B** 0.80 **C** 1.00 **D** 1.25 **E** 5.00
                                         (*N.I.*)

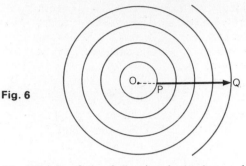

Fig. 6

11. Which of the following is (are) true both for light waves and for sound waves?

   1 They can travel through a vacuum.

   2 Speed of wave = frequency of wave x wavelength.

   3 They transfer energy from one place to another.

   A 1, 2, 3 **B** 1, 2 **C** 2, 3 **D** 1 **E** 3   (*L.*)

Fig. 7

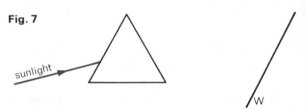

sunlight

12. Fig. 7 shows a ray of sunlight incident upon a triangular glass prism, such that a spectrum is produced on the screen W.

(*a*) Copy the diagram, continue the ray to illustrate how the spectrum is formed on a white screen at W. Mark the violet end of the spectrum V, and the red end R.

(*b*) If the white screen is replaced with a pure red screen, describe carefully what you would observe on the screen, giving a reason for your answer.

(*c*) The refractive index of the glass is 1.50 for red light. Using your answer to (*a*), state whether you would expect the refractive index of glass for violet light to be greater than, equal to or less than 1.50. Explain how you deduced your answer.

(*d*) The glass prism transmits both some ultra-violet and some infra-red radiation.

(*i*) On the diagram, mark clearly with a U the region on the screen at which you would detect ultra-violet radiation, and with an I the region at which you would detect infra-red radiation.

(*ii*) State one method by which you could detect the presence of ultra-violet radiation.

(*iii*) State whether the frequency of ultra-violet radiation is greater than, equal to or less than that of infra-red radiation.   (*N.I. part qn.*)

13. Stationary waves are set up in a long thin cord. The points where the cord appears at rest are 0.15 m apart. What are these points called? If the frequency of the vibrations is 200 Hz, calculate the speed of waves along the cord. (S.)

14. Monochromatic light is incident normally on a diffraction grating with 10^6 lines per metre. On the screen the first-order spectrum is seen at an angle of $30°$ from the direct line, as shown in Fig. 8.

Fig. 8

The wavelength of the light is

A 3×10^{-7}m **B** 5×10^{-7}m **C** 6×10^{-7}m
D 2×10^{-6}m **E** 6×10^{-6}m (O.)

15. A man standing between two cliffs X and Y at the point P fires a pistol, Fig. 9. If the speed of sound in air is 330 m/s, the first two echoes which he hears will be separated by a time interval, in seconds, of

Fig. 9

A 0.5 **B** 0.75 **C** 1.25 **D** 1.50 **D** 2.50
(N.I.)

16. A vibrating tuning fork of frequency 256 Hz is held over the top of a tube full of water as shown in Fig. 10. The water is then allowed to flow slowly from the tube, and there is a first loud response when the air column is 300 mm long.

Fig. 10

(a) What is meant by 'frequency 256 Hz'?
(b) What estimate does this experiment give the wavelength in air of the note from the fork?
(c) What is the relationship between the frequency of the fork and the wavelength in air of the sound it produces?
(d) What estimate does this experiment give for the speed of sound in air?
(e) Why is the loudness of the note heard much less when the length of the air column is less than 300 mm? (O.)

17. The pitch of the screw of a micrometer screw gauge is 0.50 mm. When this micrometer is used to determine the diameter of a wire, the screw is turned back through $4\frac{1}{2}$ turns from the closed position.
What is the diameter of the wire?
A pupil says that the micrometer has a zero error to be added. How would you verify this?
(O. and C.)

18. A solid block has dimensions 0.1 m × 0.5 m × 0.2 m, and is made of material of density 9000 kg/m³. It rests on a horizontal surface. Calculate:
(i) the mass of the solid,
(ii) the maximum pressure it can exert on the surface. (W.)

19. A force of 40 N is necessary to extend a spring by 20 mm. If the acceleration of free fall is 10 m/s², the extension, in mm, when a mass of 0.5 kg is attached to the lower end of the spring is

A 0.20 **B** 1.00 **C** 2.50 **D** 5.00 **E** 10.00
(N.I.)

20. The graph in Fig. 11 shows the displacement of a pendulum bob from its rest position as it varies with time.

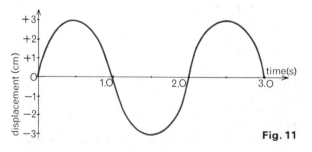

Fig. 11

From the graph, determine
(i) the amplitude of the oscillation,
(ii) the time for one complete oscillation,
(iii) the distance of the bob from its rest position after 0.8 seconds.
On a copy of the diagram, draw the graph which represents a pendulum swinging with half the amplitude and twice the frequency. (W.)

21. A uniform rod has equally spaced graduation marks on each side of its mid point at which it is pivoted (Fig. 12). Four identical metal discs are placed on the left hand side of the pivot at the three mark. Which one of the following arrangements of discs, placed on the right hand side of the pivot, could be used to restore equilibrium?

A 3 placed at the 2 mark and 1 at the 4 mark
B 2 placed at the 2 mark and 2 at the 4 mark
C 1 placed at the 4 mark and 3 at the 3 mark
D 3 placed at the 2 mark and 1 at the 4 mark
E 1 placed at the 1 mark and 3 at the 2 mark

(*N.I.*)

Fig. 12

22. Two parallel forces, of 2 N and 4 N respectively, act on a body through points P and Q as shown in Fig. 13.

Fig. 13

Their resultant
1 has a magnitude of 3 N
2 acts through the mid-point of PQ
3 is parallel to the two forces shown
Which statement(s) is (are) correct?

A 1, 2, 3   **B** 1, 2   **C** 2, 3   **D** 1   **E** 3   (*L.*)

23. Fig. 14 shows the horizontal forces exerted on a tree by two tractors in an attempt to pull it out of the ground.

Fig. 14

Draw a diagram to a stated scale and use it to determine the magnitude and direction of the resultant force exerted on the tree by the two tractors.

(*C.*)

Fig. 15

24. In Fig. 15 two forces acting at a point O are represented in magnitude and direction by OX and OY. The third force required to maintain equilibrium is represented in magnitude and direction by

A OZ   **B** ZO   **C** XY   **D** YZ   **E** XZ   (*O.*)

25. An electric motor drives a machine which lifts a mass of 2 kg through a height of 6 m in 4 s at constant speed.

(*a*) State how the work done by a force is calculated.

(*b*) How much work is done in lifting the 2 kg mass?

(*c*) How much power is used to lift the 2 kg mass?

(*d*) If the electrical power input is 40 W, what is the efficiency?

(*e*) State two causes of loss of efficiency.   (*O.*)

26. A load of 10 N is being raised slowly with the aid of the simple pulley system shown in Fig. 16. Each of the pulleys weighs 2 N.

Fig. 16

If the system has no friction losses, the effort required is

A 5 N   **B** 6 N   **C** 7 N   **D** 10 N   **E** 12 N (*O.*)

27. Fig. 17 illustrates a mercury manometer (using tube of uniform bore), connected to a gas container through a tap T, which is initially closed. Atmospheric pressure is 750 mm of mercury. On opening tap T, the mercury level in the left-hand arm

Fig. 17

A falls through 125 mm   D rises through 250 mm
B rises through 125 mm   E falls through 500 mm.
C falls through 250 mm   (*N.I.*)

Fig. 18

28. Fig. 18 represents a simple hydraulic lift. Calculate the maximum load that can be lifted using a downward effort, as shown, of 5 N.   (*W.*)

29. (*a*) Copy Fig. 19.

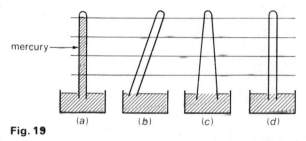

Fig. 19

(*i*) Fig. 19*a* illustrates a simple mercury barometer. State what is contained in the region above the mercury column in the tube, and mark *clearly* the height which you would measure to determine atmospheric pressure.

(*ii*) In Fig. 19*b* the tube has been tilted. Mark carefully on it the level of the mercury in the tube.

(*iii*) In Fig. 19*c*, a barometer has been made using a tube of non uniform bore. Mark carefully on it the level of the mercury in the tube.

(*iv*) In Fig. 19*d*, air has been introduced into the region above the mercury column so that it is at a pressure of $\frac{1}{4}$ of atmospheric pressure. Mark carefully on it the level of the mercury in the tube.

(*b*) On a particular day, atmospheric pressure at sea level was found to be 102 000 N/m². At the same time, the reading on a mercury barometer placed at the top of a mountain was 0.6 m. The acceleration of free fall is 10 m/s² at both sea level and the top of the mountain, and the density of mercury is 13 600 kg/m³.

(*i*) Determine the pressure of the atmosphere at the top of the mountain in N/m².

(*ii*) Calculate the difference in atmospheric pressure, in N/m², between the top of the mountain and sea level.

(*iii*) If the density of air is 1.2 kg/m³ between the top of the mountain and sea level, determine the height of the mountain top above sea level.   (*N.I.*)

30. An experiment was performed to find the connection between the pressure and volume of a fixed mass of gas when the temperature was kept constant. The graph in Fig. 20 shows the pressure (*p*)

plotted against $\dfrac{1}{\text{volume}}$ $\left(\dfrac{1}{V}\right)$

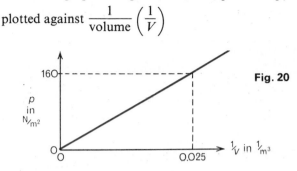

Fig. 20

(*a*) (*i*) What relationship between pressure and volume can you deduce from the above graph?

(*ii*) Give a reason for your answer.

(*b*) Using the kinetic theory of gases, explain

(*i*) how a gas exerts a pressure,

(*ii*) the variation in pressure when the volume is reduced.

(*c*) If the above experimental results show that when the pressure of the gas is 160 N/m² the corresponding value of $\dfrac{1}{V}$ is 0.025/m³, calculate the value of the volume of the gas when the pressure of the gas changes to 4800 N/m².   (*N.I.*)

31. (*a*) A cubic block, of side 3 m and density 800 kg/m³, is attached to the base of a tank containing water of density 1 000 kg/m³ by means of an inextensible cable of negligible mass, Fig. 21. The acceleration of free fall is 10 m/s².

Fig. 21

(*i*) Determine the mass of the block.

(*ii*) Determine the weight of the block.

(*iii*) Determine the upthrust acting on the block.

(*iv*) Determine the tension in the cable.

cont.

(*b*) The cable is now released, and the block rises to the surface of the water, where it subsequently floats.

(*i*) Determine the upthrust on the block when it is floating.

(*ii*) Determine the volume of the block which is beneath the surface of the water while the block is floating. (*N.I.*)

32. A hydrometer sinks to a greater depth in water than in a certain liquid L. From this it can be concluded that

1 the density of L is greater than that of water
2 the expansivity of L is smaller than that of water
3 the hydrometer displaces a greater mass of water than of L.

Which statement(s) is (are) correct?

A 1, 2, 3 **B** 1, 2 **C** 2, 3 **D** 1 **E** 3 (*L.*)

33. A radio transmitter directs pulses of waves towards a satellite from which reflections are received 10 milliseconds after transmission. If the speed of radio waves is 3×10^8 m s^{-1}, how far away is the satellite? (*S.*)

34. The velocity-time graph of Fig. 22 illustrates the motion of a ball which has been projected vertically upwards from the surface of the moon. The weight of the ball on earth, where the acceleration of free fall is 10 m/s², is 2 N.

Fig. 22

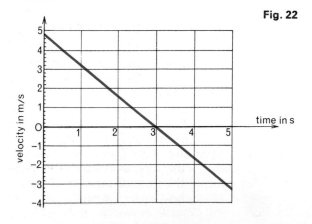

(*a*) State why the velocity becomes negative (after 3 seconds).

(*b*) Determine a value for the acceleration of free fall on the moon, showing clearly how you obtain your answer.

(*c*) Determine the total distance travelled by the ball in the first 5 seconds, showing clearly how you obtain your answer.

(*d*) Determine the weight of the ball on the moon, showing clearly how you obtain your answer.

(*e*) If the ball were projected vertically upwards with the same velocity on earth, and friction is neglected, what difference, if any, would you expect to observe in a velocity-time graph (using the same scales) for the ball on earth, compared with that given above? Give a reason for your answer. (*N.I.*)

35. Two metal spheres, of masses 4 kg and 1 kg, held at different heights above the ground, are released simultaneously, Fig. 23. If the acceleration of free fall is 10 m/s², then the difference in time, in seconds, at which they hit the ground is

A 0 **B** 1 **C** 3 **D** 4 **E** 5 (*N.I.*)

Fig. 23

36. A helicopter of mass 3 000 kg rises vertically at a constant speed of 25 m/s. The acceleration of free fall is 10 m/s². The resultant force, in N, acting on the helicopter is

A zero **B** 30 000 downwards **C** 45 000 upwards
D 75 000 upwards **E** 105 000 upwards (*N.I.*)

37. A hard ball, mass 0.50 kg, travels along a straight line with a speed 1.5 m/s. It hits a fixed sheet of metal and rebounds back along the same path with the same speed. Calculate the average force exerted on the metal during the collision if the ball remains in contact with the metal for 1.0 millisecond. (*O. and C.*)

38. Water, which flows over a weir at a rate of 900 kg/s, takes 1.5 s to fall vertically into the stream below.

(*a*) (*i*) What is the speed with which the falling water hits the stream?

(*ii*) What is the height through which the water falls?

(*b*) Calculate (*i*) the weight of water falling over the weir in 5.0 s, (*ii*) the work which has been done on this weight of water when it hits the stream below the weir.

(*c*) Calculate the power of the falling water at the instant it hits the stream.

(*d*) State the energy transformations which occur as the water falls from the weir into the stream below. (*C.*)

39. Copy and complete Fig. 24 by showing the two forces acting on a motor-cycle travelling at the appropriate speed round a banked curve. Show the direction in which the resultant of these forces must be acting. (*W.*)

Fig. 24

40. Fig. 25 shows a drawing pin which rests on the deck of a record player. The deck is horizontal and is rotating at a constant rate.

Fig. 25

Which two of the following quantities associated with the pin are changed when the drawing pin has been carried from A to B:
speed, velocity, kinetic energy, potential energy, momentum? (*O. and C.*)

41. An uncalibrated thermometer is immersed in melting ice. The length of the thread of mercury is 35 mm. When the thermometer is immersed in steam from water boiling under a pressure of one standard atmosphere the length of the thread becomes 215 mm. What is the temperature when the length of the thread of mercury is 71 mm?
(*O. and C.*)

42. Two marks on a metal bar are 50.00 cm apart at a temperature of 293 K. This distance increases by 0.096 cm when the temperature rises to 373 K. Calculate the linear expansivity of the metal. (*S.*)

Fig. 26

43. Fig. 26 shows the variation of the density of water with temperature. It may be deduced from the graph that
  1 a given mass of water has a minimum volume at 4°C
  2 between 0°C and 4°C convection will not take place in a vessel of water heated at the bottom
  3 expansion occurs when water freezes
  Which statement(s) is (are) correct?

  A 1, 2, 3   **B** 1, 2   **C** 2, 3   **D** 1   **E** 3 (*L.*)

44. An ideal gas, initially at a temperature of 27°C, is heated until both pressure and volume are doubled. The final temperature, in °C, is

  A 6.75   **B** 27   **C** 108   **D** 927   **E** 1200
(*N.I.*)

45. A quantity of helium occupies a volume 3.0×10^{-3} m³ inside a high pressure gas cylinder. The pressure of the helium is 1.5×10^7 Pa (N/m²) when the cylinder is stored at 7 °C. What volume will the helium occupy if the contents of the cylinder are used to inflate a balloon to a pressure 1.0×10^5 Pa (N/m²) when the temperature is 20°C? (*O. and C.*)

46. When a 2 kg block of metal at 600 °C is immersed in water at its boiling point (100 °C), 0.4 kg of steam is produced. Assuming that there are no heat losses to the surroundings and that the specific latent heat of vaporization of water is 2.3×10^6 J/kg, the specific heat capacity of the metal, in J/kg °C, is

  A 7.67×10^2 **B** 9.20×10^2 **C** 7.67×10^4
  D 9.20×10^4 **E** 2.30×10^8 (*N.I.*)

47. A well-lagged calorimeter contains 0.10 kg of water and has an electric immersion heater in the liquid. A second identical lagged calorimeter contains 0.10 kg of paraffin and an identical heater. Both fluids are initially at 20 °C. The heaters are switched on at the same instant. If the paraffin reaches a temperature of 30 °C in 10 minutes, how long will it take for the water to attain this temperature? Assume that the thermal capacity of the calorimeters and any heat losses are negligible. (Take the specific heat capacity of paraffin as 2100 J/kg °C and that of water as 4200 J/kg °C.) (*O. and C.*)

48. A small quantity, 0.010 kg, of water at 17 °C is added to a larger mass of ice at 0 °C contained in a vacuum flask. Calculate the greatest mass of ice which can be melted. (Take the specific heat capacity of water as 4200 J/kg °C and the specific latent heat of fusion of ice as 340×10^3 J/kg.) (*O. and C.*)

49. A heater of power 200 W was used to keep liquid boiling in a vessel. During a period of 50

seconds, the mass of liquid decreased by 0.005 kg. Assuming that all the heat energy was given to the liquid, the specific latent heat of vaporization of the liquid, in J/kg, is

    A 50 **B** 800 **C** 1.0×10^4 **D** 4.0×10^4
    E 2.0×10^6 (*N.I.*)

50. Answer each part of this question in terms of the *kinetic theory of matter*.

(*a*) A sample of liquid at its boiling point is to be converted to vapour at the same temperature. Why must heat energy be supplied to bring about this change?

(*b*) When all the liquid has been converted into vapour at the boiling point, the vapour fills a container at atmospheric pressure. Explain why the volume of the vapour is much greater than the original volume of the liquid.

(*c*) Why does the vapour exert a pressure on its container?

(*d*) If the temperature of the container is raised, why does the pressure of the vapour inside the container rise? (Assume that the volume of the container does not change.)   (*C.*)

51. Fig. 27 represents two long, straight, parallel conductors both carrying the same direct current.

Fig. 27 $\otimes$ $\otimes$

The symbol $\otimes$ indicates that the direction of the current is into the plane of the paper. Copy the diagram and add the magnetic flux pattern around the conductors. On your diagram show, by means of arrows, the direction of the forces acting on the conductors. Neglect the Earth's magnetic field.
                              (*O. and C.*)

52. (*a*) Draw a labelled diagram of a parallel plate capacitor.

(*b*) What is the relationship between capacitance, voltage and charge?
A 2 μF capacitor is charged to a potential of 200 V and then disconnected from the power supply.

(*c*) What is 2 μF expressed in farads?

(*d*) What is the size of the charge on each plate of the capacitor?

(*e*) One plate of the capacitor carries a positive charge; the other plate is earthed. Explain why the earthed plate carries a negative charge.   (*O.*)

53. When a 5 ohm resistance is connected across the terminals of a 20 V battery of negligible internal resistance, the number of coulombs passing through the resistance in 10 seconds is

    A 0.4 **B** 2.5 **C** 10.0 **D** 40.0 **E** 1000.0
                                  (*N.I.*)

54. (*a*) A wire was connected to a battery and it was found that the energy converted into heat was 30 joules when 20 coulombs of charge flowed through the wire in 5 seconds. Calculate

(*i*) the potential difference between the ends of the wire;

(*ii*) the current flowing through the wire;

(*iii*) the resistance of the wire;

(*iv*) the average power developed in the wire.

(*b*) If the current in the wire were doubled and all the energy were released as heat in the wire, how much heat would be produced in the wire in 5 seconds?   (*J.M.B.*)

55. A 9 V battery is composed of six 1.5 V cells, each of internal resistance $0.2\,\Omega$, connected in series. The greatest current that can be obtained from such a battery is

    A 0.3 A **B** 1.3 A **C** 1.5 A **D** 7.5 A
    E 9.2 A   (*O.*)

Fig. 28

56. The graph in Fig.28 shows how the current I through a tungsten filament lamp varies with the voltage V across it.

(*a*) What is the voltage when the current is 0.2 amperes?

(*b*) What is the resistance of the lamp when I is 0.2 amperes?

(*c*) What is the increase in current when V is increased from 2 V to 6 V?

(*d*) Does the resistance of the filament increase or decrease as V increases from 2 V to 6 V? What causes the change?

(*e*) Draw a diagram of the circuit you would use to take readings to plot this graph.   (*O.*)

57. An electric motor takes a current of 5.0 A from a 4.0 V supply. Calculate the power input to the motor.

The motor lifts a weight of 50 N through a vertical height of 3.0 m in 10 s. Calculate the average useful work done per second by the motor in lifting this weight.

Suggest a reason for the difference between this quantity and the power input to the motor.   (*C.*)

Fig. 29

Fig. 32

58. Two coils X and Y, having the same dimensions and number of turns, are wound around a piece of soft iron as in Fig. 29. A steady direct current passes through X and Y. Which one of the following statements is correct?

A End P becomes a North pole, while end Q becomes a South pole.

B End P becomes a South pole, while end Q becomes a North pole.

C Both end P and end Q become North poles.

D Both end P and end Q become South poles.

E Neither end P nor end Q become poles, since the effects of the two coils cancel out.   (*N.I.*)

59. A moving coil meter has a resistance of 5.0 Ω and gives a full-scale deflection for a current of 15 mA. A shunt resistor is connected to the meter in order that currents up to 1.0 A may be measured. What is the effective resistance of the shunted meter? How much power is dissipated in the meter and shunt when it is indicating a current of 1.0 A?

(O. and C.)

60. Fig. 30 shows four resistors connected to an accumulator of e.m.f. 2.0 V and negligible internal resistance. The resistances of the individual resistors are shown on the diagram. Calculate the total current flowing from the accumulator. The points B and D are now joined by a wire. Indicate, with a reason, the direction in which you would expect current to flow in the wire BD.   (*C.*)

Fig. 30

61. Each conductor in a seven-strand copper cable is 1.0 mm in diameter, Fig. 31. The resistivity of copper is 1.7×10^{-8} Ω m. Calculate the resistance of 1.0 km of such a cable.   (*O. and C.*)

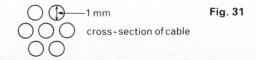

Fig. 31

cross-section of cable

62. Two coils P and Q are wound on a soft iron former as in Fig. 32. When a steady current passes through coil P, end N of the coil behaves as a magnetic north pole, while end S behaves as a magnetic south pole. Key K is initially open, and is then closed. Which one of the following statements concerning the circuit with coil Q is correct after the key is closed?

A A current will flow momentarily from X to Y through G.

B A current will flow momentarily from Y to X through G.

C A steady current will flow from X to Y through G.

D A steady current will flow from Y to X through G.

E No current will flow through G.   (*N.I.*)

63. Fig. 33 shows an incomplete diagram of a simple a.c. generator.

rotation

Fig. 33

(*a*) Copy and complete the diagram so that the following are shown and labelled

(*i*) the slip rings   (*ii*) the brushes

(*iii*) the direction of the induced current when the coil is at the position shown and the generator is connected to an external circuit.

(*b*) Sketch a graph showing the variation of output current with time. Label the axes.

(*c*) State for what positions of the coil the output voltage is (*i*) maximum, (*ii*) zero, giving a reason for your answer in each case.

(*d*) State two methods by which the output voltage of an a.c. generator can be increased.

(*e*) (*i*) A 3 V (effective value) output from an a.c. generator is applied to the primary coil of a transformer containing 30 turns. If the secondary coil contains 10 turns, determine the output voltage (effective value).   *cont.*

(*ii*) If the generator is capable of supplying 6 W, calculate the greatest output current (effective value) which can be taken from the secondary windings. (*N.I.*)

64. Fig. 34 shows how the output voltage from an a.c. generator varies with time. The frequency of the output, in Hz, is

A 0.01 **B** 0.10 **C** 10.00 **D** 100.00
E 200.00 (*N.I.*)

Fig. 34

65. The input to the low voltage unit shown in Fig. 35 below is connected to the a.c. mains and the output from the unit is approximately 15 V d.c. The unit includes a transformer. What other device must it contain?

Fig. 35

The unit is to be used to charge a 12 V battery at a current of approximately 5 A. Draw the circuit diagram, starting from the output terminals above, showing how you would carry this out, making clear the polarity of the battery terminals. (*C.*)

Questions 66 to 68
The diagrams in Fig. 36 represent five possible paths taken by atomic particles (initially travelling to the right) after they enter a magnetic field. Crosses (+) indicate a magnetic field directed into the page, while arrows pointing up indicate a magnetic field in that direction.

For each of the following particles, select the diagram which corresponds most closely to the expected path taken. Each diagram may be used once, more than once, or not at all.

Fig. 36   magnetic field into paper   magnetic field

66. electron.   **67.** α particle.   **68.** neutron.
(*N.I.*)

69. (*a*) What is meant by the *specific charge* of a particle?
(*b*) The specific charge of an electron is 1.76×10^{11} C/kg and the specific charge of a proton is 9.6×10^7 C/kg.
(*i*) Why is it reasonable to assume that an electron and a proton carry the same quantity of charge?
(*ii*) Assuming that both particles carry the same quantity of charge, calculate the mass of a proton compared with the mass of an electron. (*J.M.B.*)

70. The metallic filament F shown in Fig. 37 is heated to a high temperature in an evacuated tube. Name the particles emitted from F.

Fig. 37

Show on a copy of the diagram how you could arrange for the particles from F to be accelerated to a high speed towards M.
When the particles strike the metal block M, most of their energy is converted into heat. What form does the remainder of the energy take? (*C.*)

71. A radio-active source emits α, β and γ radiations. A suitable detector is first placed very close to the source and then moved about 10 cm away. Explain any differences in count rate that you would expect. What further effects would be obtained by your placing (*a*) a very thin sheet of aluminium, (*b*) a thick sheet of lead, between source and detector? (*S.*)

72. The radiation from a radioactive source is arranged so that it passes through a postcard and then at right angles to a strong magnetic field. A detector shows the presence of radiation straight through *and* to one side only of the original direction. Which types of radiation are being detected?

A α particles and β particles
B α particles and γ rays
C β particles and γ rays
D α particles and neutrons
E γ rays and neutrons (*O.*)

73. (*a*) Explain what is meant by (*i*) atomic mass number and (*ii*) atomic number.
(*b*) (*i*) The isotope $^{238}_{92}$U decays by alpha-emission to an isotope of thorium (Th). Compare the $^{238}_{92}$U and thorium nuclei, explaining the changes which have occurred in the uranium nucleus.

(*ii*) The thorium nucleus decays by beta-emission to an isotope of protactinium (Pa). Compare the thorium and Pa nuclei, accounting for the changes you describe. (*J.M.B.*)

74. A radioactive sample has a half-life of 20 minutes, and at a certain time a detector records 120 counts per second. Calculate the count-rate recorded by the detector one hour later.

The sample emits α particles. State briefly the nature of these particles. (*C.*)

75. (*a*) A nitrogen nuclide is written as $^{14}_{7}N$. What information about the structure of the nitrogen atom can be deduced from this symbol for the nuclide?

(*b*) A nuclide whose symbol is $^{16}_{7}N$ is an isotope of nitrogen. In what way is an atom of this type of nitrogen different from the atom in (*a*)?

(*c*) The nuclide $^{16}_{7}N$ decays to become an oxygen nuclide by emitting an electron. Write down an equation to show this process.

(*d*) The half-life of the nuclide $^{16}_{7}N$ is 7.3 s. What does this mean? A sample of this type of nitrogen is observed for 29.2 s. Calculate the fraction of the original radioactive isotope remaining after this time. (*C.*)

76. A neutral atom has a mass number of 7 and an atomic number of 3. State (*a*) the number of protons in the nucleus; (*b*) the number of electrons surrounding the nucleus. How many neutrons are present and where are they situated? (*S.*)

77. Fig. 38 represents a certain atom which is made up of protons (P), neutrons (N), and electrons (e).

Fig. 38

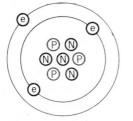

(*a*) What is meant by the *mass number* of an atom and what is its value in this case?

(*b*) What is meant by the *atomic number* of an atom and what is its value in this case?

(*c*) What is the charge: (*i*) on the nucleus of this atom; (*ii*) on the atom as a whole?

(*d*) How do protons, neutrons and electrons compare in mass?

(*e*) What happens to the atomic number of an atom when it emits: (*i*) an α particle; (*ii*) a β particle? (*O.*)

Questions 78 to 81
  A joule
  B metre per second squared
  C newton
  D kilogram metre per second
  E watt
Which of the units listed above could be used to measure

78. the tension in a stretched spring?

79. the rate at which a machine is doing work?

80. the change of momentum of a billiard ball when it bounces off the cushion of a billiard table?

81. the change in the potential energy of a falling parachutist? (*L.*)

(b) Long questions (20 to 25 minutes each).

82. (*a*) Fig. 39 shows a torch being held under water in such a way that a ray of light is produced which can strike the surface of the water at different angles *i*. Calculate a value for the critical angle; the refractive index of water is 4/3. Draw sketches to show what will happen to the ray of light after it has struck the water-air boundary when *i* is about 20° and when *i* is about 60°. Account for the different behaviour of the ray in the two cases.

Fig. 39

Why in one case has the resulting ray coloured edges whereas in the other case it has not?

(*b*) In an experiment to determine the refractive index of water a black line is painted on the bottom of a tall glass container which is then partially filled with water. On looking vertically down into the water the black line appears to be closer than it really is. Explain, with the help of a ray diagram, why this is so.

The following results were obtained in such an experiment.

Real depth/cm	8.1	12.0	16.0	20.0
Apparent depth/cm	5.9	9.1	12.0	15.1

Plot a graph of real depth (*y* axis) against apparent depth (*x* axis) and hence determine a value for the refractive index of water. (*L.*)

83. Explain, with the aid of ray diagrams, how a lens, of focal length 100 mm, can be used

(*a*) in a simple camera to photograph a distant object,

(*b*) in a slide projector to project the image of a transparency ('slide') on to a screen,

(*c*) as a magnifying glass to examine the transparency.

In each case show clearly where the photographic film or transparency should be placed in relation to the focal plane of the lens, and state the type of image being formed by the lens. The details of the other parts of the instruments are not required.

When the lens is used as a magnifying glass, the final image produced has a linear magnification of 2.5. Determine, by using a ray diagram drawn to scale, or otherwise, the distance from the lens to the object. (*O. and C.*)

84. (*a*) (*i*) Draw a ray diagram to show how a pure spectrum of white light can be projected onto a screen using a prism and any other necessary apparatus.

(*ii*) Describe and explain the appearance of a red-coloured pen as it is moved through the white-light spectrum.

(*b*) If the screen of a working colour television set is closely observed it may be seen that it is made up of a lattice of regularly arranged minute spots of light. Each spot of light emits one of the three primary colours and the lattice of these three coloured spots A, B and C is regularly arranged as in Fig. 40. Any colour can therefore be formed on the screen by various combinations of one, two or three spots emitting their individual colours.

Fig. 40

(*i*) Name the three primary colours used in the screen lattice.

(*ii*) Explain how the television screen can appear magenta using this lattice.

(*iii*) Describe and account for the appearance of a yellow coloured screen when it is viewed through a red filter.

(*c*) A student interested in astronomy attempts to identify various constellations of stars in the night sky with the aid of a book which he illuminates using a powerful electric torch. Describe the two changes in the optical system of his eye as he looks from the book to the stars and explain why these changes occur. (*L.*)

85. Write down four properties common to all electromagnetic waves.

Describe how you would make use of a ripple tank to show

(*a*) reflection of straight (plane) waves by a concave boundary, and

(*b*) diffraction of water waves.

Sketch the wave pattern you would expect to observe in each case.

A straight vibrator, vibrating at 7 Hz, causes water ripples to travel across the surface of a shallow tank. The waves travel a distance of 35 cm in 1.25 seconds. Calculate the wavelength of the waves. (*W.*)

86. Two identical dippers A and B vibrate in a ripple tank in phase with each other and with the same constant frequency and amplitude and produce waves in the tank.

The disturbance of the water at points along the line MN, shown in Fig. 41, is observed. At Q and S the disturbance is greatest, whereas at P and R the water is at rest. R is the only position between Q and S where the water is not disturbed.

Fig. 41

(*i*) Explain why the disturbance at Q is as described above.

(*ii*) Why is there no disturbance at R?

For double slit fringes (Young's slit fringes) observed with light,

$$\frac{\text{separation of fringes}}{\text{wavelength}} = \frac{\text{distance from slits to screen}}{\text{distance between the slits}}$$

Make use of this formula in answering (*iii*) and (*iv*) below.

The frequency at which the dippers are driven is slowly increased until the position of maximum disturbance, originally at S, has moved to R.

(*iii*) Calculate the new wavelength if the original wavelength was 10 mm.

(*iv*) Describe how the separation of the dippers A and B could now be changed to restore the position of maximum disturbance to S.

(*v*) The mechanism driving the dippers is altered so that they now vibrate half a cycle out of phase with each other. The frequency of vibration and the separation AB are the same as in parts (*i*) and (*ii*) of the question. At which of the points P, Q, R and S will the water be at rest? (*O. and C.*)

87. (*a*) Explain what is meant by interference of light. Draw a diagram to show why a diffraction grating illuminated with light of a single wavelength can produce constructive interference at more than one angle to the direct beam.

(*b*) Draw a diagram to show the appearance on a screen of the first-order and second-order spectra produced when white light falls normally on a diffraction grating.

(*c*) How would the diffraction spectrum of a sodium lamp differ from that of a normal electric filament lamp, and what would the differences indicate?

(*d*) A diffraction grating has 600 rulings per mm. Calculate the wavelength of light which falls normally on the diffraction grating and produces a first-order spectrum line at 20° to the straight-through position. (*O.*)

88. (*a*) Describe an experiment to show that for a body in equilibrium the sum of the clockwise moments about a point is equal to the sum of the anticlockwise moments about the same point.

Fig. 42

(*b*) A painter stands on a uniform plank 4.0 m long and of mass 30 kg. The plank is suspended horizontally from vertical ropes attached 0.5 m from each end as shown in Fig. 42. The mass of the painter is 80 kg. Calculate the tensions in the ropes when the painter is 1.0 m from the centre of the platform. State briefly (no calculation required) how you would expect the tensions in the ropes to vary as the painter moves along the plank.

Fig. 43*a* shows an end view of the plank. Figs. 43*b* and *c* show two other possible ways in which the plank may be supported by the ropes. State, giving your reasons, whether or not you would expect

(*i*) the tensions to be the same in the vertical parts of the rope in each diagram and

(*ii*) the tensions to be the same in the sloping parts of the rope in *b* and *c*. (*L.*)

Fig. 43

89. State Archimedes' Principle and describe an experiment you would perform to verify it.

Explain why a smaller volume of a block of wood is submerged when the block floats in water than when it floats in oil.

Fig. 44

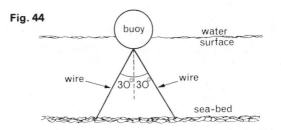

A buoy of mass 100 kg is tethered to the sea-bed by two wires, each making an angle of 30° to the vertical, Fig. 44. 0.5 m³ of water is displaced by the buoy. Calculate

(*i*) the weight of sea water, of density 1100 kg/m³, displaced by the buoy,

(*ii*) the upward force exerted on the buoy by the water,

(*iii*) the tensions in the wires. (*O. and C.*)

90. (*a*) Explain what is meant by the acceleration of free fall *g*.

(*b*) Describe carefully a laboratory experiment to obtain, as accurately as possible, a value for *g* using a free fall method.

(*c*) A helicopter which is ascending at a steady speed of 20 m/s releases a parcel which takes 10 s to reach the earth. Initially upon release the parcel moves upwards. (In the following calculations take *g* to be 10 m/s². Show your calculations clearly.)

(*i*) Find the time necessary for the parcel to reach its maximum height.

(*ii*) What is the time taken for the parcel to reach ground from the maximum height?

(*iii*) What is the velocity of the parcel when it strikes the ground?

(*iv*) What is the maximum height above the ground of the parcel?

(*v*) What is the height of the helicopter at the instant the parcel is dropped?

(*vi*) What is the height of the helicopter at the instant the parcel strikes the ground? (*N.I.*)

91. (*a*) Describe an experiment to show how the force applied to a body is related to the acceleration it produces. Sketch the apparatus you would use, state the observations you would make and show how you would use these observations to obtain the relation between force and acceleration.

(*b*) A stationary gun of mass 50 tonnes fires a shell of mass 100 kg with a velocity of 600 m/s. Calculate the initial velocity of recoil of the gun. (1 tonne = 1000 kg).

(*c*) Explain the difference between the mass and the weight of a body. State how these quantities change when the same object has its mass and weight measured, first on the earth and then on the moon. (*J.M.B.*)

92. (*a*) Describe qualitatively the expansions of the following bodies when they are heated between 0 °C and 100 °C. In each case indicate whether the expansion is relatively large or small, uniform or non-uniform, and any peculiarities which may occur.

(*i*) A copper rod.

(*ii*) A fixed mass of water.

(*iii*) A fixed mass of gas at constant pressure.

(*b*) Name the liquid most likely to be used in a thermometer required to measure temperatures

(*i*) as low as −80 °C, (*ii*) as high as 200 °C.

(*c*) The distance between the 0 °C and 100 °C marks on a thermometer is 80 mm. When the liquid meniscus is 32 mm above the 0 °C mark, what temperature is indicated?

(*d*) A bi-metallic strip can be used to control temperature. Describe

(*i*) the structure of the strip, (*ii*) how the strip changes when heated, (*iii*) with the aid of a labelled circuit diagram, how such a strip can be used to maintain an enclosure at an approximately constant temperature.

(*e*) As part of a group project to design a model steam engine, a student was given the task of designing the piston and the cylinder in which it moves. The student was given the information below and decided to leave a gap of 0.02 mm between the piston and the cylinder at 20 °C.

	Material	Diameter at 20 °C	Linear expansivity
Piston	Aluminium	40 mm	0.000 026/K

The material of the cylinder is of negligible expansion. Was the clearance sufficient to allow an operating temperature of 100 °C? Justify your answer. (*A.E.B.*)

93. (*a*) Explain how the transfer of heat energy from a warm body to a cooler body by *radiation* differs from the transfer of heat energy by *convection*.

(*b*) A solar heating system consists of a unit which may be mounted on the sloping roof of a house to produce warm water which is stored in a tank.

Fig. 45*a* shows such a unit which consists of thin-walled copper tube which is embedded, partially, in a copper plate. The surface of the copper is blackened. This is mounted within a metal frame, as indicated in the Fig. 45*b*. Sunlight irradiates the copper through a glass window and water is warmed and stored in the insulated water tank. The space behind the plate and tubes is filled with a good thermal insulator.

(*a*)   (*b*)

Fig. 45

(*i*) Why is it necessary to place the insulated water tank at a higher level than the unit? Which of the two pipes AB or CD carries the warmer water?

(*ii*) Why are the tubes and plate made of copper? Why is the tube thin-walled?

(*iii*) Explain why the unit is more effective if the surface of the tubes and plate is blackened rather than shiny.

(*iv*) The purpose of the glass plate and narrow airspace is to reduce energy loss from the copper tubes and plate to the atmosphere. Explain *two* ways by which energy loss is minimized in this design. (*O. and C.*)

94. In modern house-wiring a 'square-pin' plug is used which has three pins and a fuse. List the colour codes for the wiring of the three pins. State which lead includes the fuse.

Describe the purpose and action of the fuse and suggest an appropriate fuse value for the following appliances when used on 250 V mains.

(*i*) A 3 kW electric kettle,

(*ii*) a 1 kW electric iron,

(*iii*) a 400 W television set.

Draw a circuit diagram showing how two switches (e.g. hall and landing) can be used to control one light. (*W.*)

95. A mains supply is stated to be '240 V 50 Hz a.c.'.

With the aid of a labelled sketch graph, explain the meaning of a.c. and 50 Hz.

Describe with the aid of a labelled diagram a transformer which could be used to operate a lamp marked 12 V 36 W from the 240 V mains supply.

Assuming the transformer to be ideal (i.e. 100% efficient), calculate

(*i*) the number of turns required in the secondary coil if there are 4000 turns in the primary,

(*ii*) the current in the primary when the lamp is supplied with its normal operating current,

(*iii*) the energy given out in 300 s by the lamp under normal operating conditions. (*C.*)

96. An evacuated cathode ray tube has a circular flat screen of area 0.04 m². Calculate the force due to air pressure on the screen if atmospheric pressure is 10^5 pascal.

Give reasons why such a tube should be evacuated. If the potential difference between anode and cathode is 8 kV and the electron beam current is 1.5 mA, calculate the energy supplied per second to this beam. Describe the changes in energy when the electrons hit the screen. (*S.*)

Mathematics for physics

USE THIS SECTION AS THE NEED ARISES

Equations—type 1

An equation has sometimes to be changed round before it can be solved. In the equation $x = a/b$, the subject is x. To change it we *multiply or divide both sides* of the equation by the same quantity.

(i) *To change the subject to a.* We have

$$x = \frac{a}{b}$$

If we multiply both sides by b the equation will still be true.

$$\therefore \quad x \times b = \frac{a}{b} \times b$$

The b's on the right-hand side cancel

$$\therefore \quad b \times x = \frac{a}{\not{b}} \times \not{b} = a$$

$$\therefore \quad a = b \times x$$

(ii) *To change the subject to b.* We have

$$x = \frac{a}{b}$$

Multiplying both sides by b as before, we get

$$a = b \times x$$

Divide both sides by x

$$\therefore \quad \frac{a}{x} = \frac{b \times x}{x} = \frac{b \times \not{x}}{\not{x}} = b$$

$$\therefore \quad b = \frac{a}{x}$$

Now try the following questions using these ideas.

Questions

1. What is the value of x if

(a) $2x = 6$ (b) $3x = 15$ (c) $3x = 8$

(d) $\frac{x}{2} = 10$ (e) $\frac{x}{3} = 4$ (f) $\frac{2x}{3} = 4$

(g) $\frac{4}{x} = 2$ (h) $\frac{9}{x} = 3$ (i) $\frac{x}{6} = \frac{4}{3}$

2. Change the subject to

(a) f in $v = f\lambda$ (b) λ in $v = f\lambda$

(c) I in $V = IR$ (d) R in $V = IR$

(e) m in $d = \frac{m}{V}$ (f) V in $d = \frac{m}{V}$

(g) s in $v = \frac{s}{t}$ (h) t in $v = \frac{s}{t}$

(i) a in $F = ma$ (j) I in $Q = It$

(k) Q in $C = \frac{Q}{V}$ (l) A in $p = \frac{F}{A}$

(m) p_1 in $p_1 V_1 = p_2 V_2$ (n) a in $x = abc$

(o) t in $W = ItV$ (p) θ in $Q = mc\theta$

3. Change the subject to

(a) I^2 in $P = I^2 R$ (b) I in $P = I^2 R$

(c) a in $s = \frac{1}{2}at^2$ (d) t^2 in $s = \frac{1}{2}at^2$

(e) t in $s = \frac{1}{2}at^2$ (f) v in $\frac{1}{2}mv^2 = mgh$

(g) y in $\lambda = \frac{ay}{D}$ (h) ρ in $R = \frac{\rho l}{A}$

(i) V_1 in $\frac{V_1}{T_1} = \frac{V_2}{T_2}$ (j) T_1 in $\frac{V_1}{T_1} = \frac{V_2}{T_2}$

(k) V_2 in $\frac{p_1 V_1}{T_1} = \frac{p_2 V_2}{T_2}$ (l) T_2 in $\frac{p_1 V_1}{T_1} = \frac{p_2 V_2}{T_2}$

4. By replacing (substituting) find the value of v in $v = f\lambda$ if

(a) $f = 5$ and $\lambda = 2$ (b) $f = 3.4$ and $\lambda = 10$

(c) $f = \frac{1}{4}$ and $\lambda = 8/3$ (d) $f = 3/5$ and $\lambda = 1/6$

(e) $f = 100$ and $\lambda = 0.1$ (f) $f = 3 \times 10^5$ and $\lambda = 10^3$

5. By changing the subject and replacing find

(a) f in $v = f\lambda$ if $v = 3.0 \times 10^8$ and $\lambda = 1.5 \times 10^3$

(b) h in $p = 10hd$ if $p = 10^5$ and $d = 10^3$

(c) a in $n = a/b$ if $n = 4/3$ and $b = 6$

(d) b in $n = a/b$ if $n = 1.5$ and $a = 3.0 \times 10^8$

(e) F in $p = F/A$ if $p = 100$ and $A = 0.2$

(f) s in $v = s/t$ if $v = 1500$ and $t = 0.2$

(g) t in $V = At$ if $V = 10^{-3}$ and $A = 10^4$

(h) V_2 in $p_1 V_1 = p_2 V_2$ if $p_1 = 10^5$, $V_1 = 30$ and $p_2 = 2 \times 10^5$

(i) t in $s = \frac{1}{2}gt^2$ if $s = 125$ and $g = 10$

(j) b in $x = abc$ if $x = 0.0016$, $a = 1$ and $c = 80$

(k) θ in $Q = mc\theta$ if $Q = 8000$, $m = 2$ and $c = 400$

(l) V_2 in $p_1 V_1/T_1 = p_2 V_2/T_2$ if $p_1 = 1$, $p_2 = 2$, $V_1 = 2$, $T_1 = 300$ and $T_2 = 500$

Equations—type 2

To change the subject in the equation $x = a + by$ we *add or subtract the same quantity from each side*. We may also have to divide or multiply as in type 1. Suppose we wish to change the subject to y in

$$x = a + by$$

Subtract a from both sides,

$$\therefore \quad x - a = a + by - a = by$$

Divide both sides by b,

$$\therefore \quad \frac{x - a}{b} = \frac{by}{b} = y \qquad \therefore \quad y = \frac{x - a}{b}$$

Questions

6. What is the value of x if

(a) $x+1=5$ (b) $2x+3=7$ (c) $x-2=3$

(d) $2(x-3)=10$ (e) $\dfrac{x}{2}-\dfrac{1}{3}=0$ (f) $\dfrac{x}{3}+\dfrac{1}{4}=0$

(g) $2x+\dfrac{5}{3}=6$ (h) $7-\dfrac{x}{4}=11$ (i) $\dfrac{3}{x}+2=5$

7. By changing the subject and replacing find the value of a in $v=u+at$ if

(a) $v=20$, $u=10$ and $t=2$
(b) $v=50$, $u=20$ and $t=0.5$
(c) $v=5/0.2$, $u=2/0.2$ and $t=0.2$

8. Change the subject in $v^2=u^2+2as$ to a.

Proportion (or variation)

One of the most important mathematical operations in physics is finding the relation between two sets of measurements.

(a) *Direct proportion.* Suppose that in an experiment two sets of readings are obtained for the quantities x and y as in Table 1 (units omitted).

Table 1

x	1	2	3	4
y	2	4	6	8

We see that when x is doubled, y doubles; when x is trebled, y trebles; when x is halved, y halves and so on. There is a one-to-one correspondence between each value of x and the corresponding value of y.

We say that y is *directly proportional* to x, or y *varies directly* as x. In symbols

$$y \propto x$$

Also, the *ratio* of one to the other, e.g. y to x, is always the same, i.e. it has a constant value which in this case is 2. Hence

$$\frac{y}{x}=\text{a constant}=2$$

The constant, called the *constant of proportionality* or *variation*, is given a symbol, e.g. k, and the relation (or law) between y and x is then summed up by the equation

$$\frac{y}{x}=k \quad\text{or}\quad y=kx$$

Notes. 1. In practice, because of inevitable experimental errors, the readings seldom show the relation so clearly as here.

2. If instead of using numerical values for x and y we use letters, e.g. x_1, x_2, x_3, etc., and y_1, y_2, y_3, etc., then we can also say

$$\frac{y_1}{x_1}=\frac{y_2}{x_2}=\frac{y_3}{x_3}=\ldots\ldots=k$$

or $\quad y_1=kx_1,\ y_2=kx_2,\ y_3=kx_3\ldots\ldots$

(b) *Inverse proportion.* Two sets of readings for the quantities p and V are given in Table 2.

Table 2

p	3	4	6	12
V	4	3	2	1

There is again a one-to-one correspondence between each value of p and the corresponding value of V but when p is doubled, V is halved; when p is trebled, V has one-third its previous value and so on.

We say that V is *inversely proportional* to p, or V *varies inversely* as p, i.e.

$$V \propto \frac{1}{p}$$

Also, the *product* $p \times V$ is always the same ($=12$) and we write

$$V=\frac{k}{p} \quad\text{or}\quad pV=k$$

where k is the constant of proportionality or variation and equals 12 in this case.

Using letters for values of p and V we can also say

$$p_1V_1=p_2V_2=p_3V_3=\ldots\ldots=k$$

Graphs

Another useful way of finding the relation between two quantities is by a graph.

(a) *Straight line graphs.* When the readings in *Table 1* are used to plot a graph of y against x, a *continuous* line joining the points is *a straight line passing*

Fig. 1

through the origin O, Fig. 1. Such a graph shows there is direct proportionality between the quantities plotted, i.e. $y \propto x$. But note that the line must go through O.

Fig. 2

A graph of p against V using the readings in *Table 2* is a curve, Fig. 2. However if we plot p against $1/V$ (or V against $1/p$) we get a straight line through the origin, showing that $p \propto 1/V$, Fig. 3 (or $V \propto 1/p$).

Fig. 3

p	V	$1/V$
3	4	0.25
4	3	0.33
6	2	0.50
12	1	1.0

(b) *Slope or gradient.* The slope or gradient of a straight-line graph equals the constant of proportionality. In Fig. 1, the slope is $y/x = 2$; in Fig. 3 it is $p/(1/V) = pV = 12$.

In practice points plotted from actual measurements may not lie exactly on a straight line due to experimental errors. The 'best straight line' is then drawn 'through' them so that they are equally distributed about it. This automatically averages the results. Any points that are well off the line stand out and may be investigated further.

(c) *Practical points.*

(i) The axes should be labelled giving the quantities being plotted and their units, e.g. current in amperes.

(ii) If possible the origin of both scales should be on the paper and the scales chosen so that the points are spread out along the graph.

(iii) Mark the points ⊙ or x.

Questions

9. In an experiment different masses were hung from the end of a spring held in a stand and the extensions produced were as shown below.

Mass (g)	100	150	200	300	350	500	600
Extension (cm)	1.9	3.1	4.0	6.1	6.9	10.0	12.2

(a) Plot a graph of *extension* along the vertical (y) axis against *mass* along the horizontal (x) axis.

(b) What is the relation between *extension* and *mass*? Give a reason for your answer.

10. Pairs of readings of the quantities m and v are given below.

m	0.25	1.5	2.5	3.5
v	20	40	56	72

(a) Plot a graph of m along the vertical axis and v along the horizontal axis.

(b) Is m directly proportional to v? Explain your answer.

(c) Use the graph to find v when $m = 1$.

11. In an experiment to measure the density of copper the mass of a number of copper rivets was measured on a lever balance and the volume measured by displacement of water in a measuring cylinder. Several sets of readings were obtained by using different numbers of rivets. The readings obtained are shown below.

Reading no.	1	2	3	4	5	6	7	8	9	10
Mass (g)	18	30	36	60	42	54	66	72	78	90
Volume (cm³)	2	3	4	4.5	5	6	7	8	9	10

(a) Draw a graph of these readings choosing a suitable scale (mass on vertical axis).

(b) Does your graph pass through the origin? Explain why you think it should or should not as the case may be.

(c) Did you take reading no. 4 into account when drawing your graph? Explain.

(d) The formula for the density of a substance is

$$\text{density} = \frac{\text{mass}}{\text{volume}}$$

By measuring the slope of the graph calculate the density of the copper used in this experiment. (Show clearly on your graph any measurements you have made in order to do this.)

(e) Why is it better to use your graph to calculate the density rather than just one pair of readings? (W.M.)

12. The distances s (in metres) travelled by a car at various times t (in seconds) are shown below.

s	0	2	8	18	32	50
t	0	1	2	3	4	5

Draw graphs of (a) s against t, (b) s against t^2. What can you conclude?

Answers

1 Light rays
1. Larger, less bright
2. **(a)** 4 images **(b)** brighter but blurred
3. Shadow to left is darker

2 Reflection of light
1. **(a)** $50°$ **(c)** $50°, 40°, 40°$ **(d)** parallel
2. B
3. Top half

3 Plane mirrors
2. D
3. Away from back of mirror at 1 m/s

4 Curved mirrors
2. 7.2 cm from mirror, 1.6 cm high

5 Refraction of light
3. 8 cm
4. D

7 Lenses
1. A
2. **(c)** Image 9 cm from lens, 3 cm high
3. **(a)** 4 **(b)** 3.2 cm
4. **(a)** 0.5D **(b)** 2D **(c)** 4D

8 The eye
2. E
3. **(a) (i)** No **(ii)** Yes **(iii)** No
   (b) Concave
4. **(a) (i)** No **(ii)** Yes
   (b) Convex

9 Colour
2. D
3. **(a) (i)** White **(ii)** White
   (b) Red
   (c) Red

10 Simple optical instruments
1. Close object
2. **(a)** 4 cm **(b) (i)** larger, blurred, less bright **(ii)** moved closer to the slide
3. **(a)** 4 cm **(b)** 8 cm behind lens, virtual, $m = 2$

11 Microscopes and telescopes
1. **(a)** D **(b)** B
2. **(a)** Objective, 100 cm **(b)** 100 cm **(c)** Eyepiece
   (d) Real image formed by A: 5 cm **(e)** 105 cm

12 Further questions
1. B
3. 3.4×10^3 km
5. B
6. $100°, 80°, 100°$
8. D
10. A
12. **(a)** 0.84 cm, real, 21 cm in front of mirror
    (b) 6.0 cm, virtual, 30 cm behind mirror
13. $30°; 49°$
14. **(a)** 2.0 m **(b)** 2.7 (8/3) m
15. **(a)** Ray passes into air at an angle of refraction of $42°$
    (b) Critical angle of water $= 49°$; total internal reflection occurs in water.

16. C
17. A: convex, $f = 20$ cm; B: convex, $f = 10$ cm
18. **(d)** Object at 8.0 cm: image real, 8.0 cm from lens, 1.5 cm high
    Object at 7.0 cm: image real, 9.3 cm from lens, 2.0 cm high
    Object at 2.0 cm: image virtual, 4.0 cm behind lens, 3.0 cm high
20. **(a)** Convex—L_1 and L_2: concave—L_3 **(b)** L_1 **(c)** L_1, 0.2 m: L_2, 0.4 m: L_3, 0.05 m (5 cm)
22. Lens gets fatter and pupil contracts
23. **(a)** Long sight **(b)** Convex lens
27. **(b)** Distance between lens and film decreases
29. 40 cm : 40 cm

13 Water waves
1. **(a)** 1 cm **(b)** 1 Hz **(c)** 1 cm/s
3. **(a)** Speed of ripple depends on depth of water
   (b) AB, since ripples travel more slowly towards it, therefore water shallower in this direction.
4. **(b) (i)** 3 mm **(ii)** 15 mm/s **(iii)** 5 Hz

14 Light waves
1. **(a)** $S_1O = S_2O$ **(b)** $S_1O_1 - S_2O_1 = \lambda/2$
   (c) $S_1O_2 - S_2O_2 = \lambda$
2. $0.5 \, \mu m$
3. **(a)** There are 6000 slits per cm $= 6000 \times 100$ slits per m,
   $\therefore$ grating spacing $d = \dfrac{1}{6000 \times 100} = \dfrac{1}{6.0 \times 10^5}$
   $= 1.7 \times 10^{-6}$ m
   (b) $\lambda = d \sin\theta, \therefore \sin\theta = \lambda/d = 6.0 \times 10^{-7} \times 6.0 \times 10^5 = 0.36, \therefore \theta = 21°$
4. 2.0×10^8 m/s

15 Electromagnetic spectrum
2. D

16 Sound waves
1. D
2. **(a)** When he sees flash of light from pistol
   (b) Time taken by light to travel 110 m is negligible
   (c) Error $= 110/330 = 1/3$ s; this should be *added* to his timing
3. **(a)** $v = f\lambda$ **(b)** 300 m **(c)** 25 cm
4. 1650 m (about 1 mile)

17 Musical notes
1. **(b) (i)** 1 m **(ii)** 2 m

18 Further questions
1. $v = 33/1.5 = 22$ cm/s, $\lambda = 4$ cm, $\therefore f = v/\lambda = 22/4 = 5.5$ Hz
2. **(b)** Refraction **(c)** 0.75 cm; 0.5 cm **(d)** Equal
   (e) Speed in A greater than in B **(f)** A.
4. C
6. **(a)** We have wavelength $=$
   $$\frac{\text{slit separation} \times \text{spacing of bright bands}}{\text{distance of slits from screen}}$$
   $\therefore 6 \times 10^{-7}$ m $= 0.6 \times 10^{-3}$ m $\times \dfrac{\text{spacing of bright bands}}{2 \text{ m}}$
   $\therefore$ spacing of bright bands $=$
   $$\frac{6 \times 10^{-7} \times 2}{0.6 \times 10^{-3}} = 2 \times 10^{-3} \text{ m} = 2 \text{ mm}$$
   (b) Diffraction pattern of a single slit, see Fig. 14.1, p. 40

7. $2 \times 6450 \times 10^{-10} = 3\lambda$, $\therefore$ $\lambda = 2 \times 6450 \times 10^{-10}/3 = 4300 \times 10^{-10}$ m
8. (a) B (b) A (c) D
9. (a) 3×10^8 m/s (b) 15/4 m (c) 0.2 MHz (200 kHz)
10. E
11. 340 m/s
13. E
14. (a) Reduce length to 58 cm
    (b) Increase tension to 22.5 N
15. $21/80 = 0.26$ m; $63/80 = 0.78$ m
16. C

19 Measurements

1. (a) 10 (b) 40 (c) 5 (d) 67 (e) 1000
2. (a) 3 (b) 5.50 (c) 8.70 (d) 0.43 (e) 0.1
3. (a) 1×10^5; 3.5×10^3; 4.28×10^8; 5.04×10^2; 2.7056×10^4
   (b) 1000; 2 000 000; 69 000; 134; 1 000 000 000
4. (a) 1×10^{-3}; 7×10^{-5}; 1×10^{-7}; 5×10^{-5}
   (b) 5×10^{-1}; 8.4×10^{-2}; 3.6×10^{-4}; 1.04×10^{-3}
5. 10.4 mm
6. (a) 53.3 mm (b) 95.8 mm
7. (a) 2.31 mm (b) 14.97 mm
8. 40 cm^3; 5
9. 80
10. (a) 252 cm^3 (b) 72 cm^3

20 Density

1. (a) (i) 0.5 g (ii) 1 g (iii) 5 g
   (b) (i) 10 g/cm^3 (ii) 3 kg/m^3
   (c) (i) 2 cm^3 (ii) 5 cm^3
2. (a) 8.0 g/cm^3 (b) 8.0×10^3 kg/m^3
3. 15 000 kg
4. 130 kg
5. (a) 200 cm^3 (b) 200 cm^3 (c) 3.0 g/cm^3
6. 1.2

21 Weight and springs

1. (a) 1 N (b) 50 N (c) 0.5 N
2. (a) 120 N (b) 20 N
3. (a) 15 cm (b) 10 cm (c) 30 g
4. (a) 19 cm (b) 35 g

22 Molecules

1. E
3. (a) 1 cm (b) 1.0×10^{-7} cm
4. (a) 2×10^{-6} kg (b) $2 \times 10^{-6}/800 = 2.5 \times 10^{-9}$ m^3
   (c) $2.5 \times 10^{-9}/0.20 = 1.25 \times 10^{-8}$ m (d) 0.4 m^2

24 Further questions

1. 755.4 mm
2. 0.60 mm
3. C
4. (a) 70.5 cm^3 (b) 20 cm^3 (c) 1.6 g/cm^3
5. (b) density of block + lead = $(7.5 + 11)/16 = 18.5/16$ g/cm^3; it sinks in water since density greater than 1.0 g/cm^3
   (c) milk
6. 50 g
7. (c) Yes (d) 5 N
10. 1.6×10^{-5} cm

25 Moments and levers

1. (a) Turns anticlockwise (b) Remains horizontal
2. B
3. $X = 20$ N; $X = 5$ N
4. (i) (c) (ii) (a) (iii) (b)
5. Fishing rod

264

26 Centres of gravity

2. (a) B (b) A (c) C
3. Tips to right
4. (a) (i) 50 cm (iii) 1.2 N

27 Adding forces

1. (a) 50 N making 37° with 40 N
   (b) 60 N making 25° with 40 N
2. D
3. 200 N

28 Work, energy, power

1. 180 J
2. 1.5×10^5 J
3. (a) Electric lamp (b) Microphone (c) Battery
   (d) Water turbine (e) Electric motor
4. A
5. (a) 150 J (b) 10 W
6. B

29 Machines

1. (a) B (b) D
2. (a) 5000 J (b) 7500 J (c) 67%
3. (a) (i) 10/7 (ii) 2 (iii) 71%
   (b) (i) 2 (ii) 3 (iii) 67%
   (c) (i) 10/3 (ii) 6 (iii) 56%
4. (a) 4 (b) 5 (c) 80%
5. (a) 5 (b) 10 (c) 50%
6. $2\frac{1}{2}$

30 Pressure in liquids

2. (a) (i) 25 Pa (ii) 0.5 Pa (iii) 100 Pa (b) 30 N
3. 225 Pa
4. (a) 200 m^3 (b) 400 000 kg (c) 4 000 000 N
   (d) 200 000 Pa (e) (i) none (ii) less
5. (a) 100 Pa (b) 200 N
7. 1 150 000 Pa (1.15×10^6 Pa) (ignoring air pressure)
8. 20 m

31 Atmospheric pressure

1. (a) (i) 860 mm or 100 mm over atmospheric (ii) 860 mm
2. (c) 74 cm
3. 10 m
4. 10 cm

32 Pumps and pressure

1. (a) nothing (b) one-third previous volume
   (c) three times previous pressure
2. (a) 15 cm^3 (b) 6 cm^3
3. D
4. 10 m

33 Floating and sinking

1. (a) 10 N (b) 8 N (c) 6 N (d) 5 N
2. D
3. 8.0; 8/7 = 1.1
4. (a) 30 g (b) 30 g (c) 30 cm^3
5. (b) 1 cm
6. (i) 10 cm^3 (ii) 10 g (iii) 10 g (iv) 5 g (v) 25/4 cm

34 Further questions

1. (a) (ii) 500 N
2. 1.25 N m; 5.0 N
3. $T_1 = T_2 = 15$ N; $T_3 = 10$ N; $T_4 = 20$ N
4. Mass of boy = 60 kg
5. (b) (ii) Q (iii) (a) 600 N (b) 150 N
6. Resultant = 46 N; $P = 23$ N
7. Tension in AC = 140 N; $W = 193$ N
8. 35 N at 30° to each force; 17 N

9. D
10. (*a*) 1280 J (**b**) 1280 J (**c**) 12.8 W (**e**) 8 J (**f**) 8 J
    (**g**) Changed to heat and sound energy
    (**h**) None (**i**) 100 N
11. 6
12. (**a**) 25 (**b**) 200 (**f**) 12.5%
13. 2×10^5 Pa
14. (**a**) 4×10^3 Pa (**b**) (i) 4×10^3 Pa (ii) 400 N
    (**c**) $M = 40$ kg (**d**) (i) No (ii) M larger
15. (**a**) 4 : 1 (**b**) 2 : 1
17. 1.63 km
21. (**c**) 150 Pa
22. (**a**) 77 cm (**b**) 75 cm (**c**) 15.4 cm
23. $4/3$ cm^3
24. (**a**) 3 N (**b**) 0.3 kg (**c**) 0.0003 m^3 (**d**) 6.7×10^3 kg/m^3
25. D
26. 2145 kg; 180 kg less

35 Velocity and acceleration

1. $\dfrac{1500}{1000}$ km $\Big/ \dfrac{4}{60}$ h = 22.5 km/h
2. 82 min
3. (**a**) 2 km/h per second (**b**) 74 km/h
   (**c**) 17.5 s after reaching 70 km/h
4. (**a**) 1 s
   (**b**) (i) 10 cm/tentick^2 (ii) 50 cm/s per tentick
   (iii) 250 cm/s^2
   (**c**) 0
5. 50 s
6. (*a*) Uniform acceleration (**b**) 75 cm/s^2
7. (**a**) (i) 45 km/h (ii) $45/60 = 0.75$ km/min (iii) 12.5 m/s
   (**b**) 0.75 km
   (**c**) (i) 30 km/h per minute (ii) 0.5 km/min^2
8. (**a**) 20 m/s (**b**) 1.2 km (**c**) 10 m/s (**d**) 200 m

36 Equations of motion

1. 2.5 m/s^2
2. (**a**) 10 m/s (**b**) 25 m (**c**) 10 s
4. (**a**) 100 m (**b**) 20 m/s (**c**) Slows down
5. (**a**) $5/4$ m/s^2 (**b**) (i) 10 m (ii) 45 m (**c**) 22 s

37 Falling bodies

1. (**a**) (i) 10 m/s (ii) 20 m/s (iii) 30 m/s (iv) 50 m/s
   (**b**) (i) 5 m (ii) 20 m (iii) 45 m (iv) 125 m
2. 5 s : 31 m
3. B
4. (**a**) 3 s; 30 m/s (**b**) 30.(02) m/s
5. (**a**) 10 s (**b**) 2000 m
6. B

38 Newton's laws of motion

1. D
2. 20 N
3. (**a**) 5000 N (**b**) 15 m/s^2
4. (**a**) 2 m/s^2 (**b**) 1000 N
5. (**a**) 4 m/s^2 (**b**) 2 N
6. (i) 0.5 m/s^2 (ii) 2.5 m/s (iii) 25 m
7. $(1650 - 400)$ N/1000 kg = 1.25 m/s^2
8. (**a**) 1000 N (**b**) 170 N

39 Momentum

1. (**a**) 50 kg m/s (**b**) 2 kg m/s (**c**) 100 kg m/s
2. 2 m/s
3. 4 m/s
4. 0.5 m/s

40 K.E. and P.E.

1. (**a**) 2 J (**b**) 160 J (**c**) $100\,000 = 10^5$ J
2. (**a**) 1.8 J (**b**) 1.8 J (**c**) 6 m/s (**d**) 1.25 J (**e**) 5 m/s

3. (**a**) (i) 1000 J (ii) 20 m
4. B

41 Circular and relative motion

3. A
4. 330 km/h, 27° east of north

Fig. 1

5. In parallelogram OABC, Fig. 1, OA represents the velocity of the ship relative to the water (this is always 20 km/h whatever the velocity of the water), OC represents the velocity of the current. The ship has to sail at an angle θ west of north so that the resultant of its own velocity and that of the current is due north. OB represents the resultant velocity and equals 19 km/h 20° west of north. This is found by an accurate scale drawing or by Pythagoras' theorem—
   OB $= \sqrt{20^2 - 7^2}$; sin $\theta = 7/20$
   Time to travel 100 km = $100/19 = 5.3$ h

42 Further questions

1. (**a**) 14 m/s (**b**) 26 m/s (**c**) 1200 m (**d**) -2 m/s^2
2. C
3. (i) 0.5 m/s^2 (ii) 12 775 m (iii) 2 m/s
4. 304 m
5. (i) 45 m/s (ii) 100 m (iii) 5 m/s
6. D
7. A
8. (**b**) (i) -0.5 m/s^2 (ii) -250 N
9. 30 N northwards; 21 m
10. C
11. A
12. (**a**) 5 m/s (**b**) 0.4 kg m/s (**c**) 1 J (**d**) 0.2 J
13. (**a**) 5 m/s (**b**) 3 m/s (**c**) 37.5 J : 22.5 J
14. (**a**) Towards centre of circle (**b**) 12.5 N
15. 20.6 min; 77° east of north

43 Thermometers

1. (**a**) 1530 °C (**b**) 19 °C (**c**) 0 °C (**d**) -12 °C (**e**) 37 °C
2. C
3. E

44 Expansion of solids and liquids

2. Aluminium
4. (**a**) Aluminium (**b**) 1.009 m
5. (**a**) 0.1 m (**b**) 0.0004 m (**c**) 0.3 m
6. B
7. $0.0016/80 = 0.000\,02$ per °C; 120 °C
8. (**a**) Water (**b**) 4 °C

45 The gas laws

1. (**a**) 4 m^3 (**b**) 1 m^3
2. 546 K (273 °C)
3. (i) 100 cm^3 (ii) 400 cm^3 (iii) 178 cm^3
4. C

46 Specific heat capacity
1. 15 000 J
2. E
3. A = 2000 J/kg °C; B = 200 J/kg °C; C = 1000 J/kg °C
4. 88 000 J
5. (a) 20 000 J (b) 120 000 J
6. (a) 6000 J (b) 6000 J/kg °C
7. 1050 W
9. 45 kg

47 Latent heat
1. (a) 3400 J (b) 6800 J
2. (a) $5 \times 340 + 5 \times 4.2 \times 50 = 2750$ J (b) 8480 J
3. 680 s
4. (a) 0 °C (b) 45 g
5. (a) 9200 J (b) 25 100 J
6. 157 g
7. 2500 J/g

49 Conduction and convection
4. E

50 Radiation
1. E
6. D

52 Further questions
1. A 50 °C B 200 °C C 100 °C
4. (a) 1.4 mm (b) 35 mm (c) 65 °C
5. 0.30 mm; 0.30 mm
7. B
8. 363 K (90 °C)
9. (i) 182 mm (ii) 264 K (-9 °C)
10 C
11. B
12. B
13. 0.5 J/g °C
14. D
15. 300 °C; 0.1 kg (*Hint.* The work done in pulling the wire through the hole equals the energy that causes the temperature rise.)
16. (a) AB and CD (b) BC (c) DE
17. (a) 1 005 000 J (b) 50 400 J (c) 40 C
18. D
19. 1420 J/min
20. (a) 2300 J/g (b) 105 J/s
23. D

53 Permanent magnets
1. C
2. D
3. (a) Steel (b) N
4. B
7. (a) A (b) A

55 Static electricity
1. D
3. *a, b, c*

56 More electrostatics
1. (a) B (b) electrons repelled to earth leaving sphere positively charged

57 Capacitors
1. (b) B (c) A (d) A to B
4. (a) 1 C (b) (i) 0.001 F (ii) 0.02 C

58 Electric current
1. (a) 5 C (b) 50 C (c) 1500 C
2. (a) 5 A (b) 0.5 A (c) 2 A

4. B
5. (*b*)
6. (*d*)
7. All read 0.25 A
8. C

59 Potential difference
1. (a) 12 J (b) 60 J (c) 240 J
2. (a) 6 V (b) (i) 2 J (ii) 6 J
3. A
4. B
5. (b) Very bright (c) Normal brightness (d) No light (e) Brighter than normal (f) Normal brightness
6. (a) 6 V (b) 360 J

60 Resistance
1. 3 Ω
2. 20 V
3. C
4. D
5. A = 3 V; B = 3 V; C = 6 V
6. 3/2 = 1.5
7. (a) 15 Ω (b) 1.5 Ω
8. D
9. (a) 3 Ω (b) $\frac{1}{2}$ = 0.5 A (c) $\frac{1}{4}$ = 0.25 A
10. 4/3 Ω; 2 A
11. B, D, F = 1.5 A; C, E = 3 V; G = 6 A; H, J = 3 A; I, K = 6 V; L = 2 A; M = 4 V; N, P = 1 A; O = 2 V
12. (b) 2 Ω and 6 Ω

61 Electromotive force
1. 3 A: 9 V
2. C
3. (a) 0.5 Ω (b) 4.5 Ω
4. (a) 3.0 (b) 2.6 V (c) 2.6 V (d) 0.40 V (e) 2 Ω (f) 13 Ω

62 Further questions
1. E
5. E
6. C
9. (b) (i) no effect (ii) halved
10. (a) (i) 2×10^{-6} F (ii) 24×10^{-6} C = 24 μC (iii) 1.5 V
11. B
12. B
13. (a) 1/4 A (b) 1 A (c) 1/2 A
14. B
15. (a) (ii) 2 Ω
16. (i) (a) both lamps normal brightness;
       (b) both lamps dimmer than normal
   (ii) (a) 0.3 A; (b) 0.15 A
   (iii) (a) 0.6 A; (b) 0.15 A
17. (a) 6 Ω (b) 2 A (c) 12/7 A (d) 4/3 A
18. (a) 1/4 A, 5/4 V (b) 2/3 A, 0 V (c) 0 A, 2 V
19. B
20. (a) 5.0 A (c) 0.12 V (d) 0.06 Ω
21. (a) 18 Ω (b) 2 Ω:9 Ω
22. 2.5 A
23. 2.0 V; 1 Ω
24. (a) 1.5 V (b) 0.60 A (c) 3.5 Ω (d) 3.0 A (e) 0

63 Electric power
1. (a) 100 J (b) 500 J (c) 6000 J
2. (a) 24 W (b) 3 J/s
3. D
4. 3.12 kW
5. (a) 8 V (h) 16 W
6. (a) 3 A (b) 4 Ω
7. (a) 12 A (b) 250/12 = 21 Ω

266

9. (a) 20 units   **(b)** 60 p
10. 12 p
11. (a) Parallel   **(b)** Yes, current $= 25$ A   **(c)** 9 p
12. (b) (i) 20   **(ii)** 1200 W   **(c)** 252 p

64 Electrolysis and cells
3. 0.8 g

65 Electromagnets
2. S
5. (a) B   **(b)** Relay switch   **(c)** B, C

66 Electric motors
1. E
3. Anticlockwise
4. E

67 Electric meters
2. B
3. (a) 4.0 V   **(c)** 0.80 A   **(d)** 5.0 Ω
4. (a) 1.1 Ω shunt   **(b)** 1980 Ω multiplier

68 Electrical measurements
1. (d) 30 Ω **(e)** 340 K
2. D

70 Transformers
2. B
3. (a) 24   **(b)** 10 A
4. (b) 12 000

71 Alternating current
3. (a) 12 V   **(b)** 17 V

72 Further questions
1. (a) (i) 3 kW   **(ii)** 60 W   **(iii)** 750 W   **(b)** 4 A
2. (a) 3 A   **(b)** 36 W   **(c)** 10 800 J   **(d)** 26 C
3. 27 kWh;   81 p
6. Should be 1.0 A
7. (c) 5.6×10^{-6} m
10. (a) To complete the circuits to the battery negative
   (b) One contains the starter switch and relay coil; the other contains the relay contacts and starter motor
   (c) Carries much larger current to starter motor
   (d) Allows wires to starter switch to be thin since they only carry the small current needed to energize the relay
13. (b) 53%
14. (c) 150 mV $= 0.15$ V   **(e)** 15 mA $= 0.015$ A   **(f)** 4.35 V
   (g) 4.50 V
15. 1.8 Ω
16. 980 Ω multiplier
17. 480 Ω
18. (a) 4 Ω **(b)** Yes   **(c)** 0.5 A   **(d)** 0.5 V   **(f)** 1.2 V
   (g) No   **(h)** No
20. (a) E   **(b)** B   **(c)** C   **(d)** E
22. B
23. (b) (i) 60   **(ii)** 0.1 A
24. 3.3 A
25. (a) 5 A   **(b)** 400 W   **(c)** 80 V
27. (a) 25 μF   **(b)** 20 μF

73 Electrons
1. A

74 Radioactivity
4. (a) 8 g   **(b)** 4 g   **(c)** 1 g
5. D

75 Atomic structure
2. (a) 27 protons and 32 neutrons in nucleus: 27 electrons outside

76 Electronics
3. (a) $V_1 = V_2 = 3$ V   **(b)** $V_1 = 1$ V, $V_2 = 5$ V
   (c) $V_1 = 4$ V, $V_2 = 2$ V
5. (c) Current gain $= 60 = I_c/I_b = 30/I_b$,
   $\therefore\ I_b = 30/60 = 0.5$ mA

77 Radio and television
1. (a) (ii) 3 m

78 Further questions
2. 1.76×10^{11} C/kg
4. 1/16
5. 6 minutes
6. E
7. (i) β **(ii)** β **(iii)** α: A, D
10. (b) M_1 **(c)** collector-base
13. (c) 1/50 s

Revision questions
1. D
2. (i) between principal focus and pole   **(ii)** at principal focus   **(iii)** at centre of curvature
3. B
4. 1.73
5. (e) 53.1°
6. D
7. A
8. (a) transverse, stationary   **(b)** longitudinal, progressive
   (c) transverse, progressive   **(d)** longitudinal, stationary
9. (c) (i) BP $-$ AP $=$ even number of half-wavelengths
   (ii) BQ $-$ AQ $=$ odd number of half-wavelengths
10. B
11. C
13. 60 m/s
14. B
15. D
16. (b) 1.2 m   **(c)** 307 m/s
17. 2.25 mm
18. (i) 90 kg   **(ii)** 4.5×10^4 Pa (N/m²)
19. C
20. (i) 3 cm   **(ii)** 2 s   **(iii)** 2.3 cm
21. B
22. E
23. 4500 N at 9° to AB
24. B
25. (b) 120 J   **(c)** 30 W   **(d)** 75%
26. B
27. B
28. 80 N
29. (b) (i) 8.16×10^4 N/m²   **(ii)** 2.04×10^4 N/m²
   (iii) 1.7×10^3 m
30. (c) 1.33 m³
31. (a) (i) 2.16×10^4 kg   **(ii)** 2.16×10^5 N   **(iii)** 2.7×10^5 N
   (iv) 5.4×10^4 N
   (b) (i) 2.16×10^5 N   **(ii)** 21.6 m³
32. D
33. 1.5×10^6 m
34. (b) 1.6 m/s²   **(c)** 10.4 m   **(d)** 0.32 N
35. B
36. A
37. 1.5×10^3 N
38. (a) (i) 15 m/s   **(ii)** 11.25 m   **(b) (i)** 45 000 N   **(ii)** 506 250 J
40. velocity, momentum
41. 20 °C
42. 2.4×10^{-5} K^{-1}
43. A
44. D

45. $0.47 \, \text{m}^3$
46. **B**
47. 20 minutes
48. $2.1 \times 10^{-3} \, \text{kg}$
49. **E**
52. **(c)** $2 \times 10^{-6} \, \text{F}$ **(d)** $400 \, \mu\text{C}$
53. **D**
54. **(a) (i)** $1.5 \, \text{V}$ **(ii)** $4 \, \text{A}$ **(iii)** $0.375 \, \Omega$ **(iv)** 6W
    (b) 120 J
55. **D**
56. **(a)** $4 \, \text{V}$ **(b)** $20 \, \Omega$ **(c)** $0.13 \, \text{A}$
57. $20 \, \text{W}$, $15 \, \text{J/s}$
58. **C**
59. $0.075 \, \Omega$; $7.5 \times 10^{-2} \, \text{W}$
60. $0.8 \, \text{A}$; from B to D
61. $3.1 \, \Omega$
62. **B**
63. **(e) (i)** $1 \, \text{V}$ **(ii)** $6 \, \text{A}$
64. **D**
66. **C**
67. **B**
68. **A**
69. **(b) (ii)** 1833
72. **C**
74. 15 counts/second
75. **(d)** 1/16
76. **(a)** 3   **(b)** 3; 4
78. **C**
79. **E**
80. **D**
81. **A**
82. **(a)** $48.6°$
83. $60 \, \text{mm}$
85. $4 \, \text{cm}$
86. **(iii)** $5 \, \text{mm}$ **(iv)** halve separation   **(v)** Q, S
87. **(d)** $5.7 \times 10^{-7} \, \text{m}$
88. **(b)** $141\frac{2}{3} \, \text{N}$; $408\frac{1}{3} \, \text{N}$
89. **(i)** $5500 \, \text{N}$ **(ii)** $5500 \, \text{N}$ **(iii)** $2600 \, \text{N}$ in each wire
90. **(c) (i)** $2 \, \text{s}$ **(ii)** $8 \, \text{s}$ **(iii)** $80 \, \text{m/s}$ **(iv)** $320 \, \text{m}$
    (v) $300 \, \text{m}$ **(vi)** $500 \, \text{m}$
91. **(b)** $1.2 \, \text{m/s}$
92. **(c)** $40 °\text{C}$ **(e)** no, clearance needed $= 0.0416 \, \text{mm}$
94. **(i)** $13 \, \text{A}$ **(ii)** $13 \, \text{A}$ **(iii)** $3 \, \text{A}$
95. **(i)** 200 turns   **(ii)** $0.15 \, \text{A}$ **(iii)** $10\,800 \, \text{J}$
96. $4 \times 10^3 \, \text{N}$; $12 \, \text{J/s}$

Mathematics for physics

1. **(a)** 3   **(b)** 5   **(c)** 8/3   **(d)** 20   **(e)** 12   **(f)** 6   **(g)** 2
   (h) 3   **(i)** 8

2. **(a)** $f = \dfrac{v}{\lambda}$ **(b)** $\lambda = \dfrac{v}{f}$ **(c)** $I = \dfrac{V}{R}$ **(d)** $R = \dfrac{V}{I}$ **(e)** $m = d \times V$

   (f) $V = \dfrac{m}{d}$ **(g)** $s = vt$ **(h)** $t = \dfrac{s}{v}$ **(i)** $a = \dfrac{F}{m}$ **(j)** $I = \dfrac{Q}{t}$

   (k) $Q = VC$ **(l)** $A = \dfrac{F}{p}$ **(m)** $p_1 = p_2 \times \dfrac{V_2}{V_1}$ **(n)** $a = \dfrac{x}{bc}$

   (o) $t = \dfrac{W}{IV}$ **(p)** $\theta = \dfrac{Q}{mc}$

3. **(a)** $I^2 = \dfrac{P}{R}$ **(b)** $I = \sqrt{\dfrac{P}{R}}$ **(c)** $a = \dfrac{2s}{t^2}$

   (d) $t^2 = \dfrac{2s}{a}$ **(e)** $t = \sqrt{\dfrac{2s}{a}}$ **(f)** $v = \sqrt{2gh}$

   (g) $y = \dfrac{D\lambda}{a}$ **(h)** $\rho = \dfrac{AR}{l}$ **(i)** $V_1 = V_2 \times \dfrac{T_1}{T_2}$

   (j) $T_1 = \dfrac{V_1}{V_2} \times T_2$ **(k)** $V_2 = \dfrac{p_1}{p_2} \times \dfrac{T_2}{T_1} \times V_1$

   (l) $T_2 = \dfrac{p_2}{p_1} \times \dfrac{V_2}{V_1} \times T_1$

4. **(a)** 10   **(b)** 34   **(c)** 2/3   **(d)** 1/10   **(e)** 10   **(f)** 3×10^8
5. **(a)** 2.0×10^5 **(b)** 10   **(c)** 8   **(d)** 2.0×10^8 **(e)** 20
   (f) 300   **(g)** 10^{-7} **(h)** 15   **(i)** 5   **(j)** $0.000\,02 = 2 \times 10^{-5}$
   (k) 10   **(l)** 5/3
6. **(a)** 4   **(b)** 2   **(c)** 5   **(d)** 8   **(e)** 2/3   **(f)** $-\frac{3}{4}$ **(g)** 13/6
   (h) -16 **(i)** 1
7. $a = \dfrac{v - u}{t}$:   **(a)** 5   **(b)** 60   **(c)** 75
8. $a = \dfrac{v^2 - u^2}{2s}$
9. **(b)** Extension $\propto$ mass since the graph is a straight line through the origin
10. **(b)** No : graph is a straight line but does not pass through the origin
    (c) 32
11. **(d)** $9.0 \, \text{g/cm}^3$
12. **(a)** is a curve : **(b)** is a straight line through the origin, therefore $s \propto t^2$ or $s/t^2 = $ a constant $= 2$

Index